Marine Mining of
the Continental Shelf

Marine Mining
of the
Continental Shelf

Legal, Technical and
Environmental Considerations

Prof. Michael S. Baram
Franklin Pierce Law Center

Prof. David Rice
Boston University School of Law

Dr. William Lee
Woodward-Clyde Associates
with the assistance of Robert Kneisley

Ballinger Publishing Company • Cambridge, Massachusetts
A Subsidiary of J.B. Lippincott Company

 This book is printed on recycled paper.

"This book was prepared with the support of NSF Grant GI-39745. However, any opinions, finding, conclusions and/or recommendations herein are those of the authors and do not necessarily reflect the views of NSF."

International Standard Book Number: 0-88410-616-0

Library of Congress Catalog Card Number: 77-23831

Printed in the United States of America

Library of Congress Cataloging in Publication Data
Main entry under title:

Marine mining of the Continental Shelf.

   Includes bibliographical references.
   1. Ocean mining—United States. 2. Continental shelf—United States. I. Baram, Michael S. TN291.5.M37   333.8'5'09141   77-23831
ISBN 0-88410-616-0

To the memory of
Professor Arthur Ippen
of the Massachusetts Institute of Technology
who uniquely integrated the rational and humanistic.

Summary Table of Contents

Contents

List of Figures

List of Tables

Preface

This study of marine mining and the management of the hard mineral resources of the continental shelf was inspired by the interests of Professor Arthur Ippen of the Massachusetts Institute of Technology, was subsequently designed by Professors Ippen and Baram, and was sponsored by the National Science Foundation. It has been designed to identify and address a broad range of technical, economic, environmental, legal, and policy issues, for the purpose of informing government decision makers at federal and state levels, industrial officials, and concerned citizens. This study therefore contains information and opinion which will be useful to future processes of policy formulation and program design and implementation. It also reveals significant gaps in knowledge and various risks relevant to the proper design of future research and demonstration or prototype programs.

The project team consisted of Michael Baram, attorney and professor of civil engineering, and William Lee, doctoral candidate in civil engineering, at the Massachusetts Institute of Technology; and David Rice, professor of law, and Robert Kneisely, student at the School of Law, Boston University. Mr. Lee was primarily responsible for the development of Chapters 3, 4, and 5; all share responsibility for the other chapters.

Numerous experts were extremely helpful to us in the conduct of this study, and to them we extend our great thanks and express our appreciation. They include

Dr. Harold Hess, U.S. Geological Survey
Dr. August Stoeffler, Construction Aggregates Corp.
Mr. Tom Turner, Ellicott Machine Corp.
J.J.C.M. van Dooremalen, IMC-Holland, Inc.
Dr. Gerrit Abraham, Delft Hydraulic Institute
Dr. Helmut Beiersdorf, West German Geological Institute
Dr. J. Leslie Goodier, Arthur D. Little, Inc.
Dr. Gerhard Schreuder, Bos Kalis, N.V.
Dr. K.O. Emery, Woods Hole Oceanographic Institute

and the members of our advisory committee:

Richard L. Allen
Vice President
The Flintkote Company

Michael J. Cruickshank
Conservation Division
United State Geological Survey

Robert Edwards, Director
Northeast Fisheries Center
National Marine Fisheries Service
NOAA, Department of Commerce

D. Michael Harvey
Chief Counsel
Committee on Interior & Insular
   Affairs
United States Senate

John F. Hussey, Director
National Ocean Policy Study
Committee on Commerce
United States Senate

Melvin L. Martin, Chief
Research & Development Office
Office of the Chief of Engineers
U.S. Army Corps of Engineers

James E. Murphy
Water and Related Resources
Connecticut Department of Environ-
   mental Protection

John W. Padan
Mining Engineer
Pacific Marine Environmental Lab
NOAA, Department of Commerce

Paul Swatek
Director of Environmental Affairs
Massachusetts Audubon Society

William Van Horn
Division of Marine Minerals
Bureau of Land Management
Department of the Interior

Robert B. Ziegler
Vice President, USA
IHC-Holland, Inc.

and numerous federal and state officials and industrial and public interest representatives, including Dr. Frank Monastero of the U.S. Department of the Interior and Mr. Robert Blumberg of the Massachusetts Department of Natural Resources.

Special thanks to Mr. Arthur Konopka of the National Science Foundation for his thoughtful guidance on project management.

NOTE ON CHANGES IN LAWS

The final manuscript of the study was completed prior to January 1, 1977. However, the legal and regulatory context of environmental protection is highly dynamic and 1977 was a significant year in the occurrence of new developments. The reader is, therefore, advised of the following developments that occurred in 1977 and early 1978:

Statutory Developments:
Enactment of Clean Air Act Amendments of 1977, P.L. 95–95, 91 Stat. 687;
Enactment of the Clean Water Act of 1977, amending the Federal Water Pollution Control Act and retitling the law as the Clean Water Act. P.L. 95–217, 91 Stat. 1566;
Regulatory Developments:
Adoption by Department of Defense, U.S. Army Corps of Engineers, of revised regulations on Regulatory Program of the Corps of Engineers, 33 C.F.R. § § 320–329, 42 Fed. Reg. 37133 (July 19, 1977), rescinding 33 C.F.R. § § 209.120, 209.125, 209.131, 209.133, 209.150, and 209.260 and substituting, inter alia, 33 C.F.R. § 322 ("Permits for Structures or Work in or Affecting Navigable Waters of the United States"), 33 C.F.R. § 323 ("Permits for Discharges of Dredged or Fill Material into Waters of the United States"), 33 C.F.R. § 324 ("Permits for Ocean Dumping of Dredged Material"), 33 C.F.R. § 325 ("Processing of Department of the Army Permits"), 33 C.F.R. § 326 ("Enforcement"), 33 C.F.R. § 327 ("Public Hearings"), and 33 C.F.R. § 329 ("Definition of Navigable Waters of the United States");
Adoption by Environmental Protection Agency of Final Revision of Ocean Dumping Regulations and Criteria, 40 C.F.R. § § 220–229, 42 Fed. Reg. 2468 (Jan. 11, 1977); Amendments to Effluent Guidelines and Standards for Mineral Mining and Processing, 40 C.F.R. § 436, 42 Fed. Reg. 35843 (July 12, 1977) and 43 Fed. Reg. 9809 (March 10, 1978) and Amendments to Effluent Guidelines and Standards for Ore Mining and Dressing,

40 C.F.R. § 440, 42 Fed. Reg. 3165 (Jan. 17, 1977);

Adoption by Department of Commerce, NOAA, of revised Coastal Management Approval Regulations, 15 C.F.R. § 923, 43 Fed. Reg. 8395 (March 1, 1978) and Regulations on Federal Consistency with Approved Coastal Management Programs, 15 C.F.R. § 930, 43 Fed. Reg. 10517 (March 13, 1978);

Approval by Department of Commerce, NOAA, of California Coastal Plan, Massachusetts Coastal Zone Management Program and Washington Coastal Zone Management Plan.

The changes effected by these developments will be of particular interest to those who have a special interest in the detail of the legal and regulatory context, but it is the opinion of the authors that the new developments affect neither the validity of the methodology used nor the basic analysis presented in the study.

Marine Mining of
the Continental Shelf

✳ *Chapter 1*

The Advent of Marine Mining and Its Implications for Government Decision Making

A. MARINE MINING: INTRODUCTION

The mineral wealth of the oceans is now being exploited at an increasing pace. Most attention has been focused on the oil and gas resources of the seabed, and considerable interest has also been shown in the manganese modules of the deep ocean floor.

This study considers a third category of ocean minerals, the hard minerals of the continental shelf which can be exploited by current marine mining techniques. *Marine mining*, as the term is used herein, *is the commercial recovery of hard minerals from the surface or below the surface of the continental shelf* and excludes the recovery of oil, gas, sulfur, and minerals in seawater.

The *hard minerals* of the continental shelf, which have been determined to be of current significance and subject to exploitation by available marine mining techniques, include sand and gravel, phosphorite, manganese oxide, calcium carbonate, barite, and various types of placer minerals ranging from gold and platinum to tin, iron, and ilmenite.[1] The methods of *commercial recovery* of such minerals include dredge mining, tunneling from land or islands, solution mining, and various new and unproven submarine systems.[2] The *continental shelf* consists of the seaward extension of the continental land mass to the region where such submerged land begins to slope sharply to the deep ocean floor. Legal definition of the shelf, including division of the U.S. shelf into state-owned "submerged lands" and the federally owned "outer continental shelf," is discussed in subsequent chapters.[3]

1

Marine mining is now being conducted by several nations—principally Japan, the United Kingdom, the Netherlands, Denmark, and Indonesia and other nations of Southeast Asia.[4] Although little marine mining has been conducted on the continental shelf of the United States, federal agencies and several coastal state governments are considering programs for the exploitation of the hard mineral resources under their jurisdiction. Rough measures of the substantial economic value of such mineral resources and of competing economic interests in the marine environment have been developed;[5] exploration and mapping of marine deposits is being conducted by the U.S. Geological Survey;[6] the Bureau of Land Management is developing regulations for "hard mineral mining operating and leasing activities" on the federal outer continental shelf;[7] the coastal zone management offices of many coastal states are now considering marine mining as one of the candidates for multiple use of their coastal regions and submerged lands, in accordance with the provisions of the Federal Coastal Zone Management Act;[8] and several studies of marine mining prospects and problems have been undertaken.[9]

B. FACTORS PROMOTING MARINE MINING IN THE UNITED STATES

Factors that now promote marine mining in the United States can be organized in several categories:

1. National interests
2. Local and regional interests
3. Industrial and professional interests
4. Special needs
5. Mineral prices

Specific factors in each category are discussed in the following paragraphs. However, it should be noted that the categories are broad and that each factor seems ultimately to belong in several categories.

1. National Interests

a. *Self-sufficiency in resources.* A policy of self-sufficiency, or at least a diminution in U.S. reliance on foreign sources of essential minerals and other materials, has developed as a result of recent restrictions on U.S. oil supplies imposed by producing countries and other cases which manifest the growing role of resources in international political developments. National self-sufficiency has been formally expressed as policy in the energy field[10] and has been raised as an important reason for developing marine mining in the United States.[11]

b. *Economic health.* Numerous considerations related to productivity, employment, industrial development, growth, and the balance of payments, to the extent that such are related to the availability of mineral resources at reasonable cost,[12] have become an increasingly important concern. Dependence of the U.S. economy on foreign sources for numerous minerals has been increasing and is expected to continue to increase significantly unless new domestic sources are exploited—particularly sources on public lands onshore and offshore.[13]

c. *National leadership in New Technologies.* The importance of U.S. leadership in technology developed for the ocean environment, for military strength, and for other purposes has been frequently expressed by various interests in congressional hearings and in other forums as a basis for more aggressive minerals exploitation offshore.[14]

2. Local and Regional Interests

a. *Economic development.* New Industries, jobs, an improved tax base, and population growth incentives have long been major economic factors in promotion of the minerals industry in Western states. Economic development is now the prime factor in the promotion of marine mining in other remaining "frontier" or less developed regions of the nation, such as the Alaskan coast.[15]

b. *Alternative sources of necessary minerals not acceptable or feasible.* For example, there is a continual demand for new sources for sand and gravel, essential to construction of new buildings and facilities (e.g., airports, highways). In metropolitan regions, nearby onshore sites for extraction are not available because of urban development, or not permitted because of laws preserving the amenities and environmental quality of the outlying suburbs and rural regions, or not feasible because of distance of source from construction site with consequent high transportation costs (and attendant truck traffic–related externalities). For these and similar reasons, some states have authorized marine mining for sand and gravel in their submerged lands adjoining metropolitan areas.[16]

3. Industrial and Professional Interests

a. *Marine technology industry.* Marine engineering and technology firms have been the leading private sector proponents of marine mining. Such firms, some domestic but many foreign, now seek the development of this new U.S. market for their special skills and equipment, potentially larger than their existing markets.[17]

b. *Dredging industry.* Compared to its European counterparts, probably the least technologically sophisticated sector of the U.S. marine industry. The U.S. dredging industry is nevertheless capable of conducting some dredge mining (in nearshore regions) and therefore promotes the development of marine mining.[18]

c. *Minerals industry.* With few notable exceptions, members of the minerals industry have not played a particularly promotional role for marine mining, but have conservatively sought to continue and expand present types of mining operations on the public lands onshore and more favorable and protective federal legislation and regulation for such onshore mining.[19]

4. Special Needs and Factors

a. *Beach replenishment*, requiring offshore sand and gravel.[20]

b. *Channel dredging*, concurrently providing opportunities to dredgers for commercial recovery of dredged materials.[21]

c. *Major construction onshore* (e.g., highways), necessitating exploitation of offshore sand and gravel as the most feasible alternative sources.[22]

d. *New offshore construction*, involving land extensions, artificial islands, and large structures which necessitate offshore sand, gravel, and rock for initial construction and for subsequent maintenance.[23]

5. Mineral Prices

The influence of mineral costs on marine mining has been succintly described by Archer:

> Offshore minerals will . . . continue to be exploited only when they can be marketed competitively with land sources, the costs of which is unlikely to increase sharply because of acute shortage . . . the rapid advance of technology may lead to the development of cheaper methods of offshore prospecting, mining, processing and marine transportation. It is likely that the delivered cost of minerals produced on land will also benefit from new technology. It is, however, always possible that the exploitation of otherwise uneconomic deposits of some minerals may be subsidized by a government for strategic reasons . . . It seems more likely that for some time there will be substantially increased production from the continental shelf only of tin and . . . minerals for which transport costs contribute a substantial proportion of delivered prices so that their lower transport costs enable them to compete successfully. The main

minerals concerned are sand and gravel and calcium carbonate in various forms.[24]

This summing up has, however, been overtaken by several recent developments: the vastly increased price of rare metals such as gold and platinum on the world markets; the increasing stringency and costs of environmental controls on land-based mining, processing, and transport activities; and the advent of major offshore construction programs (offshore airports and power plants in the United States) which will require enormous quantities of sand, gravel, and rock.[25] These and other new developments have changed the data base used by Archer and others in the past. At the present time, the economic feasibility of marine mining for placer minerals, the rare metals, and sand and gravel appears increasingly favorable.[26]

C. GOVERNMENT DECISION MAKING ON MARINE MINING

The federal government is responsible for authorizing and regulating marine mining on the outer continental shelf. The governments of the coastal states bear the same responsibilities for marine mining on their "submerged lands," the nearshore sector of the continental shelf, as discussed in Chapter 6.

As pressure for marine mining slowly builds, both levels of government in the United States are becoming involved in three types of decision making: *policy* formulation, *program* design and promulgation, and *project* review and determinations.

1. Policy Formulation

Marine mining policy can be described as the aggregation of values, objectives, and law applicable to marine mining which have been articulated by legislative and executive processes. Federal policy and the policies of several states on marine mining are identified and analyzed in Chapters 6 through 10. Public values, expert judgments, private interests, and the objectives of elected officials have all helped shape current policies and have led to the prescription of regulatory functions to be conducted by agencies.

Technology assessment,[27] environmental impact assessment,[28] cost–benefit analysis, and more sophisticated analytical methods have been considered and used for informing and guiding the policy-making process on marine mining. Of course legislative and executive inaction in the face of agency and industrial activities related to marine mining leads to the establishment of policy as well.

2. Program Design and Promulgation

Within the existing policy framework, the task of establishing
a programmatic approach to marine mining regulation falls to federal
and state agencies,[29] and a detailed analysis is provided in Chapters
6 through 10. Unless a "lead agency" or coordinated interagency
approach to program design has been specified by legislative or executive action, many agencies may act in accordance with their
separately legislated responsibilities and produce, in sum, programs
applicable to marine mining which are inefficient.

Program design for marine mining regulations must eventually
include several key elements:[30] authorization of exploration, valuation
and allocation of the known resources for mining, determination of
the risks and allocation of revenues, acquisition of information,
regulation of operations, enforcement of requirements and conditions, and the development of measures of accountability to be
imposed on those charged with program implementation.[31] Such
functions are then designed for generic application to classes or
categories of marine resources and mining activities and eventually
may appear as administrative rules.

At this level of decision making, available analytical methods,
some of which have been noted above, are more useful for informing and guiding government action; and some, such as use of environmental impact assessment, may be required by law.[32] However,
techniques such as cost–benefit analysis are of limited usefulness to
program design (except as a method of organizing information)
since valuation of many of the costs and benefits would always be
arbitrary and such analyses do not necessarily force appropriate
technology nor consider distributional effects.[33] Therefore, program-
level decision making is essentially a judgmental task influenced by
information on measurable costs and benefits, public values and
private interests, and technical and economic feasibility.

3. Project Review and Determination

Finally, an agency must ultimately apply programmatic rules,
guidelines, and criteria in procedures leading to decisions on specific
mining proposals; exercise discretion in imposing ad hoc conditions
on authorized mining activities; and apply monitoring and enforcement measures as necessary.[34] Since project-related decision making
occurs within accepted policy and program frameworks, since information on mining activity (sites, minerals, environmental effects,
etc.) is relatively specific, since appropriate valuation of costs and
benefits is more achievable through citizen participation within the
local or regional context of the mining activity, and since distribu-

Table 1-1. Government Decision Making on Marine Mining

	3 Levels of Decision Making		
	1. Policy	*2. Program*	*3. Project*
Usual mechanisms for soliciting inputs	Hearings before congressional committees on executive and legislative proposals Other feedback to political processes	Administrative law: Rule-making procedures by lead agency and other agencies with responsibilities National (state) environmental policy act: program environmental assessment by lead agency, with review by others	Administrative law: Adjudicatory procedures by lead agency and other agencies with responsibilities National (state)environmental policy act: project environmental assessment by lead agency, with review by others
Inputs:			
Public values	Solicites/unsolicited	Solicited	Solicited
Expert judgment	Solicited/unsolicited	Solicited	Solicited
Private interests	Solicited/unsolicited (lobbying)	Solicited	Solicited
Other government officials	Solicited/unsolicited	Solicited/required	Solicited/required
Useful analytical methods	Technology assessment	Technology assessment and NEPA environmental analysis	NEPA environmental analysis and Cost-benefit or other balancing analysis

tional effects of possible decisions are more discernable and susceptible to trade-offs and other remedial management, the use of
analytical methods such as cost–benefit may be appropriate as a
tool for project determinations. Use of such methods supports federal agency compliance with the environmental impact assessment
requirements of the National Environmental Policy Act[35] and
with the requirements of the Administrative Procedure Act.[36]

Although responsibilities for project review, decisions, monitoring, and enforcement may fall primarily on a single resource management agency or several agencies (such as the Bureau of Land
Management and the U.S. Geological Survey for mining on the outer
continental shelf), many other agencies will also be required to
apply their regulations to keep the effects of the activities within
acceptable levels (e.g., the Corps of Engineers, Environmental Protection Agency, Coast Guard, for mining on the outer continental
shelf). Interagency coordination at the project level will be essential
to ensure efficient use of resources and the establishment of a holis-
tic and effective regulatory regime. Detailed analysis of agency
responsibilities is provided in Chapters 6 through 10.

Logic dictates that this sequence of decisions, *policy* to *program*
to *project*, is appropriate for government management of new activities such as marine mining and that the process should be dynamic
and iterative, with the learning or results of project-level activities
subsequently providing feedback which can lead to useful changes
in policy and program design.

Marine mining offers the rare case where such an idealized sequential approach to decision making can now be employed by
federal and state governments, in that no significant level of mining
project activity has yet occurred in the United States, and policy
and program decisions can therefore be made in their proper order.
Too often, in other fields where the government has assumed responsibility, the sequence is reversed: substantial project-level activities have already been conducted, attendant social and economic
interests have crystalized, and the policy and program determinations (when they later occur) are not as objective or coincident
with the national interest because of the influence of such prior
established interests.[37]

4. Resource Management

While this study focuses on marine mining and decision making
at policy, program, and project levels by federal and coastal state
governments, there is a larger need which must be addressed by the
federal government to ensure that decision making at all levels is

harmonized and consistent with the national interest—the need to develop resource management policy.[38] The need is for a federal policy on mineral and other natural resources which transcends marine hard minerals to include all minerals and materials essential to the national interest.

Developments toward a national materials policy should integrate other policy developments such as those related to specific types of minerals and materials,[39] uses of public lands onshore and offshore,[40] economic growth and the satisfaction of public and private needs,[41] the uses and regulation of minerals and materials technologies, state-level and international political developments, environmental quality, and conservation and other new "ethics" necessary to enable our stewardship for the future.[42]

Given these perspectives on decision making for marine mining, as summarized in Table 1-1, this study attempts to inform and guide the processes of *policy* formulation and *program* design through the conduct of one form of technology assessment. The approach taken to technology assessment, its utility and limitations, is described in Chapter 2.

NOTES

1. See inventory of the minerals of the continental shelf in V. McKelvey, F. Wang, et al., "Potential Mineral Resources of the United States Outer continental Shelf," (Washington, D.C.: U.S. Geological Survey, Department of the Interior, March 11, 1968), contained in *Outer Continental Shelf Policy Issues*, Hearings before the Committee on Interior and Insular Affairs, U.S. Senate, 92d Cong., 2d sess., March and April 1972.
 For a discussion of these and other mineral resources, see Chapter 3.
2. For a discussion of these methods, see Chapter 4.
3. See Chapter 6.
4. For a discussion of experience to date, see Chapter 3. Archer identifies 14 nations engaged in marine mining with measurable production of various minerals in "Progress and Prospects of Marine Mining," *Mining Magazine*, March 1974.
5. See *The Economic Value of Ocean Resources to the United States*, U.S. Senate, Committee on Commerce, 93d Cong., 2d sess., December 1974; M. Cruickshank and H. Hess, "Marine Sand and Gravel Mining," *Oceanus* 19, 1 (1975).
6. See V. McKelvey and F. Wang, *Maps of World Subsea and Mineral Resources*, U.S. Geological Survey.
7. See *Proposed Outer Continental Shelf Hard Mineral Mining and Leasing Regulations and Draft Environmental Impact Statement* (Washington, D.C.: Bureau of Land Management, U.S. Department of the Interior, 1974).
8. 16 U.S.C. 1451 et seq. For analysis of the act, see M. Baram, *Environ-*

mental Law and the Siting of Facilities (Cambridge, Mass.: Ballinger, 1976), particularly Part 2, "Environmental Law and Coastal Zone Management."

9. See, for example, *Mining in the Outer Continental Shelf and in the Deep Ocean* (Washington, D.C.: National Academy of Sciences, 1975).

10. "Project Independence," promulgated by the Ford administration after oil embargos had been imposed by members of OPEC.

11. See *Mining in the Outer Continental Shelf and in the Deep Ocean, supra* note 9, ch. 2.

12. See *Final Report of the National Commission on Materials Policy* (Washington, D.C.: U.S. Government, 1973). Note in particular the section entitled "Illustrative Data" for succinct discussion of "the role of minerals in the U.S. economy. Also see *National Materials Policy*, Hearings before the Subcommittee on Minerals, Materials and Fuels of the Committee on Interior and Insular Affairs, U.S. Senate, 93d Cong., 1st sess. (1973).

13. See the annual *Commodity Data Summaries* (Washington, D.C., U.S. Dept. Interior), and other publications of the department's Bureau of Mines, such as the *Minerals Yearbook* and *Mineral Industry Surveys. Annual Reports of the Secretary of Interior* under the Mining and Minerals Policy Act of 1970 are also useful.

14. *Proceedings* of the Ocean Science and Technology Advisory Committee of the National Security Industrial Association, Washington, D.C., reflect the promotional interests in marine mining of NSIA members, which include leading military contractors and other high technology firms.

15. Alaskan developmental policies toward marine mining, which are probably the best example, are discussed in Chapter 9.

16. See discussion of New York and New Jersey in Chapter 9, for examples.

17. The array of firms and services and their developmental interests are best captured at the world's largest conference, the annual Offshore Technology Conference. Many of the U.S. firms are subsidiaries of or otherwise affiliated with foreign (e.g., British, Dutch, German) companies.

18. Developmental attitudes of the dredging industry are generally well represented in *World Dredging and Marine Construction*, the trade magazine.

A major Dutch manufacturer of marine mining equipment and hopper dredges, the Inter-Holland Corporation, has recently established a U.S. office and is arranging a consortium of materials and transportation firms in preparation for the forthcoming leasing by the Department of the Interior of tracts for mining on the continental shelf. It is clear that Dutch, English, and to some extent, West German equipment manufacturers, shipbuilders, and dredging companies will play an important role in any exploitation of the hard minerals to be found within U.S. jurisdiction, despite exclusionary U.S. laws such as 46 U.S.C. 293 for example.

19. See *State of the Minerals Industry*, Hearings before the Subcommittee on Mining, Minerals and Fuels of the Committee on Interior and Insular Affairs, U.S. Senate, 88th Cong., 1st sess. (1963) and subsequent hearings; *Declarations of Policy of the American Mining Congress*, etc.

20. See A. Mohr, "Beach Nourishment with Sand from the Sea," in *World Dredging Conference Proceedings of 1974* (San Pedro, Calif.: WODCON Association, 1975).

21. In Chapter 9, the discussion of New York State describes such opportunities.

22. See note 16, *supra.*

23. The "Special Report—Offshore Construction" issue of *Civil Engineering* 46, 4 (April 1976) describes recent construction projects offshore. The *Sea Island Proposal* of a consortium of Dutch companies, to build a large landfill island in the North Sea for the siting of LNG and other high-risk facilities would employ enormous quantities of offshore sand, gravel, and rock, to be acquired through marine mining in nearby waters. The proposal has been developed for the consortium by Bos Kalis N.V., a leading Dutch marine engineering and technology firm, and is before the Dutch government for approval. Similar offshore island developments in the United States are being studied by the University of Delaware, under NSF grant, and *Interim Reports* were published in 1975. Finally, a study of the *Legal and Economic Considerations in the Development of Artificial Land Fill Islands for Cluster-Siting Energy Facilites* has been conducted by Professor M. Baram of MIT, for Brookhaven National Laboratory (final report published by Brookhaven in September 1976). These studies and others they cite reveal the important nexus between offshore construction needs and the future of marine mining.

24. A. Archer, "Economics of Offshore Exploration and Production of Solid Minerals on the Continental Shelf," *Ocean Management* 1, 1 (1973). Also, see extensive discussion of mineral cost factors in Chapters 3 and 4 of this report.

25. "Stationary or artificial island-based power plants or airports off the U.S. coast may each require up to a 500 acre surface area. Assuming a 30 foot water depth, some 24.2 million cubic yards of sand, gravel and rock fill will be needed for each, and it is difficult to conceive that such fill would be sought from inland sources, or that several million truck loads in transit would be tolerated by coastal communities and state governments. Floating structures would require fill for a break water only, entailing lesser but still substantial amounts of materials. Hence, offshore extraction of sand and gravel may appear desirable for economic and land-environmental reasons." William Lee, MIT, June 1974. Also see *North Sea Island Feasibility Study* Hydronamica-Bos Kalis Westminster N.V., (Rotterdam, the Netherlands, 1972).

26. Economic feasibility for U.S. commercial ventures is a difficult issue, one highly dependent on several variables, among them—the availability of land-based minerals and their transport costs, market and demand factors, and the nature of the technology to be employed. There is little U.S. experience to review, and the major offshore commercial ventures carried on today are those for tin off the Southeast Asian coast and for sand and gravel off the Dutch, English, and Japanese coasts, which cannot be readily applied to the U.S. market. The economics are the subject of considerable speculation for these reasons, as well as for the reason that firms in the industry are highly secretive and consider most of their knowledge to consist of trade secrets.

Nevertheless, given the availability of current (foreign) technology, it appears that offshore sand and gravel mining could compete with upland supplies for part of the U.S. aggregates market. This is especially true for major construction needs such as urban renewal, power plants, and airports along the metropolitan coastline regions where most of the population is congregated and where excellent deposits of sand and gravel have been located. In the aggregates industry, transportation costs (usually regulated) far exceed the extraction and processing costs, and some producers ship as far as 100 miles by rail to users. For offshore mining, the situation would be reversed: the extraction cost may be higher, but it will be offset by cheaper barge or pipeline transportation from the burrow to shore. Various estimates indicate that sand and gravel can be extracted offshore for $1 to $2 per ton. By adding royalty payments, transport costs, and profit for U.S. operators, the resultant price would compete quite favorably with pit prices from upland sources (about $3.50 per ton in Boston in 1974).

The low grade of marine phosphorite deposits (nodules) off the California coast and the depths in which they are located do not suggest current economic feasibility for mining, but several other factors point to an increasingly favorable economic trend in the near future. Technology for deep ocean (manganese) nodule extraction is advancing rapidly, and entrepreneurs now report a cost of $5 to $6 per ton for extraction at 15,000 feet (4,572 meters); phosphorite located at depths of up to 600 feet can certainly be dredged at lower cost. Another important economic factor relates to the nature of the equipment manufacturing industry: machinery for working upland phosphate deposits requires a very long lead time, while dredges for working marine deposits can currently be built in less time. Much of the data about costs for marine phosphorite mining are proprietary, but leading authorities such as John Mero of Ocean Resources think submarine phosphorite mining will occur within the near future. See J. Mero, *Mineral Resources of the Sea* New York: American Elsevier, 1965).

Calcium carbonate in the form of oyster and clam shells has been taken off the Gulf Coast of the United States for some time for use in construction and in the manufacture of cement. See *Draft Environmental Impact Statement on Shell Dredging in San Antonio Bay, Texas* (U.S. Corps Engineers, Galveston District, 1973). Upward trends in the price of gold have brought about considerable interest in the mining of gold offshore, especially off the California and Alaska coasts. See M. Mott, "Gold Potential of Beach Placers near Nome, Alaska," *Proceedings of Fifth Underwater Mining Institute*, U. Wisconsin, May 1974. (Also, personal communication, A Willard, Lands Division of State of California, April 1974).

27. Technology assessment, in its congressionally prescribed format, is described in the Office of Technology Assessment Act, 2 U.S.C. 471. For extensive discussion of different TA methodologies, see F. Hetman, *Society and the Assessment of Technology* (Paris: OECD, 1973).

28. Environmental impact assessment, as designed by Congress, is set forth in the National Environmental Policy Act of 1970. See 42 U.S.C. 4321-47 (January 1, 1970), as amended by Publ. Law 94-83 (August 9, 1975).

29. Chapters 6 through 10 of this book contain legal information on federal and state programs.

30. See note 7, *supra*, for the program approach proposed by the U.S. Department of the Interior.

31. Measures of accountability include provisions for judicial review, citizen suits, state and federal interagency reviews, annual reporting requirements, oversight arrangements to be implemented by Congress or national commissions, for example.

32. For discussion of NEPA application on a programmatic basis, see Chapter 10; and the *Sixth Annual Report* (Washington, D.C.: U.S. Council on Environmental Quality, 1976), pp. 640–46.

33. For detailed analysis of cost-benefit as a tool for government decision making, see Chapter 4 of *Report on the Use of Cost-Benefit Analysis in Controlling Ionizing Radiation* (Washington, D.C.: BEIR Committee, Natural Academy of Sciences, 1977).

34. See note 7, *supra*, for the project approach proposed by the Department of Interior.

35. See note 28, *supra*; and *Preparation of Environmental Impact Statements: Guidelines*, U.S. Council on Environmental Quality, 38 Fed Reg. 20550–62 (1973).

36. 5 U.S.C. 551 et seq.

37. See M. Baram, "Social Control of Science and Technology," *Science* 172 (May 7, 1971).

38. Discussion of this need has been the subject of congressional hearings. See *National Materials Policy*, Hearings before the Subcommittee on Minerals, Materials and Fuels of the Committee on Interior and Insular Affairs, U.S. Senate, 93d Cong., 1st sess. (1973).

39. See, for example, *Gold Production, Mining and Revitalization Incentives*, Hearings before the Subcommittee on Minerals, Materials and Fuels of the Committee on Interior and Insular Affairs, U.S. Senate, 88th, 89th and 90th Cong. (1963–1967).

40. See, for example, *Land Planning and Policy in Alaska: Recommendations Concerning National Interest Lands*, Report of the Joint Federal-State Land Use Planning Commission for Alaska, Committee on Interior and Insular Affairs, U.S. Senate, Washington, D.C. (1974).

41. See, for example, D. Brooks and P. Andrews, "Mineral Resources, Economic Growth and World Population," *Science* 185 (1974): 13–20.

42. See note 38, *supra*. In F. Huddle, "The Evolving National Policy for Materials," *Science* 191 (1976): 654–59, an inventory of such fragmented policy developments is presented.

※ *Chapter 2*

Technology Assessment and Its Application to Marine Mining

A. THE CONCEPT OF TECHNOLOGY ASSESSMENT

Technology assessment is a broad concept that systematic and interdisciplinary analyses of technological developments be undertaken for several possible social purposes:

- To examine "the effects on society that may occur when a technology is introduced, extended or modified with special emphasis on those consequences that are unintended, indirect or delayed";[1] or
- To design a particular technological development as the solution to a specific need or as the means of reaching a specific objective and to determine feasible approaches toward the achievement of the development;[2] or
- To evaluate and choose from alternative technological approaches which are available or possible to meet a specific need or achieve a specific objective;[3] or
- Some combination of the foregoing.

Therefore, technology assessment is potentially capable of providing information necessary for the promotion and limitation of technology and associated activities by decision-makers in both the public and private sectors.[4]

Timing of the assessment is critical to achieve such goals. The earlier the acquisition of knowledge through assessment occurs in the evolution of the technology involved, the easier it is for decision makers to impose controls or management plans since the social, economic, and psychological commitments that normally accompany technological developments will not have yet become significant enough to provide difficult opposition or to raise the spectre of societal dislocations if assessment results are employed.[5]

As discussed in the previous chapter, the overall purpose of this study is to inform and guide government decision making on marine mining at policy and program levels of decision. Technology assessment (TA) was chosen from among the array of available analytical methods as the most suitable method of providing results useful to government decision makers for several reasons:

- TA permits a broad, open-ended, interdisciplinary, and systematic approach to a problem with unlimited flexibility in design (one is not locked in to a formal method);
- TA does not require that economic measures be established for the valuation of unquantifiable societal and environmental impacts, and it allows full consideration of the distributional effects of alternative decisions (in contrast to cost-benefit and other economic methods of analysis);
- TA is focused on technology, and it is precisely marine technology and its industrial and professional supporters which are the major factors sustaining the promotion of marine mining (since mineral needs, mineral costs, and other promotional factors noted in Chapter 1 are sporadic and ill defined at present);
- In the absence of a national materials and minerals policy, in the absence of established principles for resource management, and in light of pressures to begin marine mining in the United States, the most urgent need of government at federal and state levels is to understand technological options prior to policy and program determinations. Through understanding of alternative technologies for exploration, extraction, transport, and processing and their limitations and externalities, which can be provided by TA, government officials can develop (*a*) appropriate incentives and subsidies for the development and use of more efficient and less harmful techniques; (*b*) better criteria for selection among applicants for marine mining activities (or rejection of all proposals for certain activities at certain sites); (*c*) effective protection of competing users of the marine environment; (*d*) sensible regulations to govern authorized activities, which may incorporate both *design* and *performance* requirements—regulations which will appropriately force advanced technologies on marine miners, as

such technologies are needed to ensure that marine mining is carried out within acceptable boundary conditions. This is the vital "technology-forcing" function which should pervade policy and program developments and which necessitates use of TA.

B. THE PRACTICE OF TECHNOLOGY ASSESSMENT

The practice of technology assessment in its various forms predates the terminology. Industry has used technological forecasting to identify new products, risks, and markets and to thereby allocate resources, a limited form of assessment. Government agencies in their *regulatory role* have established programs for the premarket review of food additives and drugs; for the technological control of air, water, and noise pollutants from various sources; and for the approval of nuclear power plant designs and sites, all of which constitute other forms of assessment. Government agencies in their *developmental role* have employed technological feasibility studies as bases for mobilizing resources and pursuing space, defense, health, and other "missions." The application of cost-benefit and cost-effectiveness analyses to the planning and management of various programs and the allocation of resources has been conducted for some time.

Most recently, large-scale environmental impact analyses have been undertaken by federal and state agencies and by institutions in several other countries as a technique for forecasting the diffuse social costs and benefits of proposed government programs, projects, and standard-setting activities (such as those involving nuclear power programs, reactor construction, and radioactive effluent limitations).

The National Environmental Policy Act (NEPA)[6] requires federal agencies, such as the Department of the Interior with its authority to allocate and regulate offshore mineral resources,[7] to undertake comprehensive environmental impact analyses of any major proposed program or project likely to have significant environmental effects. The agencies are also required to publicly disclose the resulting "environmental impact statements" and to accommodate critical review by other federal, state, and local agencies, interest groups, and the general public. Finally, the agency decision process on the program or project must utilize the findings of environmental impact analyses along with the economic, technical, and other factors it normally considers--in other words, the agency decision must be based in part on adequate consideration of a thorough environmental analysis.[8] Under NEPA, proposed agency actions have been modified to lessen or eliminate adverse environmental effects, and agency programs are being designed to deal more systematically with resource allocation and use and with potential externalities. The effect of NEPA on government in the United States has been far-reaching, and specific developments under NEPA which are relevant to marine mining are discussed in Chapter 10.

Congress has also recognized the need for a mechanism to provide it with technology assessments on subjects that may arise, and enacted the *Office of Technology Assessment Act* in 1972.[9] The office (OTA) has been funded and staffed, and has acted on a number of assessment requests since 1972, which include an analysis of offshore developments in the mid-Atlantic coastal region and an assessment of incentives and constraints affecting mining on federal lands (onshore) in the West for fuel and hard rock minerals. Several priority subject areas have been designated for future assessment activities, including "the oceans" and "materials," areas of relevance to marine mining.[10]

OTA has not chosen to develop formal, replicable methodologies for assessment but has used several different methods found suitable to the nature of the subjects and the types of results sought by Congress. Criticisms of OTA procedures and performance have been expressed, and there is little evidence that OTA has yet achieved its potential for informing and guiding Congressional decision making on policies and programs. Part of the problem has been the absence of protocols for the review and use of OTA assessments and the failure of Congress to require its own review and use of such assessments. Nevertheless, the publication of OTA assessments ensures that citizens and interest groups have access to these detailed and objective studies, which can result in appropriate pressures on the Congress for recognition and use of assessment findings in decision making.[11]

Finally, various institutions have undertaken studies relevant to marine mining which have been considered technology assessments. These include, for example, the National Academy of Sciences' report, *Mining in the Outer Continental Shelf and in the Deep Ocean;*[12] the assessments by the State of Hawaii, *Aquaculture Policy*[13] and *Exploration and Utilization of Manganese Nodule Deposits in the Pacific;*[14] the University of Oklahoma report, *Energy Under the Oceans;*[15] and the *Hydronamica–Bos Kalis N.V.* report on a proposed *Sea Island* (landfill island) for high risk facilities in the North Sea.[16]

What distinguishes this study from the others is its focus on the full array of marine mining (exploration, extraction, transportation, and processing) technologies, the environment implications of the technologies, detailed consideration of the current legal and regulatory framework, and the development of recommendations for an effective, "technology-forcing" regulatory program for social control of marine mining.

The actual methods employed in such technology assessments vary considerably and reflect the skills and biases of the assessors, the nature of the problem, and the types of results sought. Some methods used have been well established (e.g., cost–benefit analysis); others have been of an ad hoc nature—tailored to meet the problem.[17] Many elements of these methods are substantially the same, and a full-scale assessment should at least include the following elements:

1. Evaluation of the technical and economic feasibility of the technology or technologies at issue or otherwise relevant to the overall assessment objective.
2. Evaluation of the economic, human, and natural resource commitments required for the development and employment of candidate technologies.
3. Identification of the possible impacts or effects of the proposed technology to be used or of each of the proposed technologies being compared for selection.
4. Estimation of the probability of the occurrence of such impacts, keeping in mind various intervening conditions and synergistic effects between types of impacts.
5. Measurement of the impacts to the extent that this is possible.
6. Determination of the significance of each impact (and resource commitment) vis-à-vis the others (significance to the decision makers and their clients or constituency). This means valuation of each impact, using a common measure for quantification or valuation, commonly a monetary measure. However, where such valuation cannot be objectively established, as is the case with many types of health and environmental impacts, such impacts should be highlighted for valuation to be accomplished through political processes reflecting public opinion.
7. A summing up of the above, identifying, as realistically as possible, the confidence that the assessor has in the data, estimates, and other elements, and suggesting weighting factors and other features believed necessary to produce equitable results for various societal sectors. In other words, the summing up should provide the frame of reference for any actual decision making that may subsequently take place.

8. Development of recommended managerial, institutional, and legal structures, policies, and program features to ensure that appropriate technologies are selected and properly managed—as a further guide to actual decision making which may subsequently occur.

The *dangers or limitations* of technology assessment should be noted at this point. The use of systems models and other methods for organizing and relating available data can easily obfuscate the tentative quality of most inputs to the assessments or the assumptions which underlie the approach and judgments of any assessor. The results, particularly in computer print-out format, would depict an unwarranted specificity to the results. And of course the most controversial element of any assessment is the evaluation of the significance of the impacts (step 6 above), which is a subjective matter on which the assessor may provide recommendations but for which the decision maker representing various sectors of the public must provide the ultimate judgment.

A significant aspect of the assessment experience has been its use to promote the increasing *accountability of decision makers* in government agencies and in private organizations to the social implications of their activities so that their decisions thereby become more socially appropriate. This has converged with the evolution of planning and management methods for using assessment techniques, and creates powerful results. Given the growth of assessment techniques, their employment in various institutions, and their uses in decision making, a means has become available by which independently to evaluate the quality of the decisions actually made. In other words, a way has been found to determine if the decisions reasonably reflect the assessment findings and rest on substantial evidence: if the decisions are in accord with the weight of the evidence which is incorporated in the assessment or if the decisions deviate from the evidence, whether the grounds for such deviations are justifiable or reflect prejudice or capriciousness. Finally, the assessment itself can be reviewed to determine if it is coherent, objective, and substantively adequate.

Technology assessment has therefore come to mean the use of analytical techniques which (1) enable more effective planning and management decision making within an institution and (2) enable more effective review of such planning and decision making by whatever outside authorities and sectors of the public can exercise a review role. In the United States this has resulted in strong critical feedback from citizens groups, private interests, and professionals to decision makers in government agencies as well as in private industry. Despite time lags and increased immediate costs which result from this process, it has nevertheless provided important benefits: better design and implimentation of programs with fewer social costs; increased credibility for the institutions whose decision makers treat the public and interest groups as partners in their decision processes; and ultimately a long-term cost-effectiveness. Assessment is not going to be the panacea that suddenly makes institutional decision making both rational and democratic, but it does embody a number of operative principles urgently needed to improve decision processes.

C. APPLICATIONS TO MARINE MINING

In this section, translation of the technology assessment experience for application to policy and program decision making on marine mining is described.

As a first step, one must consider marine mining as a system that involves several technological features, as depicted in the following flow chart (*Figure 2-1*):

At each stage of the marine mining system, one or more types of technologies can be applied, and possible choices must be assessed in terms of technical and economic feasibility, resource commitments, and externalities (e.g., pollution). For example, the *extraction* stage, which includes dislodgment and lifting of minerals from the seabed, may involve the use of shaft or tunnel mining, several types of dredge mining, the use of submersible vehicles, or solution mining. Each of these dislodgment techniques can in turn be broken down into several different types of subtechnologies; for example, dredge mining alone may involve use of clamshell or grab dredge methods, cutter heads and suction pumps, trailer dredging, or various combinations of these methods. Full discussion of these technological methods and their feasibility is provided in Chapter 4; and information on their resource requirements and externalities is presented in Chapter 5.

The implications of these techniques for social control must then be considered, and the social control system which is applicable to marine mining must itself be carefully identified. A model depicting the dynamic processes of social control applicable to marine mining and other technological systems has been devleoped[18] and has the potential for using information on the specific attributes of specific marine mining systems. It is presented in Figure 2-2. Briefly, as inputs to and outputs from marine mining are perceived by vari-

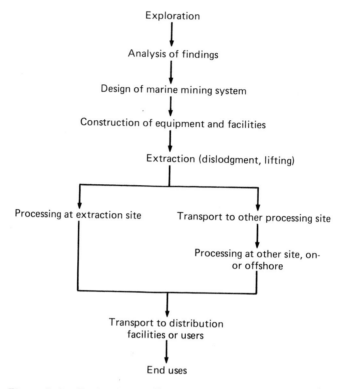

Figure 2-1. Technological Features of Marine Mining Systems.

ous interests, such interests have two alternative courses to follow in influencing decision makers: either the long-term course of lobbying and other measures for modifying present laws, institutions, and values in order subsequently to constrain or otherwise influence decision making; or the short-term course of confrontation, litigation, or other adversarial approaches to bring about more immediate and desired responses from decision makers. Decision makers are depicted as functioning at three key control points: control over the flow of resources, control over the types and levels of effects, and control over the flow of information.

This generalized model depicting the dynamic processes of social control surrounding the application of marine mining and its several technological features can be used for forecasting problems and for developing recommendations on social control, if sufficient information for each of its various elements is provided. The model can therefore be applied at *policy*, *program*, and *project* levels of marine mining and can yield results useful for forecasting and con-

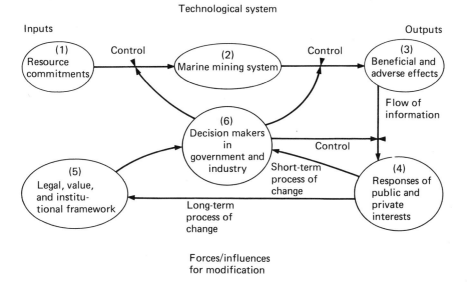

Figure 2-2. Social Control of Marine Mining.

1. *Inputs or resource commitments* include trained personnel, funds, equipment, submerged lands (sites for mining), onshore lands (sites for processing), offshore waters (at site), natural and commercial resources (finfish, shellfish) sacrificed to mining, and minerals.

2. *Marine mining system* as described in Chapter 4.

3. *Outputs or effects* as described in Chapter 5 and including various environmental and socioeconomic effects.

4. *Public and private interests* include various individuals, groups, and institutions who act on the basis of available information and suspicions, as discussed in Chapters 1 and 5.

5. *Legal, value, and institutional context.*

6. *Decision makers in government and industry;* as described in Chapters 6 through 10.

trolling the implications of marine mining at each level. This study contains much of the information which could be used for such purposes at policy and program levels; however, use at the project level would necessitate research on specific sites and specific proposed operations, and this lies beyond the scope of the study.

With these potential uses and limitations of technology assessment for purposes of social control in mind, this study has been designed to acquire, analyze, and summarize information necessary for decision making at policy and program levels. Accordingly, research was conducted to address the following issues, and findings have been presented in the chapters noted:

- Minerals availability and general economic feasibility considerations derived from working experience in Chapter 3.
- Technological aspects of marine mining in Chapter 4.
- Environmental and other externalities of marine mining in Chapter 5.
- Resource commitments associated with marine mining in Chapters 3, 4, and 5.
- Legal, institutional, and political aspects of marine mining (elements of social control) in Chapters 6 through 10.

Finally, critical issues for resource management policy have been derived from the foregoing analyses and presented in Chapter 11, with recommendations.

NOTES

1. As defined by J. Coates in "Some Methods and Techniques for Comprehensive Impact Assessment," *Technological Forecasting and Social Change* 6, (1974): 341–57. This most commonly held concept of technology assessment reveals its potential as a means by which controls or management can be imposed to contain a technological development.

2. This describes a natural but not commonly held use of technology assessment as a method for determining incentives and other considerations which would serve to promote the achievement of desired technological developments. It has been described in M. Baram, "Technology Assessment and the World Health Organization" (Geneva: Office of Science and Technology, WHO, 1974). (Unpublished report.)

3. Where a specific objective has been agreed on by decision makers in government or industry, such as a low-emission automobile engine or low-noise aircraft and engine, the task of technology assessment becomes one of choosing between alternative technological means of reaching such objective. Various studies by the National Academy of Sciences, academicians and consultants, and federal agencies reveal the use of this approach as a form of technology assessment. See, for example, F. Grad. et al., *The Automobile and the Environment* (University of Oklahoma, 1974).

4. In the private sector, particularly in large corporations such as Philips, N.V., in Utrecht, special teams have been assembled and funded to determine new and marketable technological developments achievable through use of corporate resources and experience.

5. See M. Baram, "Social Control of Science and Technology," *Science* 172 (7 May 1971).

6. 42 U.S.C. 4321 et seq. (1970).

7. See Chapters 6 and 7.

8. Calvert Cliffs Coordinating Committee v. AEC, 2 ERC 1779 (1971). Also see "Preparation of Environmental Impact Statements: Guidelines," U.S. Council on Environmental Quality, 38 F.R. 20550-62 (August 1973).

9. 2 U.S.C. 471 et seq. (Supp. 1973).

10. See *Annual Reports*, Office of Technology Assessment, U.S. Congress.

11. For useful discussion of OTA, see J.G. Speth, "The Federal Role in Technology Assessment and Control," *Federal Environmental Law*, E. Dolgin and T. Guilbert, eds. (St. Paul: West Publishers, 1974).

12. *Mining in the Outer Continental Shelf and in the Deep Ocean* (Washington, D.C.: Marine Board, National Academy of Sciences, 1975).

13. G. Trimble, *Legal and Administrative Aspects of an Aquaculture Policy for Hawaii: An Assessment* (Hawaii Center for Science Policy and Technology Assessment, Honolulu, Hawaii, 1974).

14. E. Grabbe, *Exploration and Utilization of Manganese Nodule Deposits in the Pacific* (Symposium Proceedings, Hawaii Center for Science Policy and Technology Assessment, Honolulu, Hawaii, 1974).

15. D. Kash et al., *Energy Under the Oceans* (University of Oklahoma Press, 1973).

16. *North Sea Island Feasibility Study* conducted by Hydronamica-Bos Kalis N.V. (Rotterdam, The Netherlands, 1974).

17. For a survey and analysis of TA concepts and practices, see F. Hetman, *Society and the Assessment of Technology*, (Paris: OECD, 1973).

18. M. Baram. "Technology Assessment and Social Control," *Science* 180, 4085 (1973). Also published in *Jurimetrics* (American Bar Association) 14, 2 (Winter 1973).

Chapter 3

Hard Minerals: Availability Offshore and Development Experience

INTRODUCTION

Extensive hard mineral resources are to be found in the submerged lands under the territorial waters of most nations, in the continental shelves, and in the deep seabed.[1] Iron ore and coal are currently being mined from offshore regions of Britain, Canada, and Japan. Diamonds have been mined off the South African coast, and barite off the Alaskan coast. Tin off the coasts of Thailand and Indonesia, oyster shells off the Gulf Coast of the United States, and sand and gravel off the coast of the United Kingdom are now being dredged by commercial and governmental ventures. The annual value of these operations in 1971 was estimated to be $768.5 million.[2]

Offshore mining of hard minerals is of increasing interest, and plans are now being developed for significant expansion of marine mining activities. In the United States, the Department of the Interior is developing a program for leasing areas of the outer continental shelf to enable large-scale sand, gravel, and phosphorite extraction projects to take place.[3] Considerable interest in dredging for gold and other rare metals off the Alaskan coast[4] and in the harvesting of nodules containing manganese and other valuable minerals from the deep sea bed[5] is reflected by government research, commercial exploration, and the development of new technologies for exploration and mining.[6]

This chapter provides information on the availability of hard minerals offshore and on worldwide development experience. Because of differing technological and economic considerations, the minerals are divided into two categories: high-value, low-bulk; and low-value, high bulk.

A. HIGH-VALUE, LOW—BULK MINERALS

1. Gold and Platinum

Gold and platinum are two of the most valuable metals mined. With the price of gold soaring from $35 an ounce ($1.12 per gram) in 1969 to over $200 per ounce ($6.4 per gram) in 1975,[7] gold is now being intensively sought around the world, and the search for gold is extending to offshore areas as well. The source of gold and platinum is in intrusive igneous and metamorphic rocks. Since most of these rocks accessible to surface mining operations are much removed from the oceans and since the transport distance of high specific gravity gold and platinum particles is limited to about 9.4 miles (15 kilometers),[8] very few deposits of gold are found offshore near the surface of submerged lands. Where good sources of gold or platinum are drained by steep gradient streams or glaciers to beaches, further sorting can take place. Such is the origin of the beach and offshore gold of Alaska.

Gold may occur as marine detrital deposits that originate either from source rock on land or source rock on existing continental shelves. If the source rocks are on land, then the short transporting distances will restrict sea deposits to the vicinity of present shorelines and not into deeper waters. If the site of the source rock is in the present continental shelf, then the deposits are likely to be covered by hundreds or thousands of meters of sediments, with exceptions for small areas of subaerial rock outcrops and areas of high energy erosion. Thus, Emery and Noakes have concluded that most economic offshore deposits of gold are stream or alluvial deposits close to the primary source of gold on land. If these sources on land are near the existing shoreline, the placer deposits may extend to the beach or to the nearshore submerged portion of the continental shelf. It is unlikely that gold will be found or available for economic exploitation further offshore in the foreseeable future. In addition to the beach gold deposits off the coast of Alaska, similar deposits have been found off the coast of southern Oregon and northern California.[9] No other significant offshore deposits of gold have been reported for the United States.

Mott has traced the history of gold mining in the vicintiy of Nome, Alaska.[10] Historically, the equipment used for gold mining in this area has been primitive. Simple suction dredges for extraction, with pans or coco mat to separate the gold from the overburden, have been used. The latest mining system developed by Mott of NOMECO consists of a submerged track vehicle from which the material can be pumped by a jet eductor system to an offshore "mother ship" where the first separation and concentrating steps can take place. Concentrates may then be taken ashore for further processing and refining.

Platinum has been found at many locations in the United States, but significant amounts have been produced at only three sites. One of these sites is the Goodnews Bay area in the western region of Alaska, where the swampy estuarine areas have yielded more than half a million troy ounces (15.55 million grams) of platinum since 1926.[11] The bed of the Salmon River was worked using first a drag-line and then a bucket-ladder dredge. Mining continued to within 1 mile (1.6 km) of the ocean but turned upstream thereafter. The Goodnews Bay Mining Company has apparently located an offshore deposit since it converted its offshore prospecting permit to a mining license,[12] an action which requires a demonstration that a workable mineral deposit exists.[13]

2. Tin

Southern Asia is the world's major tin-producing region, and this great tin province stretches for over 1,800 miles (2,900 kilometers), from North Burma through peninsular Thailand and West Malaysia to the Indonesian "tin islands" of Bangka, Belitung (Billitan), and Singkep.[14] Although most of the cassiterite (SnO_2) mined in this region is from inland deposits, very considerable and increasing amounts have been mined from offshore areas, particularly around Bangka, Belitung, and Phuket. Interest in offshore deposits has grown as major inland deposits have become depleted, as offshore operations have yielded good results, and as sound geological reasoning now indicates that a number of new placer deposits as yet undiscovered may exist offshore. Figure 3-1 indicates that offshore dredging contributes a growing percentage of the tin mined in Thailand.

Dredging for cassiterite, the method generally used for current offshore mining operations, actually began in 1908, and since that time the number of dredges working has fluctuated. As of 1973, ten dredges were operating in Thai waters[15] and eleven in Indonesian waters.[16]

Most of the tin mined in Southeast Asia has come from placers containing the dense, inert mineral cassiterite (SnO_2) which has been liberated from hard rock (usually granite) by weathering processes

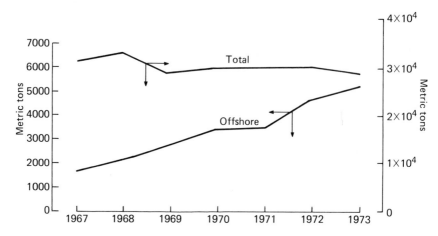

Figure 3-1. Tin Production in Thailand.

Source: Thai Department of Mineral Resources. 1974. *Mineral Production, Exports, and Domestic Consumption of Thailand, 1964-1973.* Bangkok.

during fairly recent geological periods.[17] The cassiterite is believed to have migrated, with the aid of gravity and flowing water, to form alluvial deposits. These deposits subsequently became concentrated when flowing water preferentially removed the associated lower specific gravity components of the same or somewhat greater size than the cassiterite grains. However, the brittle nature of cassiterite limits the natural transportation process to a distance of approximately 5 miles (8 km), after which the cassiterite particles become too fine to be economically recovered.[18] Cassiterite is also formed in situ, in submerged lands where the mineral was not part of a drowned drainage channel.[19]

The tin ore or *kaksa* (Chinese word for black sand) is particularly rich when found on top of bedrock and beneath an overburden of sand, clay, or silt. After the overburden has been stripped away, a bucket-ladder dredge is usually used to "clean" away the cassiterite.[20] In recent years, a subsidiary of Union Carbide has utilized a cutterhead suction dredge for this purpose. This has met with only limited success because of the nature of the dredging required and the often severe sea state in this monsoon area.[21] A series of jigs placed on board these massive dredges are used to concentrate the heavier cassiterite grains. Concentrates of about 20 percent to 40 percent tin are subsequently sent to the smelters onshore.

Exploration for new tin deposits is active along the eastern and western coasts of the Thai portion of the Malay Peninsula as well as along the western coast of Malaysia.[22] The Southeast Asian nations are aware of some of the environmental impacts of these offshore operations.[23] Since the take of cassiterite may be as low as 0.2 kg/m^3, large amounts of tailings are being discarded offshore; however, no major studies have been made of the environmental effects to date.

Tin has been found in Alaskan waters by a team from the University of Wisconsin, but no commercial interests have been announced.

3. Heavy Mineral Sands

Present data indicate that although deposits of heavy mineral sands, principally ilmenite, rutile, zircon, magnetite, and monazite, occur offshore, they appear to be of economic interest only for the future.

Titaniferous magnetite is mined from beach deposits in Japan, the Philippines, and Taiwan and from the sea floor off Japan.[24] Production from similar beach deposits in New Zealand and Australia[25] is also under consideration. Heavy mineral sands have been located along the Alaskan and the East and West coasts of the United States,[26] and exploration has been undertaken off the coast of Mozambique.[27]

The source of heavy mineral sands is crystaline rock. Deep weathering fractured the original rocks and separated out the unwanted and unstable minerals such as feldspar, garnet, and amphibole. The heavy mineral sand deposits were then formed by sorting and further weathering during transportation by running water. Economic deposits have been found only after the action of waves on beaches has sufficiently concentrated the heavy mineral sands. In general, modern beaches are richer in heavy mineral sands than submerged beaches.[28]

Given their need for iron ore, the Japanese have turned to the offshore region for iron sands. In 1961 it was reported that in the previous 4 years some 7 million tons (6.3 metric tons) of crude iron sands were dredged from 90 feet (30 m) of water in Tokyo Bay.[29] From 1962 to 1966, Yawata Iron and Steel Co. used a grab dredge to mine iron sands in Ariake Bay, off the southern tip of Kyushu Island, Japan.[30] Yawata reported an estimate of 30 million tons (27.5 million metric tons) of iron sands with assay of 56 percent iron and 12 percent titanium and employed processing to remove the unwanted titanium content. In 1966, the operation was abandoned due to the cost and competition from low-grade land reserves. Recent reports indicate that the Japanese are acquiring marine-dredged iron sands from New Zealand[31] and the Philippines.[32]

Because of the considerable deposits of these minerals onshore and available and the low grade of offshore deposits, there is little American interest in exploiting these offshore deposits.

4. Iron

Vein deposits of iron under the seafloor necessitate the use of non-dredging methods of marine mining, such as shaft mining as practiced on land. A mine is in operation near Jussaro Island, about 50 miles (80 km) southwest of Helsinki, where magnetite is mined from tabular veins under the Gulf of Finland.[33] The mine was sunk by driving shafts and drifts from land in the vicinity of the veins, with the veins being mined by shrinkstopping, a common land mining method.

In Newfoundland, an iron ore deposit which extends out under the Atlantic Ocean has been mined from entries on Bell Island. The ore reserves are estimated in the billions of tons;[34] however, the mine was closed in 1966 as operations became uneconomical.

5. Diamonds, Precious Minerals

Diamonds are one of the most elusive and valuable offshore minerals. A brief account of diamond mining offshore to date is given here, although prospects of diamonds off the U.S. coast appear negligible.

In 1927, following the discovery of rich diamondiferous marine terraces at Alexander Bay, south of the Orange River in Southwest Africa, Consolidated Diamond Mines began prospecting for diamonds offshore.[35] In 1961, further prospecting for diamonds began in earnest, and production was started in 1962.[36] Geological data suggest that the coastal diamonds were derived from inland sources within the drainage basin of the Orange River and were transported to the river mouth.[37]

Dredging for diamonds took place at depths of 30 to 120 feet (10–40 m), using suction and airlift dredges. After initial sorting by cyclones and centrifuges, diamonds were picked out of the gravels manually. However, the coast of Southwest Africa is particularly exposed to adverse weather, and several vessels were wrecked.[38] Because of the dangerous sea state and high operating costs, operations were suspended in 1971.[39] From 1962 through 1971, about 800,000 carats of diamonds were recovered by sea mining. Dredging for diamonds in Brazilian waters has recently been reported.[40]

Beiersdorf has reported on the history of marine mining for amber in the Baltic Sea.[41]

B. LOW-VALUE, HIGH-BULK MINERALS

1. Coal

The mining of undersea coal has been practiced in Great Britain since late in the nineteenth century.[47] Some collieries now extend under the sea for several miles. Standard techniques of marine mineral exploration, such as seismic soundings and drilling from offshore platforms and drillships, have been used to prove deposits.

Exploitation of undersea coal deposits has been accomplished by mine shafts sunk on land and extended underneath the seabed by tunneling. Generally, undersea coal mining is limited by the same conditions which govern mining on land: safety considerations and the costs of ventilation and transport as distance from the shaft increases. The danger of flooding from the sea is minimal if the proper precautions are taken. Safety regulations differ, but general rules, such as a prohibition on coal mining in the first 240 feet (80 m) beneath the seabed, prevail. Studies have shown that it would be feasible to extend a new undersea mine for 10 miles (16 km) offshore. Production figures for coal mined underneath the continental shelf of Great Britain are

	Production (tons)	Percentage of deep mined coal
1966–67	10,470,000	6.5
1967–68	10,908,000	7

A program of exploration has shown that there are at least 550 million tons (495 million metric tons) of workable coal reserves in the continental shelf of the British coast.

The offshore coal reserves of Japan are also considerable and are located in a large region extending from Hokkaido in the north to the southernmost island of Kyushu.[43] The most important coal fields are situated near the coast, with coal-bearing strata extending from the land to the offshore areas. Exploitation of these offshore coal reserves has been practiced since 1860, initially by shafts and tunnels from the shore and more recently by shafts and tunnels from natural and artificial islands. Bituminous coal, anthracite, and coking coals have been mined by these offshore methods.

The deepest working areas are some 1,800 feet (700 m) below the seafloor. Water depth over the working areas may be as much as 150 feet (50 m) to points some 4.4 miles (7 km) from shore. Because of the depth and distance from shore of these activities, it became necessary to sink ventilation shafts from artificial islands offshore. These artificial islands stand in water 30 feet (10 m) deep at high tide. While total production of coal from land and offshore reserves in Japan has decreased in the decade of the 1960s, the amount of coal won from beneath the seabed has increased, and by 1969, offshore coal accounted for 29 percent of coal mined in Japan. Given the extensive proven deposits of land-based coal in the United States, it is unlikely that there will be major interest in either exploring for or mining offshore coal in the United States for the foreseeable future.

2. Calcium Carbonate

Calcium carbonate is recovered from the sea in the form of shells, aragonite, coral, and the calcareous algae, *Lithothamnia.*

The United States is the largest producer of offshore-derived calcium carbonate, mainly in the form of shells. In 1970, some 21.7 million short tons (19.5 million metric tons) of shells were produced,[44] and most of the shells were dredged from off the coast of the Gulf states.

Atlantic states   1.5 million tons (1.35 million metric tons)
Gulf states   20.1 million tons (18.1 million metric tons)
Pacific states   0.1 million tons (0.09 million metric tons)

Major producers of dredged shells are located in the San Antonio Bay area of Texas, in the coastal parishes of Louisiana, and in Mobile Bay, Alabama. There is also shell dredging in the vicinity of Baltimore and in the San Francisco Bay. Live coral is also harvested for making decorations and jewelry.[45]

Dredged shells are used for the following purposes:

1. Manufacture of Portland Cement
2. Raw material for magnesium and aluminum production
3. Base material for road and highway construction
4. Raw material for caustic soda and lime production

By-products from shell dredging are also used in several other industrial processes such as those for producing fertilizer, oil rigs, dry ice, cattle and poultry feed, plate glass, and firebrick.

Reef shells began forming at the end of the Wisconsin Ice Age some 7,000 to 10,000 years ago.[46] After the rise in the sea level, oysters lived in abundance in bays and estuaries. However, this shellfish growth area gradually became smaller and shallower, and salinity decreased through natural phenomena. As a result, the oyster reefs died out and became covered by layers of sediments. Current deposits being dredged are those more accessible in enclosed bays and estuaries, with no significant overburden, and are of relatively recent origin. The deposits on the continental shelf have not been exploited. It has been estimated that up to 100 million tons (91 million metric tons) of shell lie on the continental shelf off the Gulf Coast.[47]

Shell dredging in Texas started in 1880.[48] The use of the shovel and wheelbarrow in the 1880s gave way to the mechanical dredge in 1905 and to the hydraulic dredge in 1912. In 1916, a method was found to utilize shell in cement manufacturing. Another boost to the shell industry occurred in 1929 with the discovery of a process to make lime from shell. In 1973, the shell-dredging industry in Texas had delivered more than 100 million cubic yards (7.7 $\times$ 10^7 m^3) of oyster shells to manufacturers who then turned them into more than 100 billion pounds (4.5 $\times$ 10^{10} kg) of products.[49]

Concentrated dredging started in the early 1950s in San Antonio Bay, Texas, the only bay in Texas where the oyster shells contain the chemical constituents necessary for the production of white cement. San Antonio Bay also has the dual advantage of being of only intermediate depth and immediately accessible to the Intracoastal Waterway. From 1969 to 1973, three companies held nonexclusive permits to mine shell in San Antonio Bay: Lone Star Industries, Parker Brothers, Inc., and Horton and Horton, Inc. In total, they operated from 3 to 5 hydraulic dredges, with an average combined annual production of approximately 7 million cubic yards (6 million m^3).

In Louisiana, shell dredging was initiated before 1913 to raise operating revenues for the Louisiana Conservation Commission.[50] Since 1950, the responsibility for control has been vested in the Louisiana Wildlife and Fisheries Commission. Data indicate that production rose from 0.3 million cubic yards (0.2 million m^3) in 1960 to some 10.0 million cubic yards (7.7 million m^3) in 1966, with an annual value of about $12 million by 1969. Production is concentrated in Cameron, Orleans, St. Tammany, and St. Mary parishes, in the areas of Lake Ponchartrain and Lake Maurepas.

In Alabama, shell dredging is concentrated in Mobile Bay.[51] In 1947, Southern Industries Inc. received the rights from the state of Alabama to dredge and sell dead reef oyster shells. The actual operations were carried out by Radcliff Materials Inc., who have been dredging about 1.5 million cubic yards (0.8 million m^3) per year. Since 1947, over 42 million cubic yards (32 million m^3)

of shell have been dredged. Throughout the Gulf Coast, shell recovery is accomplished by cutterhead hydraulic suction, with the use of screens and washers for sorting and initial processing.

Dredging shells in the San Francisco Bay for use in cement production has been halted. Since 1930, some 40 million tons (36 million metric tons) of shells have been dredged.[52]

In Iceland, where there are no limestone deposits, dredged shells provide the raw materials for cement manufacture.[53] The shell deposit is 10 miles (16 km) offshore in Faxa Bay, southwest of Akranes. Mining is conducted by means of a hydraulic suction dredge. The maximum digging depth of such dredges is 140 feet (47 m), and the vessels can operate in up to 6 foot waves. The deposit is free flowing and ranges from 3 feet (1 m) to 13 feet (4 m) in thickness, at a maximum depth of 140 feet (47 m) of water. The dredge has a hopper capacity of 1,000 cubic yards (765 cubic meters) each and discharges onshore by means of a wet pumping system. Production in 1966 came to 135,000 tons (123,074 metric tons).

The dredging of precious coral is a major industry in Hawaii which has grown from an annual value of $2.5 million in 1969 to $7.5 million in 1974.[54] The industry began in 1958 with the discovery of a large bed of black coral off Maui and received further impetus in 1966 with the discovery of pink coral off Makapuu, Oahu. These corals occur at 1,200 foot (400 m) depths, with harvesting by means of manned submersibles. The products are used as settings in jewelry, which increases the value of the coral by a factor of 10.

Live coral is "mined" or "harvested" for decorative purposes in Taiwan, using a two man submersible vessel.[55] For some years, *Lithothamnia* has been dredged off the north coast of Brittany. Production runs annually at the rate of about 300,000 tons (276,000 metric tons), of which 21,000 tons (74,000 metric tons) are exported as "maerl." Dredging of coral sand from Suva Harbor, Fiji, increased from some 69,000 tons (62,500 metric tons) in 1968 to nearly 87,000 tons (79,000 metric tons) in 1970. Shells are dredged from the Wadden Sea for agricultural and chemical use in the Netherlands.

Aragonite is being mined in the Bahamas for export to the United States.[56] Aragonite sand is formed by laminar precipitation of calcium carbonate from the ocean around nuclei such as shell particles or fecal pellets. Aragonite is basically a smooth-surfaced, rounded, granular particle ranging in size from 20 to 200 mesh (1.3 mm to 0.13 mm). Analysis of deposits has shown that the aragonite is more than 97.9 percent pure calcium carbonate.

The aragonite deposit is located 50 miles (80 km) east of Miami,

Florida, and is estimated to be 22 miles (35 km) long, 2.5 miles (4.0 km) wide, and about 20 feet (6.1 m) thick with a content of approximately 1 billion tons (0.9×10^9 metric tons). There is no overburden of sediment or other solids over the aragonite, a cutter-head suction dredge is used for mining, and the only production processing needed consists of dewatering. Production, which in 1974 reached 1,541,000 tons (1.5×10^6 metric tons), was unprofitable but plans are underway to expand the operation.[57] Similar deposits of aragonite exist all over the Great Bahamas Bank.

3. Sand and Gravel

Sand and gravel occur as unconsolidated, transported deposits ranging in size from silt (0.0039 mm) to boulders and are formed by the weathering of bedrock brought about by wind, ice, and water.[58] The sand and gravel industry is the largest nonfuel mineral industry, in terms of volume, in the United States,[59] and construction accounts for 96 percent of all domestic use.

Much of the sand and gravel mined today is taken from old river-beds (deposits along present and former streams that drained the melted Pleistocene ice sheets) and glaciated deposits. Where these deposits are not available, construction aggregates in the form of sand and gravel have been produced from crushed stone, but the use of crushed stone in making concrete requires more cement than is required when sand and gravel are used and more care is needed in mixing and pouring. The construction industry also consumes most of the crushed stone produced.

The historical trend in the consumption of these materials by the construction industry, shown in Figure 3-2, indicates that total consumption has tripled in the period from 1950 to 1970, with similar growth rates for crushed stone as for sand and gravel. The figure also indicates that the construction industry consumed virtually all aggregates produced in 1971, as it did in 1950. The advent of the Interstate Highway System in the late 1950s undoubtedly contributed to the rise in demand.

Although sand and gravel are the most ubiquitous terrestrial resource and crustal abundance is essentially infinite, several factors limit availability of the resource. The low value per unit of sand and gravel makes for a small profit margin. A major element of the price of sand and gravel is the transportation cost, which may exceed the cost of extraction and processing at inland plants. Thus it is uneconomical to transport aggregates over long distances for use at construction sites. Another major factor limiting supply is conflict over land use; land rich in sand and gravel deposits has become more

U.S. SOURCES AND USES OF
MAJOR NONMETALLIC CONSTRUCTION
RAW MATERIALS

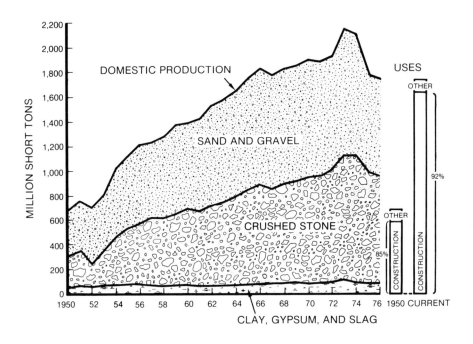

Figure 3-2. United States Supplies and Uses of Major Nonmetallic Construction Materials, 1950-1971.

Source: J.D. Morgan, Jr. 1973. "Future Use of Minerals: The Question of 'Demand'," in E.N. Cameron (ed.). *The Mineral Position of the United States, 1975-2000*. Madison: University of Wisconsin Press.

valuable for building developments or recreation or is subject to environmental or other restrictions and has thus been removed from future mineral production. Such restriction has been intensified by rapid suburban growth and developing environmental interests. A third major factor is the increasingly more stringent pollution controls on extraction of minerals and the application of common law concepts to impose restraints and liability on the "nuisance" aspects of pit and quarry operations and associated trucking. Thus higher transportation costs, built-over or restricted deposits, and stricter environmental controls have converged to limit the supply of sand and gravel.

Projections of future demands for sand and gravel are uncertain since the demand is a derived demand. Tables 3-1 and 3-2 detail the end use of construction minerals—Table 3-1 contains comparative data for 1959 and 1971 and Table 3-2 contains findings from an input-output analysis of the construction aggregates industry conducted for the Department of Commerce in 1963. The tables explain the nature of uses by the construction industry, the primary consumer of aggregates, and indicate, for example, that highway construction consumes about 50 percent of the aggregates produced.

Table 3-1. Consumption of Mineral Aggregates by the Construction Industry in the United States, 1959 and 1972 (in millions of tons)

	1959			1972		
Construction use	Sand	Gravel	Crushed stone	Sand	Gravel	Crushed stone
Building	123	114		188	153	
Paving	105	313		131	280	
Fill[a]	16	17		49	43	
Railroad ballast	1	5		1	2	
Other	6	7		10	13	
Concrete aggregates						134
Bituminous aggregates						83
Macadam aggregates			357			33
Road-base aggregates						337
Surface treatment aggregates						52
Other						113
Total construction	250	456	357	378	492	752
Cement manufacture			91			109
Percentage of total production used in construction	92.9	98.9	12.2	92.8	97.3	81.6
Total production	269	461	582	408	506	922

Source: *Mineral Yearbooks.*
[a]Fill is "unprocessed aggregates," used for road base.

Table 3-2. Percentage Consumption of Mineral Aggregates by Construction Type, 1963

Construction type	Sand and gravel	Crushed stone	Com- bined
Residential			
Single family houses	11.13	8.04	9.81
2-4 Family houses	3.30	2.68	3.04
5 or more family houses	1.80	1.08	1.49
Additions and alterations	2.53	1.75	2.20
Total residential construction	18.93	13.55	16.54
Nonresidential			
Hotels and motels	0.59	0.42	0.51
Religious buildings	0.77	0.60	0.70
Industrial buildings	3.17	2.51	2.89
Parking garages	0.23	0.10	0.17
Hospitals	1.07	1.19	1.12
Office buildings	1.84	1.30	1.61
Stores and restaurants	1.69	1.47	1.59
Schools and dormitories	3.68	3.40	3.56
Public works and utilities	4.55	3.48	4.09
Other nonresidential buildings	3.19	4.12	3.59
Additions and alterations	6.23	9.42	7.59
Total nonresidential construction	30.47	30.10	30.30
Total construction	49.40	43.65	46.84
Highways			
New highway construction	26.58	34.37	29.90
Repair and maintenance	22.34	19.93	21.32
Total highway construction	48.92	54.30	51.21
Railroads			
Railroad construction	0.75	0.84	0.79
Repair and maintenance	1.11	1.21	1.16
Total railroad construction	1.86	2.05	1.95
Total	100.00	100.00	100.00

Source: L. Bronitsky. 1973. "The Economics of Construction Mineral Aggregates with an Analysis of the Industry in the Greater New York Metropolitan Area." Ph.D. Dissertation, Rensselaer Polytechnic Institute.

A large portion of the aggregates used for highway construction is designated as "fill" in Table 3-1, and this alone accounts for much of the increase in consumption from 1959 to 1971. Thus the amount of the sand and gravel demand in the future will depend largely on the volume of future construction of highways and other major facilities. Figure 3-3 presents alternative scenarios, using 5 and 20 year trends and projections developed by the Bureau of Mines.[60] However, other expert projections that have been developed are 2 to 3 times the 5 and 20 years trends, and there is therefore considerable uncertainty of outlook.

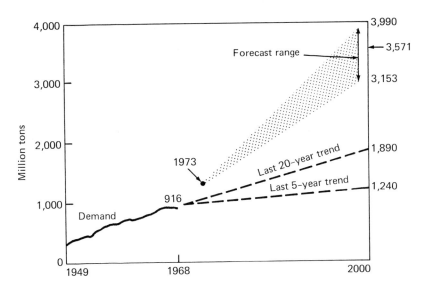

Figure 3-3. Projected Sand and Gravel Demand.

Source: J.D. Cooper. 1972. "Sand and Gravel," in 1970 *Minerals Facts and Problems*. Washington: Government Printing Office.

The offshore areas have been considered as a future alternate source of construction aggregates.[61] Offshore extraction offers several distinct advantages. First, marine transportation costs are much lower, and sand and gravel can be brought directly to urban waterfronts, close to the center of demand in coastal metropolitan regions. Second, marine dredging, when properly conducted, does not result in the nuisance and loss of amenity problems normally associated with upland pits and quarries. Finally, the marine deposits indicated for the offshore regions are so large that depletion does not appear to be a significant concern.

Geology. Sand covers much of the continental shelves of the United States. Although gravel deposits have also been determined, they are much less frequent. There are several possible origins of these offshore deposits.

One of the prime mechanisms for forming sand and gravel deposits on the continental shelf is glaciation. For example, numerous sand and gravel deposits are found in the wide shelf off New England, as indicated in Figure 3-4. The extent of the last glacial period, which includes areas such as Georges Bank where gravel is abundant, is indicated in Figure 3-5. Areas south of the limits of glaciation

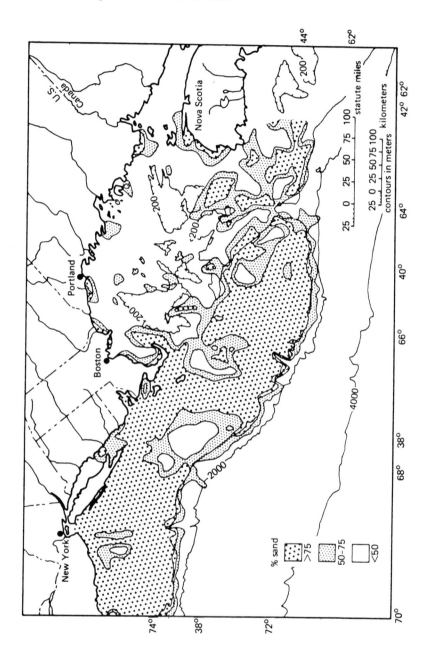

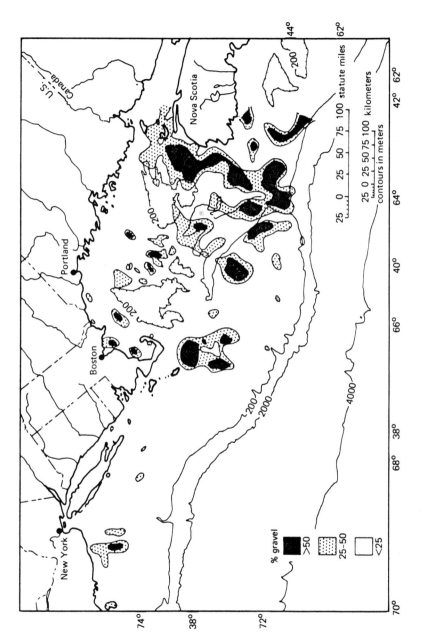

Figure 3-4. Sand and Gravel on the Continental Shelf off New England.

Source: F.T. Manheim. 1972. "Mineral Resources off the Northeastern Coast of the United States," *U.S.G.S. Circular 669.*

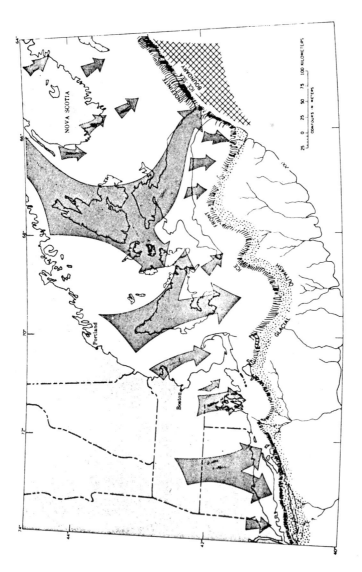

Figure 3-5. Maximum Extent of Glaciation off Northeastern United States. Arrows indicate major currents of movement of ice sheets.

Source: J. Schlee and R.M. Pratt. 1970. "Atlantic Continental Shelf and Slope of the United States—Gravel of the Northeastern part," *U.S.G.S. Prof. Paper 529-H.*

contain surficial deposits of sand and gravel which were outwashed from streams draining the ice front. These deposits are now submerged because of the subsequent rise in sea level.[62]

Another major source of continental shelf sand and gravel consists of drowned beaches and river valleys. When sea levels were much lower, river valleys extended to current submerged lands, and these ancient river beds and their flood plains became rich deposits of aggregates. These rivers also carried enormous sediment loads to the sea at flood conditions,[63] with the sediments transported by longshore currents to form beaches. Thus valuable offshore river and beach deposits lie in the drowned river valleys of the Los Angeles River,[64] and of the Hudson, Delaware, and Susquehanna rivers.[65]

Coastal erosion is thought to be another contributor of sand and gravel. The natural erosion of the coastline, particularly cliffs and reefs, has provided the sand and gravel deposits off the east coast of Florida,[66] for example. The loss of sands can also be observed in many parts of the nearshore submerged lands, especially at beaches. This dynamic nature of the movement of sand must be recognized and understood if coastal and beach erosion is not to result from offshore mining. The major sink for such sand appears to be submarine canyons,[67] and loss down submarine canyons is more dramatic if canyon heads extend close to the shore, as they do off California. The deep ocean is the ultimate sink of continental shelf sediments.

Essentially, the coastline can be compartmentalized into closed littoral cells. In these littoral cells, sediments come from rivers and streams as well as from shoreward transport by waves. Longshore currents move the sediments parallel to the coast, and sediments are then either lost to submarine canyons or deposited in quiet areas such as Cape Cod Bay. It is obvious that numerous physical principles and analytical methods must be considered as significant features in the design of any future programs for offshore mining. To illustrate with a simple example, see Figure 3–6: mining at site *B* would capture sand generally lost to deep canyons and would probably have no effect on coastal sand budget; however, mining at point *A* would disrupt the sand budget along the coast between *A* and *C* and could cause erosion, for example, at *A′*. If coastal mining is to be properly managed, such data and principles about sand transport, velocities, and budgets must be used in program design and implementation.

Experiences in Marine Sand and Gravel Mining. Of all the hard minerals currently exploited on the continental shelf, sand and gravel are by far the largest categories in terms of both volume and value. In this section, existing data about current production are briefly reviewed.

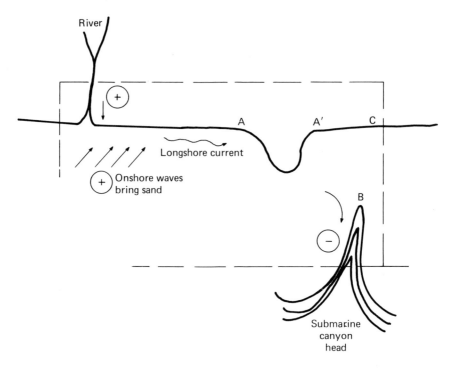

Figure 3-6.   The Littoral Cell as a Guide to Sand and Gravel Extraction.

   The largest offshore sand and gravel industry at present is based in the United Kingdom and the Netherlands. In 1955, British production of continental shelf aggregates came to 3.8 million tons (3.4 million metric tons), or 5.5 percent of total British aggregates production; by 1971, it had increased to 15 million tons (13.5 million metric tons), or 12 percent of total production. Export trade has grown as well, as gravel dredged off the eastern coast of England has been sold to users in France and the Netherlands. Hess[68] and Archer[69] have provided details about the marine sand and gravel industry of Great Britain. In 1971, 32 companies were operating with over 75 dredges, most of which were suction hopper dredges. Currently, the third generation of dredges is being used, along with highly sophisticated navigation, extraction, and processing equipment. The hopper dredges range up to 11,015 tons (10^4 metric tons) of capacity and are capable of working around the clock and in very severe sea states. The two main types of hopper dredges, the anchor dredge and the trailing hopper dredge, are discussed in the following chapter on technological feasibility; the relative environmental merits of the various types of dredges are discussed in the chapter on environmental impacts.

Some dredges contain shipboard equipment for classifying aggregates into sizes needed for local markets. Unloading at dockside is accomplished by several methods, including wet pumping, scraper buckets, and conveyor belts. All of these dredges use a plain suction head with no cutter heads. It is very difficult to project the potential costs of mining off the United States from this British data base since wages are relatively low in Great Britain, and the equipment, geological conditions, and market features differ.

Considerable interest and activities are found in other European coastal countries, especially the Netherlands.[70] However, since there are no significant gravel deposits in the Dutch sector of the North Sea, production is currently focused on inland waterways and on channel dredging projects. Plans for the construction of coastal protection facilities and for the construction of large landfill sea islands for the siting of high-risk industrial and energy facilities are being developed by Dutch officials and private interests. These could lead to greatly increased programs for offshore sand and gravel mining. The current production figures for several European nations are tabulated as follows:

Marine Sand and Gravel Production in Europe

Nation	1972 Production	
United Kingdom	12.8×10^6 yd^3	9.8×10^6 m^3
Sweden	0.72	0.55
Ireland	0.13	0.1
The Netherlands	6.5–13	5–10
Germany	3.5	2.7
France	2.6	2.0
Finland	0.5	0.4
Denmark	8.1	6.2

In recent years, Japan's building aggregates industry has undergone a transition from reliance on river production of sand and gravel, to crushed rock, to mining from the seafloor.[71] In 1971, 60 million tons (54 million metric tons) of aggregates were extracted from the sea, constituting 19 percent of total Japanese production.

Most of the ocean mining for sand and gravel in Japan is conducted by small vessels of less than 200 tons (180 metric tons) using the clamshell type of dredge. There is considerable concern in Japan that if suction type dredges are used for mining, toxic pollutants presently settled in coastal sediments will be disturbed and resuspended in the overflow from exploitation processes. This concern is derived from that nation's tragic experiences with cadmium and mercury pollution which, in recent years, entered fish and rice food chains and caused serious health problems for Japanese consumers.

The Ports and Harbor Research Institute has developed totally enclosed clamshell dredges to limit such risks arising from present operations.

Japan does not have an extensive continental shelf; but with its higher population density and land use and rugged relief, it can be expected that the role of marine sand and gravel will be expanded in the future despite potential hazards.

In the United States, there is little mining of sand and gravel on the continental shelf itself although there is some production in bays and estuaries. Often these activities are carried out in conjunction with channel dredging projects, particularly in the New York Harbor area. The state of New York licenses offshore sand extraction in an area called the East Bank, adjacent to Ambrose Channel, the main shipping channel for New York Harbor.[72] In this area, over 10 million cubic yards (13 million m^3) of high quality sand are extracted yearly to keep shipping channels open and for use as fill in highway construction and land reclamation. The Construction Aggregates Corporation has a large hopper barge, the *Ezra Sensibar*, which operates in this area.[73] It has a hopper capacity of 16,000 cubic yards (20,000 m^3) and can usually obtain 2 loads per day from the East Bank. Since propulsion is provided by a tug, the delicate coupling between the tug and the *Ezra Sensibar* makes it impossible to operate in seas of more than 3 foot (1 m) waves.

Beach and submerged beach mining have been conducted off Monterey, California, for many years. Statistics indicate that some 3 million cubic yards (2.3 million cubic meters) were mined in 18 months during 1971 and 1972,[74] using draglines and front loaders for excavation. The sands mined here are for industrial uses such as glass making and command a much higher value than sands for use as construction minerals. Sand is also mined at Papohaku Beach, Molokai, in Hawaii.[75] The operations have been minor and are now the subject of litigation by the state.

Marine sand and gravel is also exploited elsewhere.[76] For example, about 1.35 million tons (1.5 million metric tons) of sand were dredged off Hong Kong, in 1972. Production off Thailand is now also taking place, but statistics are difficult to obtain for these relatively small new operations.

Prospects for the United States. The pressures in the United States that are leading to interest in offshore sources of sand and gravel have been briefly discussed. In addition to interests in offshore sand and gravel for use as construction aggregates, the U.S. Army Corps of Engineers is concerned about obtaining vast amounts of sand for artificial nourishment of beaches and for erosion control. Their sand inventory program has become one of the major sources of data regarding exploitable offshore deposits.[77] Data on some typical nearshore marine deposits that have been delineated are presented in Table 3–3. These are gross estimates, since the test cores have not been analyzed quantitatively to date. In addition, many commercially attractive deposits exist further offshore, as depicted in Figure 3–4.

The potential deposits of sand and gravel off the northeastern coast of the United States have been delineated in detail by Schlee and his associates.[78] The continental shelf off California has also been studied extensively.[79] The state of Hawaii[80] has conducted extensive mineral surveys around the islands. Hawaii may be particularly interested in using offshore sands for construction in light of

Table 3.3. Some Typical Nearshore Marine Deposits Delineated by the U.S. Army Corps of Engineer's Sand Inventory Program

Grid Site	Approximate area surveyed (statute miles^2)	Approximate volume (million cubic yards)
Maine		
Saco Bay	10	123
Massachusetts		
Cape Cod Bay (west)	50	51
Massachusetts Bay (Boston)	70	32
Plum Island	55	54
Connecticut		
Bridgeport	50	130
Rhode Island		
Point Judith area	25	141
New Jersey		
Sandy Hook	50	475
Manasquan	25	60
Barnegat	75	448
Little Egg Harbor	120	180
Cape May	340	1880
Florida		
Fernandina	120	70
Jacksonville	60	90
St. Augustine	115	40
Cape Kennedy	190	170
Fort Pierce	250	200
Miami	17	30

Source: D.B. Duane, "Sand Inventory Program," *Shore and Beach,* 37, no. 2, 12; *Transactions of National Symposium on Ocean Sciences and Engineering of the Continental Shelf,* (Phila., Pa., 1968, 1969).

the Shoreline Setback Act (Hawaii Revised Statutes Section 205–33, amended 1973, 1974), which prohibits coastal mining of sand and gravel between the coastal setback line and an offshore point that is (1) at least 1000 feet (333 m) from shore and (2) in water at least 30 feet (10 m) deep. There is, however, some doubt whether offshore sands around the islands are of construction quality.

Commercial interest has focused on Stellwagon Bank north of Cape Cod, Massachusetts, on an area off Point Loma in the San Diego area, and on the Great Lakes.[81] In recent years, however, commercial interests offshore have been largely dormant due to uncertainties in environmental impacts, market conditions, and legal arrangements. There is, however, little uncertainty that the deposits are exploitable at prices competitive with those for sand and gravel extracted from inland sites for users in coastal cities.

Recently the Department of the Interior announced its intention to make outer continental shelf lands available for hard minerals extraction under its authority as provided by the Outer Continental Shelf Lands Act.[82] With the vast quantities of marine sand and gravel capable of being extracted, it is necessary to assess how this potential American industry would affect the natural, economic, and social environments before program implementation.

4. Phosphorite

Phosphorite on the continental shelf may be another mineral of significant economic interest. Phosphorite occurs on the ocean floor as encrustations, nodules, muds, and sands with various assays of calcium phosphate. Calcium phosphate is found in nature as apatite $(Ca_5 (PO_4)_3 F_2)$.[83]

Phosphorite contains additional elements in the crystal lattice and has a variable composition which can be represented as $Ca_5 (PO_4, CO_3)_3 (F, Cl, OH)_2$. Phosphate deposits on land are used extensively for fertilizer production. However, marine phosphorite contains an abundant admixture of other minerals which not only lowers its phosphate content but also makes it difficult to beneficiate for use. It has been suggested that phosphorus deposits on the seafloor originate from the weathering of rocks on land. When the phosphorus reaches the ocean, it either is subject to utilization and incorporation by biological organisms or remains in solution while moving to deeper waters.[84] Biologically, utilized phosphorus is precipitated to the ocean floor by excretion and death of organisms.

Another theory provides that most ocean phosphorite is formed by upwelling.[85] In certain areas of the ocean, circulation brings cold, deep waters with high concentrations of phosphorus to the surface where, as pH and temperature increase, phosphorus is precipitated either inorganically or biochemically in the form of apatite. Areas of upwelling are also areas of intense biological productivity, and organisms incorporate phosphorus into their tissues, only to release them later in excretions and death. Since phosphorite occurrence is related to upwelling, a common oceanic phenomenon, it is a reasonable speculation that marine phosphorite is widespread and abundant, although little actual survey has been performed.

Published data regarding marine phosphorite deposits are largely limited to areas off Southern California, Baja California, South Africa, and New Zealand. A mining venture was attempted by Global Marine and Collier Carbon in the Forty-Mile Bank area off San Diego.[86] Reserves were estimated to be 5 million tons (4.5 million metric tons), but the phosphorite found was of low concentration, and the site also coincided with a military munitions dump. The project was curtailed. In 1963 and 1964, Lockheed Aircraft and International Minerals and Chemicals made an extensive study of the phosphorite deposits off Southern California.[87] A potential reserve of 12.5 million tons (11.2 million metric tons) of phosphorite nodules and 50 million tons (45 million metric tons) of phosphate sands was estimated. However, phosphate concentrations of the nodules averaged 27 percent, much below that of land-based commercial deposits. It was concluded that it would be uneconomical to exploit the deposits at that time.

Santo Domingo Bay, Baja California (Mexico), was also explored for phosphorite deposits.[88] In situ analysis showed that the phosphorite sand deposits contained 5 percent to 12 percent phosphate. A deposit of 22 million tons (20 million metric tons) was estimated.

Off Savannah, Georgia, a large low-grade phosphate deposit with huge reserves has been delineated beneath 70 to 80 feet (23–27 meters) of overburden under salt marshes and coastal waters.[89]

In New Zealand, surficial deposits of phosphorite nodules, of about 20 percent to 30 percent phosphate concentration, have been found in more than 3,000 feet (1,000 meters) of water on the Chatham Rise, about 310 miles (500 kilometers) east of the North Island.[90]

Despite such large deposits of phosphorite close to shore, much of it within the technical feasibility of modern dredging techniques, marine phosphorites have not yet been developed. The explanation is twofold. First, the grade of marine deposits is too low and the impurities too difficult to remove, rendering such deposits uneconomical at present. Second, there are extensive high-grade deposits on land. In the United States alone, where annual production is 110 million tons (100 million metric tons), indicated reserves consist of 16,200 million tons (14,500 million metric tons). Reserves in North Africa may be four times as great.[91]

There are, however, special circumstances which may make marine phosphorite exploitation attractive. Nations with marine deposits may seek to mine them for particular local needs, for avoiding destruction of on-land deposit sites, or for balance-of-payment considerations.

5. Barite

Barite is one of the few minerals recovered from consolidated rock occurring on the seafloor.[92] The only current sea-mining operation is at Castle Islands, Alaska, south of Juneau. The barite recovered is used as drilling mud for oil and gas operations.

The Castle Islands lie in the limestone belt of southeastern Alaska. The limestone has been locally metamorphosed and highly faulted and folded. Some of the limestone has been replaced by barite, and in the ore now being exploited there is generally a total replacement with over 90 percent $BaSO_4$. The barite is a massive, finely crystalline rock, in color gradation from white through dark gray to bluish gray. The Alaskan barite deposit originally constituted a natural island. Mining has removed that island and now continues to exploit a submerged synclinal ore body.

Geophysical, geochemical, and drilling work has proven about 2.5 million tons (2.25 million metric tons) of drilling-mud quality ore. The ore body lies under 20 feet (6 m) of water, and the maximum thickness of the ore ranges up to 100 feet (30 m). Overlying the barite is an overburden or detrital zone up to 50 feet (15 m) thick, consisting of fine, silty, dark gray to black mud. This material contains from 10 percent to 80 percent barite, which can be separated using a series of screens and washing.

Mining is carried out by drilling, blasting, and dredging. After the barite rock is drilled and blasted, a clamshell dredge takes the broken rock to storage piles for processing at a different site. Processing consists of a crusher, screens, dryers, and grinders mounted on a beached vessel, from which pulverized drilling mud is produced.

Production at the Castle Island mine is between 1,000 and 2,000 tons (900–1,800 metric tons) per day. Mining can take place about 8 months of the year, even though tides may run as much as 20 feet (6 meters), winds 150 mph (240 km/hour), currents 5 knots (9.3 km/hour), and temperatures below 0°f (–18°C).

Although there have been reports of other offshore deposits of barite,[93] the very large supplies of on-land resources may preclude extensive consideration of offshore resources.

NOTES

1. J. Albers, "Seabed Mineral Resources: A Survey," *Science and Public Affairs* 29, no. 10, (1973): 33. Also see the inventory of OCS hard minerals contained in *Outer Continental Shelf Policy Issues,* Committee on Interior and Insular Affairs, U.S. Senate, 92d Cong., 2d sess. (1972), pp. 219-65.

2. A. Archer, "Economics of Off-Shore Exploration and Production of Solid Minerals on the Continental Shelf," *Ocean Management* 1, 5 (1973). Archer's estimate includes the extraction of bromine, magnesium, and other minerals from sea water, a process and aspect of offshore mineral resources not dealt with in this research project.

3. *Draft Environmental Impact Statement on Proposed Outer Continental Shelf Hard Mineral Mining, Operating, and Leasing Regulations* (Washington, D.C.: Department of the Interior, Bureau of Land Management, February 1974).

4. M. Mott, "Gold Potential of Beach Placers Near Nome, Alaska" (Paper presented at the Fifth Underwater Mining Institute, University of Wisconsin, Milwaukee, 1974).

5. *Mineral Resources of the Deep Sea Bed,* Hearings of Subcommittee on Minerals, Materials, and Fuels of the Committee on Interior and Insular Affairs, U.S. Senate, 93d Cong., 1st sess. (May 1973).

6. See, for example, P.A. Smith, "Underwater Mining, Insight into Current U.S. Thinking," *Mining Magazine* 7 (1972); and *Mining in the Outer Continental Shelf and in the Deep Ocean* (Washington, D.C.: National Academy of Sciences, 1975).

7. Gold prices at the London gold exchange exceeded $200 per ounce on December 30, 1974.

8. K.O. Emery and L.C. Noakes, "Economic Placer Deposits of the Continental Shelf," *CCOP Tech. Bull. (UNECAFE)* 1, 95 (1968).

9. V.E. McKelvey, "Mineral Potential of the Submerged Part of the U.S.," *Ocean Industry* 3, 9 (1968): 37; T.A. Wilson and J.L. Mero, "Economic Deposits of the California Offshore Area," in *Geology of Northern California,* E.H. Bailey, ed. (San Francisco: California Division of Mines and Geology, 1966); C.H. Nelson and D.M. Hopkins, *Sedimentary Processes and Distribution of Particulate Gold in the Northern Bering Sea,* USGS Prof. Papers 689 (1972).

10. See note 4, *supra.*

11. J.B. Mertie, Jr., *Economic Geology of the Platinum Metals,* USGS Prof. Paper 630 (1969).

12. Personal communications from Mr. Pedro Denton, chief, Minerals Section, Alaska Division of Lands, to William Lee, September 21, 1974.

13. 11 Alaska Administrative Code 86.530.

14. K.F.G. Hosking, "The offshore tin deposits of Southeast Asia," *CCOP Tech. Bull (UNECAFE)* 5, 112 (1971).

15. Thai Department of Mineral Resources, *Mineral Production Exports and Domestic Consumption of Thailand, 1964-1973* (Bangkok: Economic and Information Division, 1974).

16. A. Tajib, "Tin Dredging Developments in Indonesia," *Proc. VI World Dredging Conference* (San Pedro, Ca.: WODCON, 1975), p. 5.

17. See note 14, *supra.*

18. See note 8, *supra.*

19. Personal interview with M.C. Piriyadis Diskul, chief, Economic and Information Division, Thai Department of Mineral Resources, Bangkok, Thailand, October 6, 1974.

20. See note 16, *supra.*

21. Information about the cutterhead dredge and its problems obtained from personal interviews with G.A. Nelson, vice chairman, Thailand Exploration and Mining Co., Bangkok, Thailand, October 7, 1974; and engineers from IHC-Holland, who designed the dredge.

22. See note 2, *supra.*

23. See note 19, *supra.*

24. See note 8, *supra.*

25. G.A.Brown and L.R.F. McCulloch, "Investigations for Heavy Minerals Off the East Coast of Australia," *Preprints, Marine Technology Society Conference*, 983 (1970).

26. V.E. McKelvey and F.F.H. Wang, *World Subsea Mineral Resources*, USGS Mis. Inv. I–623 (Revised) (1969).

27. H. Beiersdorf, "Prospects for Marine Heavy-Mineral Deposits," *Meerestechnik* 3, 217 (1972).

28. See note 8, *supra.*

29. "Japan's Big Iron Source—Bottom of Tokyo Bay," *Mining Engineering* 13, 1303 (1961).

30. "Grab Dredge Will Mine Sand-Iron," *Engineering and Mining Journal* 163, 4 (1962): 94.

31. "$189 Million for Offshore Iron Sands," *Hydrospace* 4, 3 (1971): 28.

32. I.O. Hidalgo, "Dredge Mining for Magnetite/Iron Ore in the Phillipines," in *Ocean Mining Symposium III* (San Pedro, Ca.: World Dredging Conference, 1973).

33. J.L. Mero, *The Mineral Resources of the Sea* (New York: Elsevier, 1965).

34. J.F. Pepper, "Potential Mineral Resources of the Continental Shelves of the Western Hemisphere," in *An Introduction to the Geology and Mineral Resources of the Continental Shelves of the Americas*, USGS Bulletin 1067, (1958), p. 43.

35. D. Borchers, C.S. Stocken, and A.E. Dall, "Beach Mining at Consolidated Diamond Mines of South West Africa, Ltd.: Exploitation of the Area Between the High and Low-Water Marks," in M.J. Jones, ed., *Mining and Petroleum Technology* (London: Institute of Mining and Metallurgy, 1969).

36. See note 2, *supra.*

37. See note 35, *supra.*

38. A.C. Nesbitt, "Diamond Mining at Sea," Proceedings of First World Dredging Conference, 697 (Palos Verdes Estates, Ca.: WODCON, 1967).

39. See note 2, *supra.*

40. See note 2, *supra*, and A.A. Archer, "Progress and Prospects of Marine Mining," *Mining Magazine* 68, 3 (1974): 150. See "World Dredging and Marine Construction," 12, 8 (July 1976): 20–21.

41. H. Beiersdorf, "Mining for Amber on the Sea-bed in Kursiumario," *Meerestechnik* 3, 100 (1972).

42. Information regarding the undersea coal industry in Great Britain from K.C. Durham and J.S. Sheppard, "Superficial and Solid Mineral Deposits of the Continental Shelf around Britain," in M.J. Jones, ed, *Mining and Petroleum Geology* (London: Institution of Mining and Metallurgy, 1970).

43. Toyohiko Hirota, "Japan's Seabed Coal Mining," *Mining and Safety* 16, 524 (1970). [in Japanese]; and S. Tokunaga, "Outline of Exploration for Off-shore Extensions of Coal Fields in Japan," *CCOP Tech. Bull. UNECAFE* 2, 117 (1969).

44. Statistics for shell production in the United States are from the *Minerals Yearbook* (U.S. Bureau of Mines, Washington, D.C., 1970).

45. State of Hawaii, *Hawaii and the Sea—1974* (Honolulu: Department of Planning and Economic Development, 1974).

46. K.C. Price, *Environmental Impact of Dead Reef Dredging in Mobile Bay, Alabama* (New Iberia, La.: Guld South Research Institute, 1972).

47. R.E. Boykin, L.F.Miloy, and K.J. Jensen, eds., *Texas and the Gulf of Mexico* (College Station: Texas A&M University. 1972).

48. A. Kerr, *The Texas Reef Shell Industry* (Austin: Univ. of Texas Bureau of Business Research, 1967).

49. Texas A&M University, *Environmental Impact Assessment of Shell Dredging in San Antonio Bay, Texas* (College Station: Texas A&M University 1972).

50. U.S. Army Corps of Engineers, *Final Environmental Statement on Crude Oil and Natural Gas Production and Other Mining Operations in Navigable Waterways Along the Louisiana Coast* (New Orleans: New Orleans District, 1973).

51. See fn. 46 supra.

52. Personal interview with Ed Welday, geologist, California Division of Mines and Geology, by William Lee, San Francisco, March 1974.

53. "Cement," *Mineral Trade Notes* 64, 12 (1967): 3.

54. See note 45, *supra.*

55. Information in this paragraph from A.A. Archer, "Progress and Prospects of Marine Mining," *Mining Magazine* 68, 3 (1974): 150.

56. R.C. Schmit and W.T. Aldrich, "Underwater Mining of Aragonite Sands in the Bahamas," in *Preprints, 1970 Marine Technology Society Conference,* 973 (1970).

57. Cyprus Mines Corporation, *Annual Report* (1974).

58. W. Yeend, "Sand and Gravel" in D.L. Probst and W.P. Pratt, eds., *United States Mineral Resources,* USGS Professional Papers 820 (1973).

59. W. Pajalich, "Sand and Gravel," in U.S. Bureau of Mines, *1972 Minerals Yearbook,* vol. 1 (Washington, D.C.: Bureau of Mines, 1974).

60. J.D. Cooper, "Sand and Gravel," in U.S. Bureau of Mines, *1970 Mineral Facts and Problems* (Washington, D.C.: Bureau of Mines, 1972).

61. See notes 58, 59, and 60 *supra,* for example. Also see *World Dredging and Marine Construction,* May 1976, and other issues; and the works of Albers, Hess, and others cited in this and other chapters.

62. J. Schlee and R.M. Pratt, *Atlantic Continental Shelf and Slopes of the United States—Gravels of the Northeastern Part,* USGS Professional Papers 529-H (1970).

63. F.P. Shepard, *Marine Geology,* 3rd ed. (New York: Harper & Row, 1973).

64. Personal interview with Mr. Ed. Welday, California Division of Mines and Geology, by William Lee, March 1974.

65. J. Schlee, *Sand and Gravel on the Continental Shelf off the Northeastern U.S.*, USGS Circular 602 (1968).

66. See note 63, *supra.*

67. D.L. Inman and B.M. Brush, "The Coastal Challenge," *Science* 181, 20 (1973).

68. H.D. Hess, *Marine Sand and Gravel Mining Industry in the U.K.* (Tiburon, Ca.: NOAA Marine Minerals Technology Center, NTIS COM-71-50585, 1971).

69. A.A. Archer, "Sand and Gravel Demands on the North Sea—Present and Future," in E.D. Goldberg, ed., *North Sea Science* (Cambridge, Mass.: MIT Press, 1973).

70. From papers presented at an International Committee for Exploration of the Sea (ICES) working session on "The Effects on Fisheries of Marine Sand and Gravel Extraction," Lowestoft, U.K., April 1974.

71. Personal communications from Dr. Kazuro Sasaki, National Research Institute for Pollution and Resources, to William Lee, September 1974.

72. Personal communications from Mr. Charles Marotta, New York State Office of General Services, to William Lee, January 1974.

73. Personal communication from Mr. August Stoeffler, Construction Aggregates Corp., to William Lee, December 1973.

74. F.F. Davis, "1971-1972 Mining Activity in California," *California Geology* 25, 231 (1972).

75. See note 45, *supra.*

76. See note 40, *supra.*

77. D.B. Duane, "Sand Inventory Program," *Shore and Beach* 37, 2 12; and D.B. Duane, "Sand Deposits on the Continental Shelf: A Presently Exploitable Resource," *Transactions of the National Symposium on Ocean Sciences & Engineering of the Continental Shelf* (Philadelphia, March 1968 and 1969).

78. See notes 62 and 65, *supra;* and J. Schlee, "New Jersey Offshore Gravel Deposit," *Pit and Quarry* 57, 81 (1964).

79. U.S. Bureau of Reclamation, *Study Work Plan for California Undersea Aqueduct, Reconnaissance Investigations* (Denver: Bureau of Reclamations, 1971). This project studied the type of unconsolidated sediments on the California continental shelf (California Division of Mines and Geology); depth of unconsolidated sediments (USGS) and engineering properties of the sediments (USBR).

80. F.M. Casciano and R.Q. Palmer, *Potential of Offshore Sand as an Exploitable Resource in Hawaii* (Honolulu: U. of Hawaii Sea Grant Publication 69-4, 1969).

81. D.L. Woodrow, T.L. Lewis, and R.G. Sutton, "Lake Ontario as a Source of Sand," *Rock Products* 74, 4 (1971): 72.

82. 38 *Fed. Reg.* 4105 (February 1, 1974).

83. B.J. Skinner and K.K. Turekian, *Man and the Ocean* (Englewood Cliffs, N.J.: Prentice-Hall, 1973).

84. R.L. Bowen, "Continental Shelf Phosphates—One Answer to Future Needs," *Preprints, 1972 Offshore Technology Conference*, II-399 (1972).

85. V.E. McKelvey and L. Chase, "Selecting Areas Favorable for Subsea Prospecting," in *Transactions of the Second MTS Conference—Exploiting the Oceans* (Washington, D.C.: June 1966, 1966).

86. M.P. Overall, "Mining Phosphorite in the Sea, Part I," *Ocean Industry* 3, 9 (1968): 44.

87. A.L. Inderbitzen, A.J. Carsola, and D.L. Everhart, "The Submarine Phosphate Deposits off Southern California," *Preprints, 1970 Offshore Technology Conference*, II-287 (1970).

88. See note 86, *supra.*

89. F.F.H. Wang, *Mineral Resources of the Sea* (New York: U.N. Secretary General [E/4973], 1971).

90. *Id.*

91. J.B. Cathcart and R.A. Gulbrandsen, "Phosphate Deposits," in D.A. Brobst and W.P. Pratt, eds., *United States Mineral Resources*, USGS Professional Paper 820, (1973), p. 515.

92. R.M. Thompson and K.G. Smith, "Undersea Lode Mining in Alaska," *Preprints, 1970 OTC*, II-819 (1970). J.F. Stevens, "Mining the Alaskan Seas," *Ocean Industry* 5, 11 (1970): 47.

93. U.S. Senate, *The Economic Value of Ocean Resources to the United States*, Washington: National Ocean Policy Study, 1974. See Wilson & Mero, note 9, *supra.*

Chapter 4

Technological Feasibility of
Marine Mining

INTRODUCTION

That there is an abundance of hard minerals on the continental shelf is now well established. That it may be technologically feasible and economically practicable to exploit some of these mineral resources is the issue addressed in this chapter.

The following analysis of the alternative methods for marine mining, present and near future, encompasses the technologies available for navigation, exploration, and extraction—to the extent these features of marine mining are distinct from land-based mining. Technologies for the processing of offshore minerals are also dealt with, insofar as such processing methods are unique to marine mining. Therefore, the relatively simple methods of sorting, dewatering, and washing minerals, which can be conducted at sea, are discussed. Excluded from this analysis are the more sophisticated methods of minerals processing, which are, of course, chosen on the basis of the desired end use of the mineral, since it has been assumed that such activities will take place in facilities onshore or on offshore structures or islands; and that such facilities and processes will not differ in basic design or types of externalities from facilities currently employed to process similar classes of minerals derived from inland sources.

The scope of this chapter is quite extensive and is global in its coverage of developments. However, considerable judgment has been exercised as to which of the numerous current technologies and future developments are likely to be considered for marine mining off the coasts of the United States, and only these are discussed.

A. NAVIGATION TECHNOLOGY[1]

1. Position Finding

Techniques for precise positioning of a ship at sea are crucial to exploration and mining and to the avoidance of lease boundary violations—if mining is to be limited to specific sites to prevent conflict with other uses of the sea. Determining the position of a vessel at sea can be accomplished in a variety of ways the choice of which depends on the scope of the operation, accuracy required, system mobility, distance from shore, costs, and various engineering requirements.

The methods of position determination at sea can be broadly categorized as dead reckoning, bottom sounding, satellite, acoustic Doppler sonar, inertial guidance, automatic celestial trackers, determinations using visual objects, and electronic methods. The traditional methods of visual navigation and the simple use of contoured bathymetric charts in conjunction with echo sounders give, at best, only approximate locations. More accurate positioning with highly advanced electronic techniques such as satellite radio telemetry, inertial guidance, and tracking systems are possible but expensive.

Simpler electronic methods of position determination are now well developed, and because of their efficiency and moderate costs, it is likely that most offshore mining operations would use one or more of these systems. For continental shelf applications, a lines-of-position (geometrical) method would probably be adequate. In this system, position is basically determined by the intersection of two hyperbolic lines or circles.

Hyperbolic. All hyperbolic position-determining systems define hyperbolic lines of position by measuring time difference or phase difference between radio signals transmitted simultaneously, or with a fixed delay, from two fixed stations. The constant time difference or distance difference from the two fixed stations determines a hyperbolic line of position on which the ship is located. For a fix, two lines of position must be generated. This requires three shore stations, with one, a "master" station, intercommunicating with the other two "slave" stations. A receiver on board ship measures the difference in transmission time between signals from shore stations and computes its own position. The widely used LORAN system is one example of this hyperbolic mode.

Circular or Ranging. In the circular or range method, the position of the vessel is defined by the intersection of two circular arcs, each centered on a fixed shore station. This is sometimes called "range-range," to denote that two ranges are needed to obtain a fix. In this method, the master station is carried aboard ship and interrogates the shore stations, the shore stations respond, and the round-trip time is measured at the master station. The principal difference between the range-range and hyperbolic systems is that in the range-range system the master station is on board ship rather than on shore. SHORAN is an example of this type of system.

There are advantages and disadvantages to each of these systems. The circular or ranging method is more accurate than the hyperbolic method, but at the expense of greater complexity, in that often several frequencies are utilized to transmit the required information. "Range-range" systems require a transmitter aboard ship, operating continuously, and can serve but one ship at a time. Two or more ships' units must work on a shared time basis. Hyperbolic systems require only a receiver aboard ship, so any number of ships can be served simultaneously. The hyperbolic system requires families of hyperbolic curves which must be computed for each station and plotted, which is not a simple task without a computer. Ranging systems need only a series of concentric circles centered on the stations. The simple geometry of the range-range system facilitates easy conversion into geographical coordinates. A large number of commercial systems in both modes offer a variety of operating distances and accuracies.

Other less common methods can also be used. The satellite navigation system determines the position of the vessel by means of information transmitted from the satellite to the ship giving data about the position of the satellite. An onboard receiver processes the information and calculates its position using a computer. Doppler sonar and inertial systems of navigation do not use radio waves. The doppler sonar utilizes the reflection of sound waves from the ocean bottom, with an operating depth to about 1,000 feet (300 m). As the ship moves, a hull-mounted sonar transducer continuously emits sound waves. The reflections from the ocean floor are processed by an onboard computer, to provide the direction and velocity of the vessel. With an independently known starting point, the position of the vessel is determined. Inertial systems utilize a gyroscope to sense accelerations from which ship speed and direction are derived and integrated by a computer, providing distance and direction from an independently known starting point.

Position finding is also possible using underwater beacons. Acoustic positioning is done by measuring the relative location between a reference sound source and a receiving array. The method may use 3 beacons mounted on the seafloor receiving signals from a ship or 3 hydrophones mounted on a ship receiving signals from a free-running seafloor beacon. To measure position, the source emits a "ping," a short burst of high-frequency sound waves. The ping travels through the water and is received by the hydrophones. The measured time of travel between the source and the hydrophones is used to estimate the position of the sound source relative to the known position of the hydrophones. Different systems with different ranges and accuracies are available commercially.

2. Position Control

It is extremely important to be able to maintain the position of a vessel when exploring or mining, especially for placer deposits. Maintaining and relocating the position of a vessel at sea is a complicated operation, even under ideal conditions. Some of the factors that affect this position maintenance operation are

1. Sea state (wave characteristics)
2. Seafloor characteristics (type, strength, etc.)
3. Weather (wind)
4. Current (velocity)
5. Vessel characteristics (propulsion, size, natural periods)
6. Vessel anchoring facilities (anchor, mooring lines, other types of mooring)

The two common methods of maintaining position are anchoring and dynamic positioning. A number of mooring systems are available. Dynamic positioning is a relatively new development which utilizes sonar beacons dropped to the ocean floor. Several extendable hydrophones mounted on the vessel home continuously on these sonars. Signals from the bottom are directed to a shipboard computer, which maintains the vessel's position by controlling thrusters and propellers.

B. EXPLORATION TECHNOLOGY

Exploration activities are carried out to detect mineral ore bodies and to reduce uncertainties about the location, quality and extent of the deposits. The application of field exploration techniques should be preceded by a thorough review of geological knowledge about the mineral being sought and the area being explored. Chapter 3 provided some information as to the geological environment in which the several offshore minerals are likely to be found. In this section, the various techniques for marine minerals exploration usually used in combination are discussed.

The existence, quantity, and quality of a mineral deposit is essentially a random variable, and the process of verifying the deposit is further complicated because of the blanket of water. A number of field methods can be used progressively to reduce the uncertainty surrounding a specific region or suspected mineral deposits. If one imagines a map of the seafloor, perfectly horizontal, the probability of mineral exploitability can be plotted along a vertical axis arising from the map. Without any information, one can assume that there is uniform probability for the seafloor area in question. With the help of marine geologists, areas such as submerged beaches, where the likelihood of finding certain minerals is high, can be identified. These areas can be then plotted in relief—rising vertically from the map. By sequential application of the geophysical, geological, and geochemical techniques to be described, certain areas of the map with very high probability of mineral occurrence will develop steep peaks rising from the map. Armed with this relief map of probabilities of specific minerals occurrence, the selection and design of further exploration and extraction programs and techniques can be conducted with more confidence. However, experience with land mining indicates that the uncertainty surrounding the sites and probable quantity and quality of deposits is never completely defined.

1. Geophysical Methods

Geophysical techniques are remote methods to "see" beneath the water and layers of soil on the ocean floor. These techniques are usually carried out using surface vessels without physical contact with the seafloor.

Bathymetry. Bathymetric surveys, or the determination of the depth of the water, are always performed as a first step since it is a fundamental parameter in offshore mining. The depth is found by measuring the time for a short pulse of sound to travel from a ship-mounted transducer down to the seafloor and to be reflected back to the transducer. Depth is calculated after compensations have been made for temperature, salinity, and pressure of the water. Bathymetric surveys are often made systematically for mapping.

Photographic and Visual Techniques. The ocean water constitutes a barrier to visual observation of the continental shelf, as light decreases exponentially with water depth. In order to observe the seafloor, it is necessary to provide powerful illumination. There are several possible ways to photograph or observe the shelf in order to determine deposits of minerals lying on the seafloor. The most elementary visual method is still photography. Still photographs, at various scales, can provide the basis for detailed mapping of the seafloor. The cameras may be fixed or towed when operating. There are a variety of methods for triggering the shutter, such as bottom contact, remote control, or programmed sequence. Films sensitive to different portions of the light spectrum can be used to reveal several features such as color variation or abnormal heat on the seafloor. Stereo photographs are useful in showing bottom relief.

Motion picture and videotape cameras can be used to provide a continuous visual record and can cover large areas of the seafloor in a short time. Videotapes have the advantages of real time pictures, controllability, and extended duration on the seafloor. Companies interested in mining for deepsea manganese nodules have made numerous visual records of this type at depths of 13,000 to 15,000 feet (4,400 m to 5,000 m). While it may be expensive to knock the towed camera assembly on the seafloor or against rock outcrops, these actions give some gross indications of the soil mechanics of the surface sediments and may serve as a guide to selection and design of mining equipment. Television cameras may also be valuable tools for monitoring and controlling the subsequent mining operations.

Observations and photography by divers, with or without the aid of submersibles, are also used; but advantages of direct control and the possibility of in situ measurements are offset by high costs and various physical limitations.

Another method of obtaining a picture of the seafloor is to use the side-scan sonar, a device similar to sonars used for hunting submarines. In this system, a survey vessel tows a compact "fish" containing a set of transducers which generate high-power, short-duration sound pulses. The pulses are emitted in a thin, fan-shaped beam that spreads downward from either side of the fish in a plane perpendicular to its path. As the tow vessel moves forward, this beam scans a seafloor segment ranging from directly underneath the fish to a distance as far as 1,500 feet (500 m) away from the fish. The side-scan sonar has excellent capability for distinguishing small features or objects on the ocean floor and is therefore especially useful in delineating some minerals, since it can differentiate between sand, mud, gravel, shells, or rock, for example. The sonar display is analogous to an oblique aerial photograph on land. Commercially available side-scan sonars are reported to have sufficient resolution to distinguish a 2 inch (5 cm) diameter cable at a distance of up to 450 feet (150 m) from the fish.[2]

In actual practice, the side-scan sonar has also proved to be useful in environmental surveys and monitoring. Dickson and Lee[3] used a sector-scanning sonar to detect and measure the identations made on the ocean floor by gravel dredges and found that the accuracy of measurements using the sector-scanning sonar was comparable to those developed by divers.

Seismic Surveys. Bathymetric and photographic techniques provide easily obtained topographic pictures of the ocean bottom. However, seismic surveys provide information about the physical properties and dimensions of the various types of rock and sediments that act as the "liners" of the ocean basin without requiring the use of expensive techniques of coring and drilling. Since these geophysical methods are remote and indirect, the interpretation of the data is open to some degree of ambiguity.

Seismic Reflection (Figure 4-1). Seismic reflection profiles are most useful in delineating sedimentary layers beneath the ocean floor. As such they are most important in mineral surveys. For example, the depth of an exposed sand or gravel deposit or the depth of the layer of overburden over a gold or coal deposit can be determined.

Seismic profiling is similar to echo sounding, except that it uses low-frequency sound impulses rather than high-frequency ones. The sound impulse is emitted from a towed electronic transducer, such as a sparker (which produces electric sparks at intervals), compressed air gun (bubble impulse), boomer (electromechanical impulse), or gas explosion. The echoes are received by hydrophones towed by the survey ship. Since sound travels at different velocities through different materials, the echoes from different layers arrive at the hydrophones at different times. The results when depicted on a graphic recorder may indicate, for example, a recognizable section of the subbottom with shallow layers of sediment, configuration in the bedrock, faults, and other features.

Seismic Refraction. Seismic refraction complements seismic reflection in providing a more generalized picture of the structures beneath the ocean floor and deeper penetration. Like seismic reflection, seismic refraction utilizes the principle that sound travels at different velocities through different materials. In the case of seismic refraction, a higher energy sound source is used, and the time it takes for the refracted sound waves to arrive at another point is determined. To achieve that higher energy required, explosives are usually set off at regular intervals. The refracted signals are measured by another ship away from the point of explosion or by floating hydrophones.

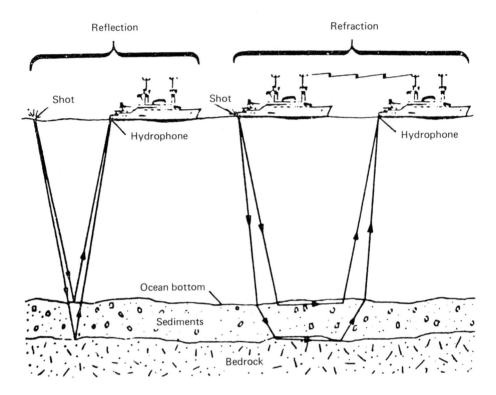

Figure 4-1. Geophysical Surveying Techniques. In the seismic reflection technique, sound waves from a source at the ship bounce directly back to the ship from sediment and rock layers. In the seismic refraction technique, the sound waves from a "shooting" ship travel along the sediment and rock layers before propagating back to a "receiving" ship.

Source: P. Rona. 1972. *Exploration Methods for the Continental Shelf: Geology, Geophysics, Geochemistry.* NOAA TR ERL 238-AOML 8.

The recorded results show the depth of interface between layers and the velocity of sound waves in different layers. By comparing the sound velocities with known velocities, some predictions can be made about the nature of the rock in various layers. However, seismic refraction cannot be used to detect a sediment layer beneath a rock layer.

Seismic refraction is not in common use because of the improved capabilities and lower costs of seismic reflection techniques. Refraction is still used in cases where information about deep layers is required, but this is not a priority need in the foreseeable future for those interested in solid minerals on the continental shelf.

In recent years, systems for "high-resolution subbottom profiling," or "continuous reflection profiling," have become popular.[4] High-resolution geophysical studies usually involve use of sound-generating devices, sound receivers, and graphic recorders to define the water depth and to provide a cross-sectional display of the subbottom layer structure in the first 500 feet (150 m) or so beneath the sea-floor. Typically, such a system employs a combination of several acoustical devices simultaneously, in order to gather data obtainable by using varying sound frequencies. "High resolution" is achieved, to the extent that these systems can determine the boundaries between rock and sediment layers to within 1 foot (0.3 m) at some 500 feet (150 m) into the seafloor, below 1,000 to 1,500 feet (325 to 500 m) of water. These systems are of great interest to those interested in promoting the use of some continental shelf minerals, since, for example, the depth of sand and gravel deposits can now be delineated. The range of existing systems appears to be adequate for providing the information about seafloor structure at all depths under consideration for shelf mining in the foreseeable future.

Recently, there have been attempts to correlate information on the types of sediments or rocks in different layers with the data obtained from high-resolution subbottom profiling, and this combined process is known as "acoustic coring."[5] The intensity of the sound reflection in an acoustical survey is proportional to the velocity of sound travel and the density of the material. Independent determination of both the intensity of sound reflected and the velocities of sound travel from various layers of rock and sediments permits the characteristic densities of these layers to be determined. This technique is much improved if the results can be correlated to an actual core analysis. The use of acoustical coring could greatly reduce the need for and costs of physical coring in mineral exploration programs.

Magnetic Measurements. Magnetic measurements are used to detect magnetic minerals on or beneath the seafloor and to measure the thickness of sediments over magnetic basement rocks. The magnetic method depends on accurately measuring anomalies of the local geomagnetic field produced by variations in the intensity of magnetization of sediments and rocks. The intensity of local magnetic fields is a function of the presence of iron-rich minerals with magnetic properties, especially magnetite, which is present in many volcanic rocks.

Magnetic intensity measurements on the continental shelf can be made inexpensively with a total intensity magnetometer towed from a ship or airplane. Computer techniques are used to process the data and obtain information such as the thickness of sediment layers with magnetic properties. Magnetometers can also be used to detect munitions, wrecks, cables, and pipelines which would have to be avoided during mining operations.

Gravity Measurements. Gravity measurements of the surface of the earth locate anomalies in gravity by observing minor distortions in the earth's main gravity field. These distortions in local gravitational fields may be caused by ore minerals which have specific gravities exceeding those of common rock.

In this process, the gravitational force field is measured at a number of points on the surface of the earth, and several devices can be employed on shipboard, such as pendulums and torsion balances. The most commonly used instrument is the Worden type gravimeter, which measures the pull of gravity against a delicately calibrated spring.

Other Methods. Other geophysical methods have been developed and have potential for offshore exploration, such as heat flow measurements, electrical measurements, and measurements of natural radioactivity. These have provided onshore data to geophysicists but have not been practiced or fully demonstrated in the offshore environment.

2. Geological Methods

Geological methods of exploration basically seek to prove the presence of a mineral deposit by physical sampling. Sampling involves securing a small quantity of a deposit for several purposes: e.g., for assay, basic scientific data, determination of engineering properties, pilot processing, and site evaluation. Information obtained from a sample is limited to the site of the sample; thus, to evaluate a deposit, a sampling program must be properly designed to yield the desired information. The usual methods of sampling are surface grabs, shallow coring, dredging, and deep drilling (see Figure 4-2).

Surface Sampling. Surface grab sampling obtains a bite of the sediments from the seafloor, usually the top few inches, and therefore the amount of sample obtained is a function of the equipment used; however, the characteristics of the sample may or may not be representative of the sediments at the site. Gravel or shell caught in the closing jaws of the grab sampler can cause occasional loss of the sample. Other simple devices may also be used for surface sampling;

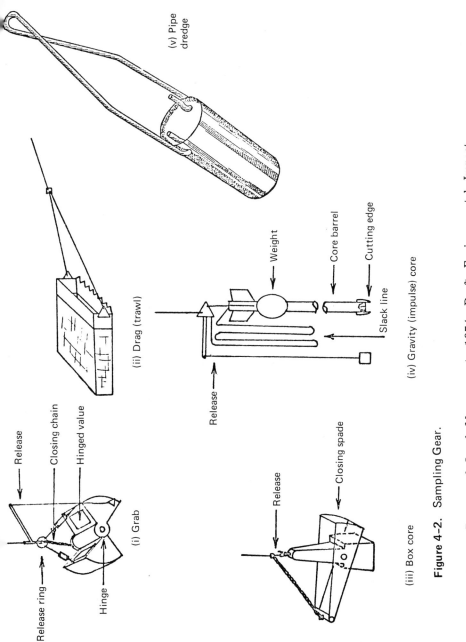

Figure 4-2. Sampling Gear.

Source: Bureau of Land Management. 1974. Draft Environmental Impact Statement for OCS Solid Minerals Mining.

for example, the drag sampler, which resembles a dustpan and which is dragged along the seafloor. While the drag sampler covers larger areas, the sample becomes homogenized, thereby diminishing the site-specificity of the resultant data. Surface samplers such as these are not effective for hard seafloor surfaces.

Shallow Coring.   Cores of the seafloor are in many ways superior to surface samples. For example, cores make it possible to examine the depth distribution of materials which may be critical, since many submerged mineral deposits, such as sand and gravel, may be economic only for deposits of certain thickness. Other minerals, such as gold or cassiterite, may be covered by a thick overburden and not determined by surface sampling.

A great variety of coring devices are available. The basic method involves a core barrel, consisting of a tube several inches (centimeters) in diameter and up to several feet (meters) in length, which is driven to penetrate the seafloor. The depth of penetration is a function of the type of seafloor encountered and the driving mechanism, and the latter is used as the basis for classifying coring methods or devices. The simplest type of device is the *impulse corer*, which uses gravitational impact or some explosive mechanism to drive the corer into the soil in one motion but to no considerable depth. *Piston corers* are used to facilitate penetration a few feet into the soil. *Percussion coring* is done with repeated impulse loading, and penetrations of several tens of feet (3–10 m) can be achieved. *Vibratory corers* are driven by acoustical or mechanical vibrations at a frequency close to the natural frequency of the material to be penetrated, and penetrations of 5 to 40 feet (1.5 m to 12 m) can result. To obtain relatively undisturbed samples, *box corers* may be used. These are impulse corers with a large cross-sectional area and achieve penetration of only about 3 feet (1 m).

In addition to depth limitations, coring devices cannot take samples in gravelbeds. However, the Alluvial Mining and Shaft Sinking Co. of the United Kingdom has developed a successful coring system for gravel—the AMdril. The AMdril lifts the materials penetrated by pumping compressed air down to provide buoyancy as the drill is driven deeper into the seafloor. Maximum seafloor penetration of 39 feet (12 m) in water depths in excess of 325 feet (100 m) has been achieved.[6]

Dredging.   To obtain larger samples of surficial sediment or rock samples from the seafloor, dredges are used, particularly the frame dredge or the pipe dredge. The frame dredge is a closely knitted network of chains with a frame at the mouth and is dragged along the bottom like a dustpan. The openings or mesh size of the chain bag can be regulated to pick up only material above a certain size. The pipe dredge is merely a section of a large diameter pipe, similarly dragged along the bottom for collection.

Exploration for sand and gravel may use regular dredges to bring up mass samples, and if necessary for gravel samples, an airlift dredge can be successfully employed.

Drilling. Drilling is required for penetration into consolidated deposits of minerals or for deeper penetration than that afforded by coring. Drilling can be performed from "jack-up" drilling rigs, semisubmersible drilling platforms, and drill ships. Such equipment stands on legs and is either anchored or dynamically positioned over the drilling site. Rotary drilling is routinely used for oil and gas exploration on the continental shelf, and penetrations of several miles (km) have been achieved.[7]

3. Geochemical Methods
Geochemical methods are used to analyze constituents in sediments and rocks for indications of the presence of ore bodies. Geochemical methods can be divided into laboratory analysis and in situ techniques.

Laboratory Analysis. When surface grab samples or cores are retrieved from the seafloor and brought into the laboratory, an array of chemical analysis techniques can be used to determine the presence of ore bodies. Visual or microscopic observations are frequently sufficient for sand and gravel as well as for some heavy mineral sands deposits.

After sample preparation by separation and concentration, spectroscopic techniques can be employed efficiently for metals analysis: examples include atomic absorption, flame, and X-ray spectrometry. Neutron activation analysis is more powerful and accurate if a neutron source is available. All these methods can now be carried out on shipboard.

In Situ Analysis. In situ analytical techniques are unsophisticated. Most of the research has centered around the application of neutron activation analysis, using a towed source and detector or submersibles. Because neutron activation techniques create artificially generated radioactive isotopes and measure the decay radiation, they leave a trail of radioisotopes on the seafloor. Depending on the half-lives of the created radioisotopes and the quantities activated, this may be an environmentally undesirable method of exploration.

C. EXTRACTION TECHNOLOGY[8] AND ASSOCIATED PROCESSING FEATURES

In this section, the state of the art of extraction technologies is addressed, and judgements are made as to their feasibility for use on the continental shelf of the United States and for exploiting the hard minerals therein. In addition, a process for the selection of marine mining systems is developed in terms of technical and economic factors, and basic variables believed to be controlling in the selection process are identified and discussed.

1. Existing and Future Mining Methods

The demonstrated methods of marine mining are tunneling, solution mining, and dredge mining, and each method has its advocates, technical and economic limitations, and externalities. Other methods are now being developed for possible use in the future.

Each of the demonstrated methods is basically a well-known process with origins in terrestrial mining or coastal construction activities. Extension of each method to the offshore, continental shelf environment has been accomplished largely as a result of incremental changes, as necessary modifications, in the several technical steps which constitute each method.

Therefore, in this chapter on technological feasibility, each method is of interest primarily as it technologically differs offshore from its onshore applications, and this is reflected in the following discussion. However, a brief review is also presented of the technological features of each method that are virtually the same for both offshore and onshore applications, since the application of these technological features to the offshore environment produces a range of new environmental effects—as discussed in the next chapter on environmental impacts.

Tunneling. Minerals in hard rock, such as coal and iron ore, have been commercially developed by means of tunneling from shafts sunk on land or on islands, natural and artificial. Experience with this practice is discussed in the preceding chapter, and as noted, ventilation for worker safety, depth of tunneling below seafloor to protect the integrity of the tunnels, and transportation distances from tunnel outer limits to shaft and surface transport facilities are critical factors in terms of costs but present no particular technological difficulties.

However, for most of the offshore minerals and sites determined to be on the continental shelf of the United States, and further determined to be of interest to meet national or regional needs in the foreseeable future (as discussed in the preceding chapter), tunneling, while technically feasible, has distinct economic limitations. For the low-value, high-bulk minerals such as sand and gravel, tunneling entails a substantial economic investment in fixed facilities which is not justified by the profit margins or the dispersed, surficial nature of most deposits. In addition, tunneling necessitates extensive transport facilities below the seafloor and from the shaft to markets, which facilities (rail, truck) are more costly than the water transport system (barges, ships) needed to support dredge mining for such minerals. For the high-value, low-bulk minerals discussed earlier in terms of sites and interest (e.g., gold), the nature of the deposits (widely scattered small deposits) and their accessibility to other, less expensive, more flexible marine mining techniques (e.g., dredge mining) appears to preclude use of tunneling for marine minerals on the American shelf for the foreseeable future.

Solution Mining. Hard rock deposits amenable to hydrometallurgical treatment of their ore can be recovered by solution mining. In this process, the ores are transformed into a fluid state through heat treatment or use of a solvent and are removed from the rock through a bore hole. Sulphur is commonly mined in this manner by the Frasch process. Presently determined mineral deposits in offshore regions under federal and state control are amenable to simpler techniques of extraction, and solution mining appears to be unnecessary for the foreseeable future.

Dredge Mining. The primary method for extracting and recovering marine minerals is dredge mining. There is considerable similarity between dredge mining and the dredging commonly conducted for purposes of navigational channel clearances in the sense that both operations involve the taking of materials from the seabed by means of similar equipment and techniques. Dredge mining has, in fact, evolved from traditional channel and riverbed dredging. However, in certain countries, such as Holland, the need for extensive coastal construction for the protection of lowlands from ocean and river flooding and the desire to reclaim submerged lands for agriculture led to the more rapid evolution of the sophisticated equipment and techniques now being employed in the European marine mining industry.

The equipment used to remove seabed materials is commonly called the dredge, and it is usually fixed to a stationary platform, a barge, or an oceangoing ship. Two types of dredges are in general use: the *mechanical dredge,* which removes materials by means of a grabbing or excavation type of action; and the *hydraulic dredge,* which employs the vacuum action of a pump to suck up material from the seabed to the surface of the overlying water. Since the hydraulic dredge creates a sediment-water slurry which is easily controlled and transported by piping, the hydraulic mode of dredge mining is generally more cost-effective and therefore dominates modern practice.

Subsequent discussion in this chapter deals with such dredge mining systems and subsystem elements, variations or available alternatives for such subsystem elements, and their limitations. Tables 4–1 and 4–2 and Figures 4–3 through 4–9 provide further detailed information summaries on both types of dredge mining systems.

A key element of the hydraulic system of dredge mining deserves further discussion at this point—the dredgepump. Pumping the dredged material from the seafloor to the surface vessel is a critical and limiting element of the dredge mining process. Normally, the dredgepump is mounted at the lowest possible point on a hydraulic dredge, to take full advantage of the maximum "pulling" vacuum generated by the pump. Physical principles dictate that for this process the slurry of materials and water must decrease in concentration (of materials) as dredging depth increases, a limiting factor. The solution is to mount the pump as close to the material being dredged as possible, so that the material can be "pushed" upward. In the use of the cutterhead dredge, submerged pumps have been mounted on the hefty, rigid ladder which extends to the seafloor. However, hopper dredges designed to work in heavy seas have suction pipes that are flexible, articulated, and connected to the hull through a swell compensator (Figure 4–9) for carrying the dredged material from the seafloor to shipboard. It has been difficult to design a suction pipe that will bear the weight of a submerged pump and enable transmission of energy to the pump.

These engineering problems have now been solved, and the trailing dredger *Maas* built by IHC-Holland Inc. has a draghead-mounted dredgepump that is hydraulically driven. Work is in progress at IHC-Holland on more efficient electrically driven submerged dredgepumps. This development will undoubtedly be widely adopted because of its several significant implications for dredge mining:

1. The concentration of solids in the slurry reaching the surface will be much higher, which means that *less* volume of water with fine sediments will have to be discarded, providing for economic and environmental benefits.

2. Theoretically, unlimited dredging depth can be attained. Previously, minerals at greater depths (beyond 20 to 30 m) such as phosphorite could only be brought to the surface by airlift means or not at all. Such minerals can soon be dredged and pumped, using these new submerged pumps, from all points on the continental shelf—to the 200 m isobath or outer bound of the shelf. This significantly expands the range of technological feasibility and economic feasibility for dredge mining.

Other features of dredge mining are discussed in detail in the following section of this chapter.

Other Marine Mining Systems: The Underwater Bulldozer. There is now some interest in the use of recently developed submarine bulldozers for marine mining. These underwater bulldozers are presently in the prototype or testing stage and are not yet commercially available. The capabilities of underwater bulldozers are similar to those of land bulldozers, except that they can operate underwater under diver or remote control. While such equipment has potential for such tasks as removing seabed overburden in marine mining, it appears that they will have limited utility for further mining functions. If operated for mining itself, they can function only in a manner similar to a grab or mechanical dredge, would suffer the same low production rates, and would probably cost much more. The underwater bulldozer may also have limited potential as an exploration tool or for the extraction of very small deposits.

2. Design of Marine Mining Systems
The design of a marine mining system involves two levels of analysis. The first level is a determination as to which mode of marine mining is most suitable to work desired deposits—tunneling, solution mining, or dredge mining. As earlier discussion on working experience (Chapter 3) and on the technological feasibility of various extraction techniques (earlier in this chapter) has indicated, a number of factors influence the choice of mode. Among these factors are the following:

a. *Deposit*
   • Amount, volume
   • Area, depth of seafloor involved
   • Concentration, other physical properties of minerals involved
   • Quality, value of minerals
   • Processing requirements, capabilities for integration with ex-

Table 4-1. Mechanical Dredges

Dredge type	Dragline on barge	Dipper dredge
Dredging principle	Scrapes off material by pulling single bucket over it toward stationary crane. Lifts bucket and dumps dredged material in a conveyance	Breaks off material by forcing cutting edge of single shovel into it while dredge is stationary. Lifts shovel and deposits material in a conveyance
Horizontal working force on dredge	Medium intermittent force toward bucket	High very intermittent force away from bucket
Anchoring while working	Dragline mounted on barge secured with spuds or anchors	Several heavy spuds
Effects of swells and waves	Can work up to moderate swells and waves	Very sensitive to swells and waves
Associated transportation	Work with barges	Work with barges
Production rate	10-30 tons/cycle 1000-3000 tons/hour	< 130 cu. yd./load
Operating depth	< 5000 feet	15 feet
Dredged material density	Approaches in-place density in mud and silt, dry density in coarser material	Approaches in-place density in mud and silt, dry density in coarser material
Comments	The dragline is frequently used on land also. It has potential for use in manganese nodule and phosphorite mining in deep water	Used primarily for excavating hard material. Because of its depth limitation the dipper is an unlikely candidate for ocean mining
Figure	4-6	4-5

Adapted from A.W. Mohr. 1974. "Development and Future of Dredging," *Proc. A.S.C.E., 100*, WW2, 69.

Clamshell or grab dredge	*Bucket-ladder dredge*
Removes material by forcing opposing bucket edges into it while dredge is stationary. Lifts bucket and deposits dredged material in a conveyance	Removes material by forcing single cutting edge of successive buckets into material while dredge is slowly moved between anchors. Lifts buckets (on a continuous belt) and deposits dredged material in a barge or its own hopper
No forces	Medium constant forces away from bucket
Several spuds or mounted on barge or ship hull	Mounted on barge hull
Can work up to moderate swells and waves if mounted on barge hull	Can work in moderate swells and waves
Work with barges	Work with barges
< 30 tons/cycle 800–1000 tons/hour	0.65–6 cu. yd./bucket 100–2500 cu. yd./hour
< 150 feet	< 150 feet
Approaches in-place density in mud and silt, dry density in coarser material	Approaches in-place density in mud and silt, dry density in coarser material
Simple and portable machine, suitable for small operations. Has low production rate for its size	A highly developed machine. This is the most widely used dredge for tin mining in Southeast Asia. It is also widely used for harbor dredging in Japan and European countries. Not used in the United States. High production rate
4-7	4-8

Table 4-2. Hydraulic Dredges

Dredge Type	Cutterhead dredge	Dustpan dredge	Hopper dredges (stationary and trailing)	Airlift
Dredging principle	Material is dislodged with a rotary cutter and sucked up to the surface by the dredge pump. While working dredge swings around spuds toward an anchor	Material is dislodged with water jets, sucked up thru a wide but shallow suction opening to the surface. While working the dredge is slowly pulled toward two anchored spuds or anchors	Material is removed and picked up together with dilution water by draghead sliding over bottom (or stationary) and flows through suction piping, pump and into the hopper of the dredge	Material is removed and picked up together with dilution water through buoyancy provided by injected compressed air
Horizontal working forces on dredge	Medium intermittent force opposing swing to side	Medium constant force opposing forward movement	Slight or no constant forces opposing forward movement	Slight or no constant forces opposing forward movement
Anchoring while working	Two spuds and two swing anchors	Two spuds or anchors secured upstream while working	Dredge moves under own power to form a trail or is anchored to dig a hole	Dredge moves under own power or anchored
Effects of swells and waves	Very sensitive to swells and waves	Very sensitive to swells and waves	Unaffected	Unaffected
Material transport	Discharges into pipeline and sometimes into barges	Discharges into pipeline or barges	Material is taken to shore in the hoppers. Upon arrival material is pumped or grabbed out	Transport in hoppers, barges, or pipeline

Production rate	325–2600 cu. yd./hour	325–2600 cu. yd./hour	260–4500 cu. yd./hour	1000 cu. yd./hour
Operating depth	< 75 feet	< 75 feet	< 128 feet	< 16,000 feet
Comments	This is the main type of dredge used in the U.S. Highly developed machine with high production rate. Application to ocean mining only in case of very hard minerals	This is a sand and silt dredge specially developed for use in the Mississippi River. It has high potential for nodule mining in the ocean	Highly developed and highly efficient machine. Because it is unaffected by waves it is most suitable for ocean mining except for hard rock	Experimental machine for deep ocean manganese nodules extraction but can also be used for many continental shelf hard minerals
Figure	4-9, 4-10	None	4-11, 4-12	4-13

Adapted from A.W. Mohr. 1974. "Development and Future of Dredging," *Proc. A.S.C.E.*, *100*, WW2, 69.

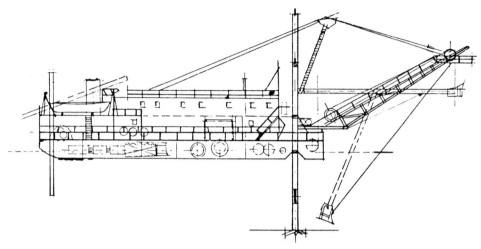

Figure 4-3. A Dipper Dredge.

Source: IHC-Holland Sales Brochure.

traction program at site or elsewhere offshore
  - Overburden, dislodgement
b. *Site*
  - Seafloor characteristics, geology
  - Water depth, currents, other features
  - Weather, working season
  - Distance from shore or transhipment facility
  - Other activities (e.g., shellfishing, shipping, etc.) nearby
c. *Operating or Performance Requirements*
  i. *Government-imposed*
    - Pollution control
    - Occupational safety
    - Boundaries, volume, duration, renewal, and other parameters of permit
    - Royalty payments, performance bonds
    - Limitations re: other minerals at site
    - Limitations on availability of coastal sites for necessary facilities on shore
    - Limitations re: other activities at site
    - Allocation of liability, clean-up costs, etc.
  ii. *Management-imposed*
    - Profit and risk minimization determinations
    - Market position

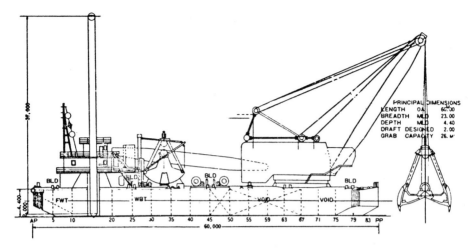

Figure 4-4. A Grab Bucket or Clamshell Dredge.

Source: H. Tatsumi. 1975. "Large-Scale Reclamation on Soft Subsoil," *Proc. Sixth World Dredging Conference* [Taipei]. San Pedro, CA: World Dredging Assn, pp. 61-138.

- Clients, consumers
- Investment limitations
- Growth potential
- Experience and other advantages for future follow-on ventures
- Availability of equipment, skilled labor, etc.

Further specification of these and other factors to be considered in the choice of the marine mining method to be employed is possible and useful only when actual site and deposit conditions are determined. As indicated earlier in this chapter, dredge mining appears to be the most feasible method for extraction of those minerals of interests which are presently determined to lie in or on the continental shelf of the United States.

The second level of analysis necessary for the design of a marine mining system is essentially a "fine-tuning" process to determine the specific features, equipment, and operating procedures necessary for optimal implementation of the marine process selected at the first level of analysis.

On the assumption that dredge mining is the method most likely to be selected at the first level analysis for the minerals of interest, the several aspects of dredge mining can now be addressed. These aspects or component subsystems consist of the following (Figure 4-10):

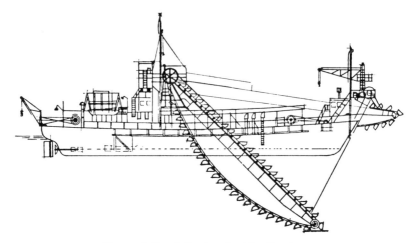

Figure 4-5. A Bucket-Ladder Dredge.

Source: IHC-Holland Sales Brochure.

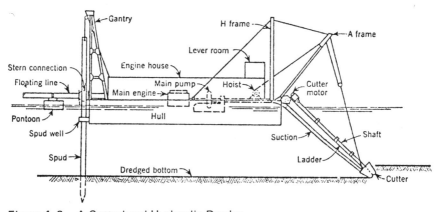

Figure 4-6. A Cutterhead Hydraulic Dredge.

Source: J. Huston. 1967. "Dredging Fundamentals," *Proc. A.S.C.E.*, *93*, WW3, 45.

1. Dislodgement technique
2. Lifting method
3. Stable surface platform
4. Transport mode to processing and transshipment facilities

Choice of Dislodgement Technique. Marine hard minerals exist in various forms, ranging from free-flowing sand and gravel deposits to cassiterite which rests on top of or in hardrock. The deposits must

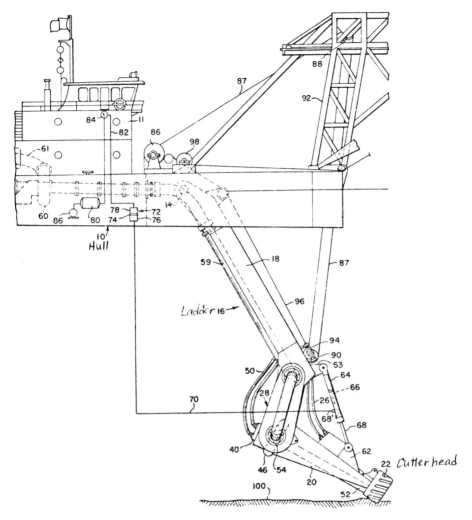

Figure 4-7. Design for a Compensated Cutterhead Hydraulic Dredge.

Source: U.S. Patent 3,777,376 (1973).

be separated or dislodged from the seabed or the rocks in the extraction process. Different types of mining equipment can be used for this dislodgement function. For example, a plain suction head would not be effective for mining barite, which occurs as bedrock, or tin, which is richest just above bedrock but which lies beneath an overburden of sediments. But plain suction heads are very useful for obtaining loose deposits of sand or gravel. To obtain barite or cassiterite, bucket-ladder dredges with buckets which can be knocked against

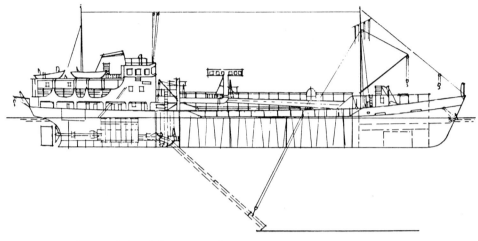

Figure 4-8. A Stationary Suction Hopper Dredge.

Source: IHC-Holland Sales Brochure.

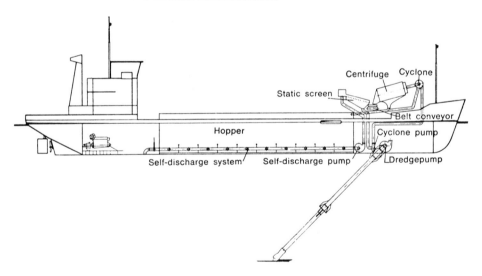

Figure 4-9. A Trailing Suction Hopper Dredge.

Source: IHC-Holland Sales Brochure.

bedrock, or cutter suction heads with rotary cutters, or water jets, or combined air and water jets, or microwave beams are alternative measures which can be used to dislodge the minerals. On the other hand, these techniques would not be necessary for harvesting phosphorite, which commonly occurs as nodules resting on the ocean floor.

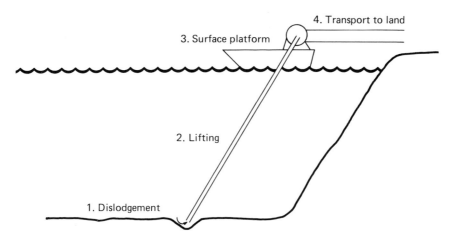

Figure 4-10. Marine Mining Subsystems.

Other than such mechanical methods of dislodgement, chemical and thermal methods can also be used. The use of solvents or leaching solutions has been considered for underwater copper mining, similar to the use of heat in the Frasch process, the common method for obtaining sulphur from subsurface deposits in coastal regions.

No common engineering parameter characterizes the mode of mineral occurrence. One can conceive of some rough measure of "cohesion" as a surrogate parameter. Free-flowing sand and gravel would be low on this cohesion scale, and hard rocks such as barite and cassiterite (tin ore) would be high. It follows from the energy required to "break" this degree of cohesion that the cost of this dislodgement function would be proportional to the degree of cohesion. Figure 4-11 depicts this relationship.

Choice of Lifting Method. Marine minerals are located either on or beneath the seafloor and then have to be lifted through the water to the surface, either directly to land or, more commonly, to the sea surface and then to land. Because these minerals lie beneath water after dislodgement, several lifting schemes are possible.

For minerals completely underneath the seafloor, such as coal or copper lodes, it is possible to lift them after dislodgement without contact with water. This containment can be achieved by means of a waterproof shaft which can be built around traditional solids handling equipment, such as continuous line buckets and conveyor belts. Although such installations are not presently employed, they are technically feasible and would incur economic costs and environmental benefits.

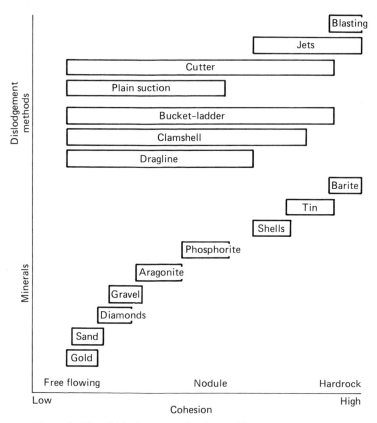

Figure 4-11. Dislodgement Needs for Mining Marine Minerals.

For most marine mining, it is inevitable that there be contact with water, which can be either a curse or a blessing. It can be a curse because unwanted water must be lifted, and it can be a blessing because convenient and inexpensive dredging methods may be used. For this situation, the depth at which the mineral is located becomes a primary design variable. Figure 4-12 indicates both typical depths at which minerals have been found and the typical capabilities of various types of dredges.

The choice becomes one of using mechanical or hydraulic dredges. Mechanical dredges physically lift the bottom material. There are no theoretical depth limits for mechanical dredges, but there may be engineering limits. Hydraulic dredges lift a slurry of soil and water. If the dredge pump is mounted on the surface mining vessel, the lifting force is the vacuum created by the dredge pump, and thus the maximum depth is limited to about 120 feet (40 m). Dredge pumps can also be located on the seafloor or somewhere in between, as discussed earlier in this chapter, and in such cases the operating depth is virtually unlimited. By examining Figure 4-12, one can roughly determine the type of lifting mechanism that must be used.

Design of a Stable Surface Platform. With the exception of mining by tunneling from land, it is necessary to have a platform on the sea surface to perform operations for other marine mining methods, such as dredge mining. The choice of a platform depends largely on

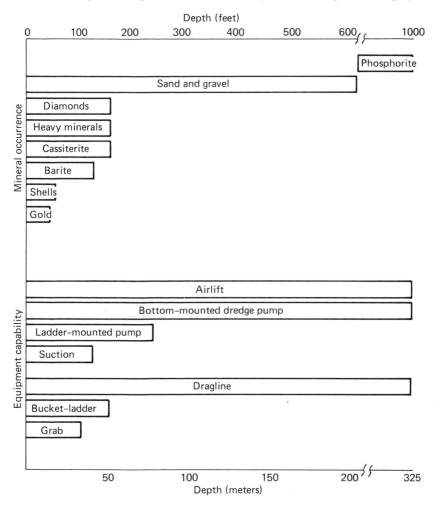

Figure 4-12. Depth Location of Marine Minerals and Equipment Capability.

the environmental conditions at the mining site. The key variable appears to be wave height, which affects the stability of the platform. The platform choices range from barge hull, to ship hull, to a semisubmersible hull, to a drilling platform or artificial island. These represent increasing abilities to withstand adverse wave conditions and ensure continuous and safe mining operations. For example, dredges for navigation channel maintenance are traditionally mounted on barge hulls for work in quiescent, nearshore waters; and cannot operate effectively in open waters over the outer continental shelf, for they must seek shelter whenever swells become too rough. Hopper dredges on ship hulls usually are equipped with swell compensators, so that they can work continuously in very severe seas, and this has been proven by Dutch and English ocean miners. Bucket-ladder and cutterhead dredges have heavy ladders which may be driven into the soil at the trough of a swell and cause breakup of the dredge when the shock is transmitted back through the ladder. Catamarans and other forms of semisubmersibles have better stability characteristics and can work in heavy seas. Being "able to operate" in different sea states means (1) ability to perform the mining operations continuously; and (2) ability to discharge the minerals through to the associated transportation scheme continuously. The ability to continue mining in high swells implies that some device to compensate for the heave (up and down) motion of the vessel must be used. This is easily accomplished in plain suction hopper dredges. However, this has not been successfully achieved for suction dredges with a heavy cutterhead or bucket-ladder dredges. In bucket-ladder dredges, the ladder is extremely heavy, and adequate compensation devices are yet to be developed. Cutters at the extremity of the ladder also create complicated forces which are difficult to cope with. Although designs for compensated cutterhead dredges exist, they have not been proven in practice.

The ability to continue discharging minerals in heavy seas depends on the choice of transportation mode. If a submerged pipeline is used, discharge operations can continue even in heavy seas. However, if barges or ore boats are used, the coupling between the mining vessel and the barges becomes a very difficult problem in heavy seas. Even with a stationary dredging platform and barges, the problem is considerable. If the mining vessel also serves as the mode of transportation, the coupling problem is eliminated and replaced by the lesser problem of maintaining vessel operations in heavy seas.

From the above discussion, it is clear that because of its seaworthiness, use of the hopper dredge with a ship hull is the most attractive alternative for minerals such as sand and gravel.

Transportation to Processing and Transshipment Facilities. The last important function of offshore mining is to transport the mineral or ore to land or nearshore sites for processing and sale. The choice of transportation mode depends on the distance and size of the mineral deposit from processing and transshipment facilities. The major criterion for this choice is economic. For short distances of up to 2.5 miles (4 km), it may be cheapest to pump the mineral to the facility by means of a pipeline. For longer distances, barges, ore boats, and the hopper of the mining vessel itself can be used. Other than the primary technical variables, secondary economic parameters control the detailed specification of systems. These parameters include

1. *Production rate.* The production rate of a mining system is a design variable, determined mainly by demand or lease conditions. For example, nearshore sand and gravel can be extracted by a variety of methods. In the absence of government-specified production rates or volumes, the mining system must be designed so that the market will not be saturated. Hopper dredges would enable a high production rate to be achieved, one which could flood the market. Clamshell dredges on barges have lower production rates, which may be more appropriate for the regional sand and gravel markets of American coastal areas.
2. *Size and composition of deposit.* Exploration provides some idea of the size and composition of the deposits. Decisions must be made as to the time pattern for production before initiating mining activities. A small or inferior deposit would probably not justify a large initial investment; a large and valuable deposit might justify such commitments.
3. *Processing needs.* Processing and refining of marine minerals can take place either onshore, on an island or structure, or on the mining vessel. For example, gravel is a valuable resource, but is usually mixed with sand. It is possible to have screens on mining vessels separate the gravel from the sand before transportation to shore. If this is desired, then the mining sytem, such as hydraulic dredging, must be compatible with the processing system. In min-

ing high-value but low-concentration minerals such as gold or tin, it would not be economical to transport the voluminous raw ore to shore for separation and other primary processes.

4. *Mobility requirements.* Related to the distance of the ore body from shore are mobility requirements. It is necessary to design and select a mining system that is highly mobile and therefore capable of tracing the deposit or of moving to shore quickly for shelter to avoid ocean traffic and other factors?

5. *Control requirements.* Is it necessary to have sophisticated controls over the mining process? For example, the precision mining of sand and gravel using hopper dredges can be accomplished with a minimum of mining instrumentation, but better instrumentation will mean much higher efficiencies and reduced externalities.

6. *Environmental quality requirements.* A variety of environmental considerations are central to mining system selection. For example, the use of suction dredges for marine aggregates extraction is discouraged in Japan for fear of agitating sediments that contain mercury, cadmium, and other toxic metals. Therefore, some kind of mechanical dredge is dictated. Various types of equipment and special operating procedures may be necessary adjuncts to mining systems to prevent water pollution and the destruction of living marine resources.

In Chapter 5, the comparative environmental impacts of several dredge mining techniques for "winning" minerals will be discussed in detail. In short, anchor dredges create deep craters on the ocean floor, while trailer dredges skim the seafloor and leave shallow trails. Because of complaints by Dutch fishermen who have lost trawls in some deep dredge holes, Dutch authorities have prohibited the use of anchor dredges, necessitating the use of trailer dredges for their considerable offshore sand and gravel mining.

7. *The security of tenure.* Mining systems entail major capital investments, which must be amortized over a number of years. If the term of a license or lease is short, then a less capital-intensive mining system will probably be chosen. For example, consider the virtually unlimited supply of sand and gravel on the outer continental shelf. If the license term is limited to 2 years only, then the marine miner will probably employ a clamshell dredge, rather than invest in capital-intensive hopper dredges.

8. *Miscellaneous considerations.* As noted in the earlier discussion of a first level of analysis for selecting marine mining systems, a number of other factors have to be considered prior to start-up. For example, the following economic factors have obvious influence on mining ventures:

a. Desired rate of return
b. Labor costs
c. Fuel costs
d. Interest rates

To sum up, this discussion indicates that the detailed design of the chosen mining system depends initially on an assessment of technological feasibility for accomplishing four primary functions: dislodgement, lifting, stable surface platform, and transportation. Respectively, the major design parameters are cohesion of minerals, depth of deposit, wave height, and distance to shore. The design of the mining system subsequently depends on consideration of a number of economic and legal factors, such as size of deposit, market situation, and environmental control requirements. It is inappropriate to declare generic economic viability for any one type of mineral or mining method because each deposit and site provides different values for the variables. Economic feasibility can be determined only in a mineral-specific deposit and a site-specific context.

To illustrate the usefulness of the above approach to the design of marine mining systems, two likely, hypothetical cases are briefly presented here:

First Case. Firm A is granted a 2 year nonexclusive license to mine phosphorite nodules resting on the seafloor off the California coast. The nodules, virtually inexhaustible and of uniform commercial quality, occur at 600 to 1,000 feet (200 m to 340 m) of water. Distance to the onshore processing facility is about 6 miles (9.6 km). Moderate wave heights in the area of about 6 feet (2 m) must be considered. Regulations stipulate that "no indentations" be made on the seafloor. What design for the mining system?

The nodules are known to lie on the seabed, so no significant dislodgement equipment is needed. However, the depth of the nodules and the short tenure of the mining license preclude the purchase or lease of expensive hydraulic dredges. Simple and inexpensive mechanical dredges, such as a dragline mounted on a ship hull, might be appropriate. The relatively calm sea and the short distance to shore sugest that a simple dredge, operating with barges or ore boats, would be sufficient. A typical design for this case might involve use of a dragline on a ship hull operating with barges.

Second Case. Firm B has been granted a 10 year license to mine for sand and gravel in an area 1 mile (1.6 km) square on the outer continental shelf, 25 miles (40 km) from shore. The deposit is loose gravel, 50 feet (20 m) deep with no overburden. Water depth is 90 feet (30 m). However, this area experiences very high wind-generated swells, with significant wave heights reaching 15 feet (5 m) or more. Regulations stipulate that no mined area may have an artificial slope of more than 10 percent. What design for the mining system?

The mode of gravel occurrence and the depth are not severe limitations, but the very high swells disqualify all but hopper dredges and semisubmersible platforms. The use of platforms with pipelines is precluded by the transport distance to shore, and the sea state precludes the use of platforms working with barges. Thus only the hopper dredge is suitable. The deposit contains 62×10^6 cu. yds. (48×10^6 m^3) of gravel and at \$2.80/yd^3 (\$4/m^3) is worth \$174 $\times$ 10^6. It may be well worth investing \$10 $\times$ 10^6 or so in a sophisticated hopper dredge. The stipulation regarding slope in the dredge area excludes stationary hopper dredges. Thus the mining system will probably consist of a trailing hopper dredge, with hull-mounted dredgepumps.

This discussion and these cases represent an objective attempt to consider concisely the major variables which control the selection of a marine mining system—an attempt to develop a coherent approach and to offset the extensive advertising literature, and interest groups in the field. This section of the chapter also provides the necessary background for subsequent, detailed consideration of environmental impacts and regulatory issues.

D. PROCESSING TECHNOLOGY ONSHORE

Any marine mining operation will need some shoreside facilities for unloading, processing, and stockpiling the minerals prior to sale and transport to users of the minerals. This section describes some of these shoreside operations and technical features.

1. Unloading

Marine minerals arrive at the dock by means of barge, ship, or pipeline, and several methods are then available for unloading:

1. Shore-mounted grabs
2. Vessel-mounted grabs
3. Scraperbucket and conveyor belt combinations
4. Hydraulic pumping using either vessel or shore-based pumps
5. Bottom dumping

The selection of the method of unloading depends heavily on the desired efficiency and economy of the system and the application of water pollution control and other laws.

Grab offloading, using either dock-mounted or vessel-mounted grabs, is commonly used in sand and gravel mining in Western Europe. This method is reliable but slow, and thus costly if the expensive mining vessel spends a large portion of its active time in port unloading.

Unloading using elevators or scraperbuckets operating with over-the-side conveyer belts is a recent development in sand and gravel operations in Western Europe. In the scraperbucket discharge system, drag scraperbuckets are controlled to scrape the vessel holds, lift the aggregates up into a hopper, and discharge the materials onto conveyer belts running over the side of the ship to shore.

In hydraulic pumping, the dredging process is repeated on board the vessel, and a sediment-water slurry is sucked up from the vessel and pumped ashore. The efficiency and speed of this mode is virtually unlimited. This is a common mode of operation for sand and gravel miners who operate in the bays and estuaries of the United States. Since the slurry is 10 to 20 percent solid, a large volume of water containing fines must be discharged on- or offshore. Because of this discharge function, hydraulic unloading is seldom used in sand and gravel mining operations in Western Europe. Experimental work is now underway in the Netherlands to develop a closed loop, complete recycle, hydraulic unloading technique.

It is also possible simply to dump the minerals through bottom doors on certain vessels so equipped. In at least one gravel operation in Rotterdam, the bottom-dumped gravel is redredged using a dockside bucket-ladder dredge as needed. In this case, the river bottom serves as a temporary stockpile site. This mode of operation creates water quality problems, involves additional operations, and will probably not be widely employed.

2. Processing

The processing facilities onshore for most marine minerals must perform several basic functions: separation, reduction, and cleaning. When the minerals arrive on shore, they must be separated from impurities, such as tin from plain sediments, gravel from sand, and sand from fines. Such separation is usually accomplished by use of a gravity separator, one employing jigs or screens. For tin mining in Southeast Asia, a series of jigs is used to separate the cassiterite ore from the overburden. In sand and gravel operations in Western

Europe, a series of screens is used to tailor the final product to the specifications of the client. Similar mechanical processes can be employed for marine gold and other minerals.

A reduction operation is a necessary condition precedent to chemical treatment of the minerals or to the reduction of oversize material to usable sizes. In tin mining, the cassiterite is reduced by crushing before going to a smelter. In sand and gravel operations, oversize materials are crushed to make gravel and sand to the specifications of the users.

A simple cleaning operation may then be employed physically to remove attached impurities. In marine sand and gravel mining, it is sometimes necessary to wash the aggregates with fresh water to remove fines and salinity.

Finally, the minerals must be stockpiled for availability upon demand and subsequent transport to users. No special techniques are required for this operation.

NOTES

1. This section is derived largely from B.B. Barnes, "Navigation and Survey," in *Peele's Handbook for Mining Engineers*, 2nd ed. (1973).

2. E. G. & G. Co., "Mark 1B Side Scan Sonar," Sales Brochure, Waltham, Mass., Environmental Equipment Division, 1975. See special issue on deep sea photograph, *Oceanus* 18, 3 (1975), Woods Hole Oceanographic Institution, for survey of techniques.

3. R. Dickson and A.J. Lee, "Gravel Extraction: Effects on Seabed Topography," *Offshore Services* 6, 6–7 (1973): 32, 56.

4. H.C. Sieck. "High-Resolution Geophysical Studies for Resource Development and Environmental Protection," *Preprints, 1975 Offshore Technology Conference*, II–321 (1975).

5. D.L. Bell and W.J. Porter, "Remote Sediment Classification Potential of Reflected Acoustic Signals," in L. Hamptin ed., *Physics of Sound in Marine Sediments* (New York: Plenum, 1974).

6. Alluvial Mining and Shaft Sinking Co., 1974 Sales Brochure.

7. See H. Menard and G. Sharman, "Scientific Uses of Random Drilling Models," *Science* 190 (1975): 337–43.

8. This section on Extraction Technology has been derived from a large number of sources among which are:

Ellicott Machine Co. 1974: Various sales brochures and U.S. Patent 3,77,376.
IHC-Holland, 1974: Various sales brochures, issues of *Ports and Dredging*, and interviews of their engineers.
Ocean Science and Engineering, Inv., 1971: *The Economics of Offshore Mining*.
U.S. Bureau of Land Management, 1974: *Draft Environmental Impact State-*

ment, *Proposing Outer Continental Shelf Hard Mineral Mining Operating and Leasing Regulations.*

World Dredging and Marine Construction, miscellaneous issues, Symcon Publ., San Pedro, California.

Various research reports on mining systems, e.g., F. Casciano, *Development of a Submarine Sand Recovery System for Hawaii,* U. Hawaii Sea Grant Program, 1973.

Personal communications with officials of Bos Kalis N.V., IHC Corporation, and the Delft Hydraulics Laboratory.

Chapter 5

Environmental Effects of Marine Mining

INTRODUCTION

Marine mining involves a sequence of technical and analytical activities which are discussed in the preceding chapters and
can be generally depicted by a flow chart such as that shown in
Figure 5-1. Alternative technologies and methods are available for
conducting each of the activities in this sequence. The selected technology or method for each activity will incur costs and benefits upon
application either *directly*, as in the case of extraction by dredging
which produces a sediment plume and other environmental costs,
or *indirectly*, as in the case of the use of an analytical method on
collected data to determine the nature of a deposit (which thereby
provides the justification for subsequent extraction and processing
activities which will then have direct effects).

This chapter focuses only on those activities which *directly* bring
about environmental consequences or effects. In addition to immediate or primary effects on the environment, this assessment includes
in its scope some of the more probable secondary or long-term
environmental and social effects, such as the various effects on the
coastal ecosystem and amenities which are likely to arise from
processing and trucking activities.

However, discussion of such secondary effects is limited to the
discrete region most directly impacted and is presented largely in
terms of physical, biological, and esthetic considerations. The
broader social consequences for the region, and indeed for the
nation, of the sudden availability of additional minerals from off

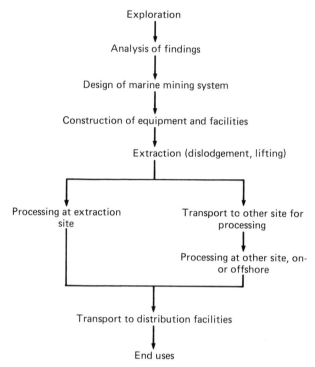

Figure 5-1. Sequence of Technical and Analytical Activities for Conduct of Marine Mining.

shore at prices competitive with or lower than similar minerals imported or derived from mining on land are extremely significant but are excluded from this assessment. The broad implications of new marine gravel supplies for construction of highways and buildings, consequent suburban sprawl, and changes or extensions of cultural and demographic patterns, for example, are not treated herein and await determination through subsequent research.

Therefore, this assessment should be recognized for what it is—an *analysis of the primary effects and probable secondary consequences of a regional nature in terms of their physical, biological, and esthetic features, which are likely to materialize as a direct result of technological activities associated with marine mining.*

Now that the limitations of this assessment have been articulated, a revised model is offered in matrix form in Figure 5-2 for guidance as to the subsequent discussion. With this organizational framework at hand, along with detailed knowledge of the technologidal activities and their implications, assessment can be formalized and applied to each technological activity as a five step process:

Inputs ——————→ Marine mining steps ——————→ Outputs

General categories of environmental inputs or resource commitments for marine mining, reversible and irreversible					Sequence of activities for conduct of marine mining with direct and probable secondary consequences on regional basis	General categories of regional environment outputs or costs and benefits, onshore and offshore, arising from marine mining			
Coastal land and biota	Coastal waters (inland) and biota	Offshore land and biota	Offshore waters and biota	Other		Physical	Biological	Aesthetic	Other
					Exploration				
					Construction of equipment and facilities				
					Extraction (dislodgement, lifting)				
					Transport				
					Processing				
					Transport				

Figure 5-2. Matrix for Organization of Environmental Assessment on Marine Mining.

1. *Identification* of associated inputs and outputs, as these terms are defined on the matrix itself
2. Estimation of the *probabilities of occurrence* of such inputs and outputs
3. Estimation of the *magnitudes* of such inputs and outputs
4. Determination or judgment as to the *significance* of the inputs and outputs—i.e., the weight or value to be accorded each input and output
5. Development of *conclusions* for each technological activity— including selection of most desirable alternative, determination of appropriate controls, findings of no acceptable alternative, etc.

This assessment approach is suggested for application prior to policy and decision making on marine mining but has not been applied in this chapter because the chapter presents data and opinion on environmental effects at a preliminary and generic level only. Application of such an assessment method would not be feasible, given the general nature of findings herein. However, given actual sites, deposits, desired productivity, and other specific features, the approach can be applied to specific proposed activities at programmatic (i.e., proposed regional mining programs) or project (i.e., specific permit issuance process) levels.

Finally, the paucity of knowledge on marine ecosystems must be addressed. In conducting assessments of the environmental effects or outputs of proposed marine programs or projects, the lack of baseline data and other critical information on marine ecosystems essentially precludes use of any "systems" approach, unless one is willing to make somewhat arbitrary assumptions. Therefore, to focus on the determination and valuation of the marine environmental outputs or effects of a proposed activity, it is useful to resort to an approach which treats the marine ecosystem at stake as a "black box"—in full recognition that lack of detailed knowledge forces this simplistic approach. By applying available information and opinion to the contents and workings of the black box, particularly our knowledge of the living and mineral resources involved[1] and of the structure and workings of marine physical and biological processes,[2] we can generate some rough conclusions as to the nature and significance of the direct consequences of marine mining. Consider the diagram shown in Figure 5-3.

In a typical marine ecosystem, there are inputs, $I(\bar{x})$ (sunlight, food, nutrients, water), which are acted upon by a "transfer function" $T(\bar{x})$, to give outputs $O(\bar{x})$, which may include the quality of water, amount of algae, or volume of shellfish. Because of very

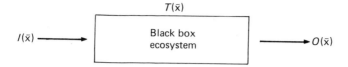

Figure 5-3. Conceptualizing the Marine Ecosystem.

inadequate knowledge of $T(\bar{x})$, one cannot predict with confidence the response when the system is perturbed by changing $I(\bar{x})$ to $I'(\bar{x})$—for example, how the number of fish will change if one perturbs the system by introducing some suspended solids from dredge mining.

There is a subtle but more important impediment to complete understanding of the marine ecosystem: Current sampling and essay techniques do not allow one to distinguish an actual adverse impact from human activities as distinct from one arising from natural variations in the system. When $O'(\bar{x})$ is observed instead of $O(\bar{x})$, one does not know whether $O'(\bar{x})$ is from $I(\bar{x})$ or from $I'(\bar{x})$. For example, in a hypothetical situation, a background environmental survey yielded line *a* in Figure 5-4a. Mining was initiated, and the next year line *b* was observed. Was there a mining impact? A similar and adjacent area was monitored for 5 previous years and the data are shown in Figure 5-4b. Was there an impact? It has been observed that ocean biological systems are perverse and resilient.[3] It may be that the system is one where only catastrophic and nonreversible impacts can be observed.[4] The point is that it would be exceedingly difficult, involving large amounts of monetary as well as human resources, to unambiguously attribute adverse environmental effects to marine mining in most cases.

In light of the foregoing discussion in this lengthy introduction, it is clear that several caveats must be kept in mind. First, this chapter is not an exhaustive scholarly treatise on marine ecosystems but a survey to discover whether there are principles of ecosystem management which should be incorporated into the design of a regulatory framework for marine mining.

Second, there is, of course, a clear need to gather more data to improve our understanding of the ecosystem. Our current understanding is represented by $T(\bar{x})$. By making decisions using current knowledge and perhaps allowing limited and monitored demonstrations of the different modes of marine mining, we may be able to improve our understanding through actual experiments and to develop successively more accurate approximations of real transfer functions, $T(\bar{x}')$, $T(\bar{x}'')$, and so on.

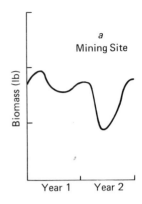

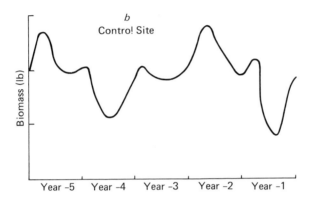

Figure 5-4.   The Sampling Problem in Assessing Environmental Impacts.

Finally, one must bear in mind the relative features or scale of the environmental impacts. As described in the following sections, the area where environmental effects may be felt as a result of a specific lease or mining project is on the order of hundreds of square miles at most, while the total area of submerged lands is on the order of millions of square miles. This assures that any trade-offs to be made between the economic gains and the environmental damages from a demonstration marine mining project can be relatively low in societal risk if the project is carefully sited and conducted on a reasonably limited scale.

A. EFFECTS OF EXPLORATION[6]

This section deals with the probable environmental impacts from activities for the exploration of marine minerals. The reader is referred to the sections of Chapter 4 on mineral exploration technology, which have been divided into geological, geophysical, and geochemical methods. For the current discussion, it is therefore useful to organize discussion of environmental effects in the same manner.

Geophysical. A number of geophysical exploration techniques are passive, involving measurements of the environment. These include the taking of magnetic and gravimetric measurements, as well as the use of spectrometers to measure natural radioactivity. The environmental effects of these activities are minimal—e.g., the collision of towed instrument assemblies with pelagic organisms, the possibility that lost instruments may become a hazard on the seafloor.

Other exploration techniques use artificial sound waves to measure the depth of water and sediments. Organisms in the immediate vicinity of the sound sources may be harmed. Although sound from these exploration methods may cover large areas, such possible damage is confined to a small area in which actual physiological damage may occur to marine organisms—within a few meters of the sound source. In the region of the beam direction and for an area ranging from a few meters to a few hundred meters, sharks, porpoises, and other organisms which use sonarlike navigation systems may experience confusion for short periods of time, but from which they recover. Outside such limited regions, sound intensity is not high enough to cause any damage.

Explosives have been used to generate sufficient pressure to reveal deep layer structure by seismic refraction. Such techniques are now seldom used because of their expense and the high resolution offered by seismic reflection using air guns. It has been reported that Soviet scientists use taped sounds of predator fish to scare fish away from areas where explosives are to be used.[6]

Geological Sampling. In methods of surface sediment sampling, various amounts of the seafloor and the attendant benthic organisms are removed. Coring removes a column of sediments and its organisms, although life is rare beneath the top few centimeters of the soil. Dragline type samplers remove the top few centimers of sediments, but over a relatively larger area. In all cases, the benthic population is the recipient of the impact. While the area affected by each sampling and coring operation is small, the density of the sampling or coring is the key parameter in determining the overall environmental impact.

Geochemical. The possible use of in situ neutron activation analysis on the seafloor raises obvious environmental issues. The method, discussed in Chapter 4, inevitably subjects benthic and pelagic organisms to ionizing radiation and may destroy or irreversibly and harmfully change such organisms. Further, the deposits of activated isotopes left on the seafloor remain radioactive long after exploration has ceased, and effects over half-life periods must be considered before permitting this exploratory process. The degree of damage will depend on the intensity of the source, the frequency of irradiation, the types of minerals activated, the half-lives of the isotopes created, and the receptor populations.

Other Aspects of Exploration. Other environmental effects of exploration will be largely those stemming from the use of ships and coastal facilities and would be of little significance. Therefore, with the possible exception of in situ neutron activation analysis, exploratory activities will, of themselves, not create significant environmental effects. However, exploration is the key to subsequent extraction, and therefore the specificity and precision of exploratory findings will be critical to the siting and types of extraction activities to follow—and to the reduction of unnecessary extractor costs and unnecessary social costs that arise from environmental degradation.

B. EFFECTS OF EXTRACTION

This section deals with the probable environmental effects arising from the extraction of offshore hard minerals. As the earlier discussion of technological approaches for offshore mining indicated, the primary technique to be employed on the continental shelf of the United States will be some variant of dredge mining. Therefore, this section focuses largely on the environmental consequences of dredge mining, as the most feasible technique to be used, and develops a taxonomy of environmental effects for consideration in program design and the regulation of actual projects. No attempt has been made systematically to list impacts on specific biological organisms, since this can only be attempted on a site- or area-specific basis. The reader is referred to other sources for such inventory.[7]

The discussion herein is organized as follows: Dredge mining is seen to consist of a sequence of activities—dislodgement, lifting, and shipboard processing and/or overflows—each with several potential effects, which are discussed in turn. Impacts resulting from the dislodgement operation of dredging the seafloor are summarized in Table 5-1. The effects of lifting, overflowing the hopper of a

Table 5-1. **Environmental Impacts from Strip Mining the Seafloor**

Potential direct or indirect impact	Level of ecosystem affected							
	Geomorphology	*Water quality*	*Phytoplankton*	*Zooplankton*	*Benthos*	*Shellfish*	*Juvenile fish*	*Adult fish*
Changing the sea-floor Bathymetry	—							
Coastal erosion	—							
Physical removal of organisms					—	—		
Particle size change					—	—	—	—
Oxygen depletion and free sulfides	—	—	—	—	—	—	—	

Note: + indicates beneficial, — indicates detrimental

hopper dredge, and discarding of tailings or other undesired materials are summarized in Table 5-2. These tables also depict the levels of the ecosystem impacted and estimate the beneficial or detrimental nature of the effects.

1. Dislodgement

Changing the Seafloor Bathymetry. The mining of hard minerals requires the removal of parts of the seafloor. Mechanical dredgers, such as clamshell and bucket-ladder dredges, create a crater or track that is more or less intentional. The shape and stability of the craters or indentations will depend on such factors as wind velocity, current velocity, depth of hole, depth of the water, and soil characteristics in the vicinity of the borrow. Cutterhead suction dredges also make cuts in the seafloor.

As indicated previously, most offshore mining in the foreseeable future will probably employ some type of hopper dredge, of which there are 2 basic types. One type anchors and dredges large pits through a forward facing pipe. The position of the vessel can be changed somewhat by adjusting the extended length of anchor chain, giving the dredgemaster some control on the exact site at which the mineral is taken. This type of extraction or dislodgement results in the formation of large round holes in the seafloor. Again

Table 5-2.　Environmental Impacts from the Discharge of Fines or Tailings[a]

Potential direct or indirect impact	Level of ecosystem affected							
	Geomorphology	Water quality	Phytoplankton	Zooplankton	Benthnos	Shellfish	Juvenile fish	Adult fish
Suspended solids and turbidity dispersion	—	—	—				—	
Reducing sunlight in the water column		—	—	—				
Oxygen demand from sediment dispersion		—		—			—	—
Release of nutrients		+	+	+	+	+	+	+
Release of metals		—	—	—	—	—	—	—
Release of pesticides		—	—	—	—	—	—	—
The rain of fines interfering with marine organisms					—		—	

Note: + indicates beneficial, — indicates detrimental
[a]Impacts are assumed here to occur. For estimates of probability of occurrence see text.

the shape and size of the holes are functions of local currents, wind velocity, water depth, hole depth, and soil characteristics.

The second type, trailer dredgers, dredge through one or two rear-facing suction pipes while the vessel is moving at a speed of 3 to 5 knots. This technique produces tracks on the seafloor from 6 to 12 feet (2-4 m) wide and about 8 inches (19 cm) deep.

The disturbance at the seafloor is also a function of the type of draghead used. In mining sand and gravel in the North Sea, all dredges employ plain suction heads with grids to exclude boulders. In the case of an anchored dredge, however, the draghead is buried in the seafloor deposit, and little disturbance is created on the seafloor other than the subsequent crater. In trailing dredges, the draghead scrapes the top layer of sediments, and the flow of materials into the draghead is prompted by the turbulence created around the edges of the draghead. The trailer dredge "stripmines" a much larger seafloor area for the same amount of minerals removed.

Hard rock minerals, such as cassiterite or barite, must first be dislodged and then removed. In these cases, many techniques are available, such as the cutterhead, water jets,[8] air and water[9] jets, and microwave[10] penetration. The use of these techniques would result in considerable disturbance of the seafloor on an ongoing basis as mining proceeds.

It is interesting to observe the fate of these seafloor indentations. Dickson and Lee[11] have performed the most detailed studies to date of the effects of aggregates mining on seafloor topography. Using a sector-scanning sonar, they were able to identify seafloor features created by dredgers. Trailer tracks were occasionally observed, although others have since found it difficult deliberately to follow such trails.[12] Of two craters created by anchor dredges which were definitely visible, the fate of one crater over a period of 2 years was monitored, and no substantial refilling was determined. Measurements by divers and sonar showed that far from filling in, the pit deepened over time.

This crater phenomenon is confirmed by several other less rigorous observations. In 1955, a portion of Long Island Sound was dredged to obtain fill for the construction of the Connecticut Turnpike, and a seafloor pit was created. Soundings taken in 1973 showed that the pit still remained,[13] with no significant refilling with original materials.

In the same vicinity, a borrow area has been studied by the Corps of Engineers.[14] In 1957, 437,700 cubic yards of material were dredged, but in the following 3 years, only 24,000 cubic yards of material accumulated in the hole by means of natural processes. Sieve analysis determined that the refilled material was silt of smaller sized particles, despite the fact that the surrounding material is composed of sand and larger-sized material.

There are several adverse environmental impacts from these craters on the ocean floor. Since silt and clays are most likely to accumulate in these craters, the filled craters are liable to become anaerobic. The biological impact of these holes is magnified if they are located in the spawning grounds of those species which require a stable bottom for deposition of eggs.[15] Rolfe and his colleagues have suggested that if ocean mining is to occur, a minimal layer of the original material should be left as substrates for species recolonization.[16]

Another implication of anchor dredging is that the craters which develop are hazardous to trawl fishing: when trawls fall into such craters, they foul, snap, and are otherwise damaged or lost. This hazard is similar to the problem created by the markers and wellheads left behind by oil and gas exploration and production activities.

While trailer dredging does not leave craters, it may nonetheless produce environmental impacts of significance. Trailer dredging may leave behind a rough surface and large stones or boulders which may snag fishing gear.[17] Intensive trailer dredging in any one seafloor plot may resemble frequent vacuum-cleaning operations, removing the benthic organisms with the surface sediments and preventing the resettlement of the juveniles of different species. Finally, changing the seafloor must be carefully conducted to avoid the disturbance of cables, pipelines and other undersea activities—including shellfish beds, discussed subsequently.

A change in the seafloor bathymetry appears to be an inevitable result of marine mining. However, this appears to be less important than the subsequent impacts on biological organisms.

Coastal Erosion. One of the primary concerns about marine mining is its potential for inducing coastal erosion. There is little actual evidence of coastal erosion to date resulting from extensive sea dredging off the United Kingdom,[18] where mining has been conducted for some 25 years. However, several erosion cases of questionable origin have been noted, the most dramatic in Start Bay, where a small seacost village, Hallsands, with a population of about 100, reportedly slumped partially into the sea as a result of gravel dredging. The condition, however, is believed to have been caused by gravel recovery operations conducted strictly on the beach, rather than offshore. The actual cause-effect mechanism was apparently that offshore conditions were not conducive for natural replenishment of the gravel taken from the beach and, as mining proceeded, the beach was further denuded and the rock face under-cut by excessive wave action.

There are several ways in which offshore mining, especially the removal of bulk quantities such as in sand and gravel extraction, can influence the coastal regime.[19] First, since a beach and adjoining submerged lands form a dynamic "cell" in which materials are constantly exchanged, the removal of aggregates from the submerged portion may result in a permanent drawdown of the beach. Second, mining may intercept the natural littoral drift of materials to or along the coast, thereby reducing the amount of littoral materials that protect other beaches. Third, mining may remove materials that serve as banks for natural coastal protection against wave attacks. Fourth, increased depth in the mined area could lead to increased wave heights inshore of the dredged site, increased wave energy at the shoreline, and accelerated erosion of the shoreline. Fifth, the increased depth at the borrow site can alter the angle of incidence of waves onto the coast and the tidal current circulation patterns inshore, thereby changing the rate and/or direction of littoral drift and the incidence of erosion and accretion.

Fortunately, the field of coastal engineering is now well developed, and techniques exist to determine whether the above impacts will occur. In order to ensure that coastal erosion will not result from a prospective offshore mining operation, the British Crown Estate Commissioners consult the Hydraulic Research Station before issuing an offshore mining license.[20] The Hydraulic Research Station performs hydraulic model tests and calculations to ensure the adverse impacts will not occur. In the United States, the Army Corps of Engineers has similar capabilities in its Waterways Experiment Station and Coastal Engineering Research Center.[21]

The lack of apparent coastal erosion problems associated with marine mining off the United Kingdom is partly due to the fact that the Crown Estate Office has had a longstanding safety-margin rule that no mining is permitted within 3 miles of the coast. In the Netherlands, with its history of concern over coastal integrity, a similar exclusionary zone for marine mining has been established at 20 km.[22] Recent studies conducted over a 2 year period in severe seas using radio-tracer tagged pebbles by British researchers has shown that gravel movement offshore of the 54-foot (18 m) contour will be negligible at all times,[23] and it is now believed that gravel mining below this depth is unlikely to cause coastal erosion.

Physical Removal of Organisms. The most apparent environmental effect of marine mining is the removal of benthic organisms. These organisms are sucked up and churned up by the action of the dredge pump or disturbed by other dislodgement methods. It is believed that few organisms can survive this action and be redeposited on the seafloor to propagate anew. Disruption and loss of substrate will have short-term effects on the benthic biota. However, this impact may well be within natural background occurrences since Swift et al.[29] reported natural shifts of offshore sediments which create depressions of several feet. Some experiences with estuarine dredging[25] indicate that while there is an immediate decrease in the faunal populations after dredging, there is a fairly rapid repopulation.

The stripping of benthic organisms is an important local environmental impact and must be regulated properly. Marine mining should not be permitted in areas of important shellfish grounds, spawning grounds for fin fisheries, and other areas of biological importance.[26] Fortunately, such impact areas are localized, and when compared to the total area of submerged lands and mineral sites, not overly critical to the future of offshore mining. It is clear that offshore mining must be regulated so as to avoid conflicts with the numerous other users of the seabed.

Particle Size Change. A more subtle and chronic environmental impact of marine mining is the change in texture of the seafloor. For example, a dredge mining for gravel may completely denude the gravel bank and leave behind a seafloor of clay or silt. The biological (and commercial) impact will be determined by which species repopulate the dredged area—the original species or a different group.

The dependence of marine animal populations on specific particle size distributions on the seafloor is well established. Rhoads and Young[27] reported that suspension feeders and benthic fauna are largely confined to sandy or firm mud bottoms. Sanders[28] showed that suspension feeders in Long Island Sound comprised 80 percent of the organisms on coarser sediments, but only 6 percent on fine sediments, with deposit feeders the dominant form on fine sediment areas. As marine mining changes the bottom texture of the seafloor, the distribution of benthic populations may be seriously affected.

The importance of this change lies in the relative value of the predredge and postdredge fauna as food for fish and marine mammals.[29] Organically rich, muddy sand typically provides rich feeding grounds where dense populations of invertebrates occur. These communities, characterized by a diverse fauna, are basically stable but would be disturbed by continuous mining. The result might be an unstable community characterized by one or two resistant organisms, the destruction of a rich fish food area, and the elimination of a rich fishing site.

Change in bottom texture is also a threat to fish spawning grounds, either through gross changes in bottom texture or more subtly through alteration of the suitability of the area for spawning. Fisheries research has shown close relationships between bottom substrate composition and spawning. The International Council for Exploration of the Sea (ICES) is currently trying to determine spawning grounds more precisely, especially for herring and sand eels in the North Sea, with the objective of prohibiting sand and gravel mining in those areas to protect commercially valuable fisheries.[30]

This potential environmental impact must be given a highly important rating since the stability of regional ecosystems and commercial fisheries may be at stake. Regulatory programs should specifically prescribe that marine mining should not be conducted in spawning and feeding ground areas of commercially important fish.

Oxygen Depletion and Free Sulphides Release.[31]   Marine mining operations disturb seafloor sediments and may lead to the release of organic and inorganic materials (such as sulphides), which deplete oxygen in the overlying waters. Depending on the nature of the sediments, significant depletion can take place. Mining may also expose benthic deposits of high oxygen demand which were previously covered by clean sediments. This oxygen demand is probably chemical rather than biological in nature and may be caused by the oxidation of various iron sulphides. The adverse impact of reduced dissolved oxygen (DO) on marine organisms is well documented in the sanitary engineering literature.

High concentrations of free sulfides within the mineral deposits and the release of the sulfides to the overlying water as a direct or indirect result of mining operations can be environmentally significant for a number of reasons. First, the release of free sulfides can increase the benthic oxygen demand rate and thus lead to a decline in the aerobic zone of the deposit and a rapid lowering of the DO concentrations within the overlying waters. Second, free sulfides, particularly hydrogen sulfide, are toxic at low concentrations to fish, crustaceans, polychaetes, and a variety of benthic microvertebrates.[32]   Actual toxic concentrations reported in the literature usually represent only initial sulfide concentrations and thus may be too low due to chemical oxidation throughout the test period. In tests that maintained nearly constant conditions, hydrogen sulfide concentrations below 0.075 mg/l (pH 7.6–8.0) were found to be significantly harmful to rainbow trout, sucker, and walleye, particularly to the eggs and fry of these fish.[33]

This is another potentially important environmental impact. However, the nature of the impact will vary with the type of minerals sought. Valuable heavy minerals such as gold may occur in rather polluted aquatic environments where sludges and sulfides are present. Commercially attractive sand and gravel deposits will probably be located in clean environments. In the latter case, regulations should probably prohibit mining in a polluted environment, while in the former case, specific criteria may be needed to regulate mining-induced releases of oxygen-depleting sulfides.

2. Lifting, Ship Overflow, and Discharges

In most marine mining operations, there will be some solids discharged in the lifting process and from the mining vessel in the form either of hopper overflow or in the discarding of unwanted tailings.

The nature, volume, and amounts of solids "dumped" vary in accordance with the minerals sought. In the case of sand and gravel mining using hopper dredges, the overflow will consist of very large volumes of water with a fairly low concentration of unwanted fines. Boehmer et al.[34] have suggested that the fines concentration will be 5 percent, with all particles smaller than 2.95×10^{-3} inches (0.075 mm) in diameter. This may result in a slurry that spreads rather than settles. In the case of gold mining, where the gold may be in concentrations of ounces (grams) per ton (tonne), the discharge will be a heavy slurry that settles rapidly. The potential impacts are discussed in the following sections.

Suspended Solids and Turbidity Dispersion. As the slurry of solids and water is discarded from a mining vessel, various environmental impacts are possible. This discussion focuses on such significant impacts as burial of benthic organisms, relase or adsorption of heavy metals, and the effects on juvenile forms of fish. However, before these impacts can be dealt with, the pattern of sediment dispersion must be discussed. Boehmer et al.[35] have shown that many organisms are adversely affected by the direct discharge from a sand and gravel mining dredge and that this discharge is readily and substantially diluted by the surrounding water. If the amount of "near field" dilution is comparable to that offered by submarine sewage outfall diffusers, the concentration of solids a short distance away from the discharge point may be as much as two orders of magnitude below the toxic levels found in Massachusetts experiments.

The first prerequisite to a detailed knowledge of dispersion patterns is information on the hydrodynamics of the area, such as (1) the magnitudes and directions of tidal and nontidal currents, (2) distribution of the velocities in the vertical direction, (3) the vertical and horizontal dispersion rates, (4) the effects of winds and waves, and (5) other parameters. All of these depend upon the geometry and the geographical location of the body of water in question, as well as on meteorological conditions. This discussion assesses several approaches to such predictions.

Mathematical models of the physical processes which determine the ultimate fate of dredged materials using local hydrodynamic conditions; characteristics of the material such as densities, size distribution, and settling velocities of the particles; and the initial conditions imposed by the method of dredge mining appear to be the most promising tool for assessing the impact of discharges of solids.

Unfortunately, the ocean environment is complex, there is little data on the physical aspects of water movement, and reliable mathematical models have yet to be developed. For example, the problem of how to deal with ocean stratification has beset the most sophisicated modelers of ocean water circulations.[36] Thermal and salinity stratification in ocean waters may cause sediments to be trapped at the pynocline and prevent their settling to the seafloor.[37] The problem is further complicated when one attempts to trace the descent of a solids slurry which has different densities and settling velocities and which undergoes different phases, such as convective transport, dynamic collapse, and long-term diffusion. It is reasonable to conclude that no existing model is capable of adequately describing the pattern of solids dispersion in the ocean.

One of the major models developed to deal with the physical fate prediction of particulate matter is that of Koh and Chang,[38] who assumed three phases of dispersion: convective, collapse, and long-term diffusion. Their model further assumes that ocean current is unidirectional, constant in time, and has a special vertical profile. Concentration of solids was calculated by the method of moments rather than by solving the diffusion equations. Because of these assumptions, the Koh and Chang model can only be used for prediction of the fate of particles in a small localized area in the open ocean environment. It cannot be used where tidal currents are present, as in estuaries and nearshore coastal waters.

Several models of sediment dispersion have been developed at the Massachusetts Institute of Technology. The late Professor Arthur Ippen and his colleagues developed an analytical model of three-dimensional solids dispersion which predicts the quasi-steady-state sediment concentration as a function of space, tidal time, and the depositional pattern in the region surrounding a continuous vertical line source.[39] The inputs to the model are settling characteristics of the sediments, hydrodynamic conditions of the area, and dispersion coefficients. This model is used primarily for prediction of a far-field dispersion pattern and can be used in nearshore waters. There are a number of limitations to this model, particularly because it relies on the concepts of vertically integrating the water column and neglecting stratification. Leimkuhler has developed a numerical modification to this earlier analytical model,[46] with many mathematical advantages, but it is still unable to handle the temperature stratification situation in the ocean. Wang has indicated that models with this capability may be unachievable for some time to come.[47] The U.S. Army Corps of Engineers has made a commitment to field-test and improve the Koh and Chang model.[42] The cancellation of the NOMES demonstration project for offshore mining off the

Massachusetts coast resulted in the loss of opportunities to test such models.

Given this inability to deal with sediment dispersion in a quantitative manner, one must rely on qualitative and observational approaches at present.[43] Investigators who have adopted this approach have generally concluded that a sediment plume is so transient as to constitute an insignificant impact.[44] This conclusion was reached following two determinations: First, the sediment plume occurs over only a small localized area which pelagic organisms can avoid; second, these observations were carried out with fine dredge spoil in estuarine environments which are inherently turbid. In coastal oceanic waters, the sediments would probably settle faster in the absence of extreme tidal currents (but organisms there may not have grown up in a turbid environment).

The environmental impact of a single sediment plume or plume of limited duration is probably not important per se; however, if the plume is of extensive duration, the impacts on organisms may be significant. In any case, any plume will have an esthetic impact on conservation and recreation areas when visible to tourists and other users.

Reducing Sunlight in the Water Column. Another possible environmental impact can materialize from the presence of plumes with abnormally high concentrations of sediments if they interfere with the passage of light into the water column. Light penetration depends primarily on the concentration of suspended material in the water column, including particulate organic and inorganic matter and plankton.[45] The more turbid the water, the shallower the depth of light penetration. Since the euphotic zone is where most primary production occurs, the depth of the euphotic zone determines the amount of gross primary production at a particular location. It is possible that there will be a reduction in the photosynthetic production of dissolved oxygen by algae as the euphotic zone depth is reduced. This constitutes a 200 percent impact, since some algae in the water column continue to use up dissolved oxygen although not producing it. Since photosynthetic phytoplankton occupy the lower trophic level, and higher organisms depend on them for food, reduction in the population of plankton by blocking out light would have ramifications further up the food chain.

Sherk[46] reviewed the literature on estuarine environments where turbidity had increased due to dredging or similar operations and concluded that while turbidity may not eliminate photosynethsis at shallow depths, photosynthesis could be curtailed at deeper levels which could have been part of the euphotic zone. After suspended material settles, however, and renewed penetration of light into deeper waters occurs, any unfavorable effects could be offset if inorganic nutrient levels have been raised.[47] Flemer[48] found no gross effects on phytoplankton from the disposal of fine material due to dredging and concluded that the effect of turbidity from dredging on phytoplankton was temporary for a given location.

Zooplankton respond to light intensity by means of diurnal migrations through the water column, generally moving toward the surface during the night and away from the surface during daylight hours.[49] Light limitations of increased turbidity could upset their feeding habits because of disruption of their normal diurnal migrations. Studies in an acid dumping area of the New York Bight[50] have shown that the resulting ferric hydroxide floc changed the light conditions and disrupted the normal vertical distributions of copepods in the water column. However, the total numbers of zooplankton in the affected area were not significantly different from the numbers of zooplankton found at 5 nearby but unaffected areas. Sediment plumes from marine mining could have impacts similar to these determined to arise from channel dredging and dumping.

The effects of blocking light in the water column are potentially severe, but the area affected will be small, and the adjoining areas, with similar amounts of phytoplankton and zooplankton, may be unaffected. Thus this effect of offshore mining is probably less important than other effects discussed here.

Oxygen Demand from the Dispersion of Sediments. Bottom sediments brought up by the mining system and subsequently discarded may exert oxygen demand as they descend in the water column. This potential effect is similar to that discussed in Section B.1 of this chapter, except that for this case the problem is more widespread as the sediments disperse.

The severity of this impact is a function of the original materials mined. In the case of sand and gravel mining, it is anticipated that extraction will generally take place in clean deposits and that the relatively small amounts of fines to be discarded should not create a significant oxygen demand problem. However, for the case of heavy minerals extraction, the bulk of sediments returned and the probability that these sediments will be organically rich could result in a substantial oxygen demand problem. Thus, the impact will depend on the nature of the deposits and sediments and should be considered in the evaluation of mining proposals accordingly, in terms of preleasing studies and postleasing monitoring requirements.

Release of Nutrients. The possibility of accelerating net photosynthetic production by means of the introduction of nutrients into waters where such nutrients were previously present only in limited quantities must also be considered. The primary candidates for the role of "limiting nutrient" are inorganic carbon, nitrogen, and phosphorus. Experimental studies in coastal environments have shown that nitrogen is the limiting nutrient for phytoplankton productivity in coastal waters for most of the year.[51] It should be kept in mind that such increases may not necessarily be of net benefit to the marine community or associated commercial fishing. An increase in phytoplankton may accelerate silting and fouling of normally clear water by means of the death and decay of additional cells and the resultant deoxygenation. In the marine environment, relationships between "red tide" blooms[52] and abnormally high levels of an essential nutrient have been suggested.

Phosphorus. Net transport of phosphorus runs generally from water to sediment. However, dissolved phosphate may also be transported from sediment to water. The direction of dissolved phosphate transport is a complex function of physical, chemical, and biological interactions in the environment.

Sediments act as reservoirs of phosphorus in natural ecosystems and therefore play a role in the cycle of phosphorus.[53] Numerous studies have been performed on the transport of dissolved phosphorus from sediments to the water column.[54] The factors which influence this transport include mixing and turbulence, bacterial and other biological activity, dissolved oxygen content, the chemical form of phosphorus, the ion-exchange capacity of the sediments, adsorption, pH and buffer capacity of the water column—many of which factors are substantially modified by dredge mining. The release of phosphorus from sediments is a very fast reaction, which occurs at a rate of about 1 micromole PO_4/m^2/day.[55]

The movement of phosphates from the water column to sediments has been studied extensively using radioactive isotopes.[56] Within seconds of application, most of the phosphorus becomes attached to some particulate surface. Correll et al.[57] reported a phosphorus flow rate of 4.3 μg P/cm^2/day from water to soil, which indicates that the movement of phosphorus from the water column to the sediments is faster than the reverse movement by three orders of magnitude. Dredge mining followed by the movement of fine particles disposed from a dredge may therefore result in a net removal of phosphorus from solution.

Nitrogen. Nitrogen in sediments has not been studied as extensively as phosphorus. The transfer of nitrogen from sediments to water column and the reverse transfer is governed by many factors, including the chemical forms of nitrogen, mixing and turbulence, ion exchange capacity, dissolved oxygen content, pH and buffer capacity of the water—all of which may be affected by dredge mining with subsequent changes in nitrogen transfer.

Windom has studied the changes in ammonia concentrations arising from dredge spoil disposal and has found that, in general, ammonia has increased by about one order of magnitude after spoil disposal.[58] Nitrates also increased by a similar amount, but after a delay of about 5 days, probably as a result of the nitrification effect. Windom's data are not extensive enough to determine any occurrence of a general reversal to original nitrogen concentrations.

Presently available information indicates that any release of phosphorus attributable to the rain of fines brought about by dredge mining is not likely to produce an artificial fertilization effect on coastal waters. More research appears to be needed before one can determine whether the transfer of nitrogen, the limiting nutrient in coastal waters, would be changed, and this must be rated as a potentially important environmental effect. However, it should be noted that the effect may be beneficial if it enriches coastal waters and makes them more productive.

Release of Trace Metals. The possible release of toxic trace metals from dredge mining and the discharge of tailings has been a widely shared concern and has been the major consideration cited in decisions to prohibit offshore mining in Long Island Sound and San Francisco Bay. Such metals occur in coastal sediments both naturally and as a result of runoff and effluent discharges from industrial and agricultural processes.

Equilibrium relationships governing the solubility of the metals in solution should provide a basis for determining whether the leaching of metals from the mined sediments would take place.[59] Such calculations show that solubility would depend heavily on pH, redox potential, and buffering systems and may also depend on other mechanisms such as complexation and ion-pair formation. Similar reactions which remove the reactivity of metals, are chelation and organic complexes. These methods of coordination chemistry allow one to predict whether metals will be released from mined sediments.[60]

Most experimental studies have shown that metals are removed from solution when exposed to dredge sediments. Windom has reported that the concentration of metals in a dredge discharge pipe was considerably lower than concentrations in the river water upstream of the dredge and in the weir effluent from a diked disposal area.[61] Gustafson, who conducted a limited leaching study of dredged sediments from the San Francisco Bay area, has reported that 4 of the 5 metals studied (mercury, zinc, lead, copper) had a lower concentration after 30 minutes of mixing with sediment.[62] The fifth metal, cadmium, was the only exception.

It is suggested by such research that suspended solids and dissolved sulfides would tend to remove metals from solution by entrapment, reaction, and adsorption and that the redox potential of the water column is the key determinant of whether metals will be released. Under reducing conditions, but not under oxidizing conditions, metals may be released.

The foregoing discussion indicates clearly that the sediments released by mining—whether tailings or hopper overflow—will have impacts on water quality and productivity. Local sediment plumes and dissolved oxygen depletion are virtually inevitable features of dredge mining. But since ocean waters are highly buffered, large changes in pH and redox potential that would allow major releases of heavy metals are unlikely. Thus the potential environmental effects of the release of trace metals arising from the various stages of mining, particularly from hopper overflow or tailings dumping, may not be as important as previously estimated.

Release of Pesticides. Fear that pesticides in mined sediments and materials will be released into the water column has been a concern similar to that expressed about trace metals. There appears to be no substantial basis for such concern. Lee and Plumb[63] reviewed several studies of the fate of pesticides in lakes and found that lake sediments serve as terminal sinks. In general, pesticides are believed to be adsorbed effectively by suspended solids. A study by May[64] indicates that no release of pesticides occurred as a result of several dredging and spoil disposal operations. The threat of pesticides release as a result of offshore mining has not been verified and presently cannot be considered as a proven environmental impact.

The Rain of Fines Interfering with Marine Organisms. In this section, the direct impact of the rain of fines produced by dredge mining on biological communities is discussed. Extensive literature has been generated on the effects of high levels of suspended sediments on estuarine organisms.[65] The general conclusion has been that such organisms have, in general, natural resistance to heavy suspended solids. Hitherto it has been necessary to apply the evidence arising from studies of estuarine environments to the open ocean environment, a process of dubious validity since organisms on the outer continental shelf have in most cases evolved in an environment considerably different from the estuarine environment and have developed highly efficient filtering mechanisms necessary to trap food particles from a rather sparse nutritive suspension. The introduction of heavy solid concentrations might therefore be more damaging to ocean organisms than to estuarine organisms. Several studies are now available that deal directly with such effects on ocean or shelf organisms,[66] but these are experimental studies[67] performed in the laboratory and are not conclusive. In the ocean, mobile organisms can evade the rain of fines, while in the laboratory, the same organisms are subjected to toxic levels of solids. Therefore, these recent studies are of interest to marine physiologists but presently are of limited usefulness for decision making. Because of these uncertainties, this potential of marine mining remains a troublesome issue and must be dealt with cautiously through demonstration programs and monitoring.

Plankton. The most elementary form of life in any aquatic ecosystem is plankton—the plants and animals that float or swim weakly in the water. The plants are known as *phytoplankton*, and the animals as *zooplankton.* The phytoplankton are the primary producers in the water column in that they perform photosynthesis for growth and reproduction and occupy the first trophic level. The zooplankton feed on the phytoplankton or other zooplankton and are members of the second or higher trophic levels, depending on food availability and feeding preferences.[68]

The first impact from the rain of fines on plankton is reduced sunlight penetration. This was dealt with in Section B.2 of this chapter. There does not appear at present to be any report of physical impact on the phytoplankton from the rain of fines.

Two other factors are considered to be more important to zooplankton than light limitation: food availability and ingestion of nonliving suspended matter. During periods of prolonged high turbidity arising from either natural conditions or dredge mining, those zooplankters whose feeding specificity limits the type of food acceptable would be expected to undergo some degree of starvation. It is known that one major constitutent of the zooplankton, the chaetognaths, can survive starvation periods of over one week with no apparent ill effects.

Many zooplankters, including the herbivorous copepods, do not feed on large particles, their food collecting apparatus being modified to sweep the water with small filterlike appendages.[69] Particle size may therefore be a factor in their feeding preference. It is possible that copepods which filter particles of a similar size range would ingest silt and other nonnutritive particles when the turbidity caused by these particles is of sufficient intensity. Such animals ingesting these nonnutritive particles could experience a temporary reduction in growth and reproductive potential.

A secondary effect for zooplankton from their ingestion of suspended, nonliving particles may occur from their concentration of various heavy metals or other potential toxic substances. It is known that certain trace metals are required by many phytoplankters and zooplankters for their physiological well-being. However, concentrations of trace elements and nutrients at levels higher than required for normal physiological processes is possible.[70] In the event that the rain of fines contains high concentrations of trace metals and is widely distributed in the water column, prolonged uptake could reduce photosynthesis[71] or be accumulated for transfer to higher trophic levels. The literature on the effects of heavy metals on marine organisms is scarce; the final deposition of heavy metals which move through the food chain has not been adequately researched.

Impact on Benthic Organisms, Including Shellfish. Benthic organisms are those living on the seafloor. Substrate composition determines the types of organisms that inhabit a certain locale. Some species prefer sandy areas, while others prefer silty sand or gravelly environments. The alteration of the substrate is of prime concern for benthic organisms during marine mining operations, but changes in physical and chemical parameters are also important. The following discussion treats this topic by seafloor habitat and primary forms of animal life thereon.

Typical Benthic Habitats.

• Sandy Areas. The sand habitat merges with the shore zone and extends to approximately 150 foot (50 m) depths, depending on the bottom topography. Areas exhibiting sand fauna include the Nantucket shoals and vicinity, nearshore Rhode Island, and the open coast from north of Cape Cod to Cape Hatteras.

The sandy sediments are constantly shifting, subjecting the fauna to considerable physical stress, and are usually sparsely populated. Benthic forms of life in this area are adapted for movement and recovery from burial. Although the predominant faunal group found in the sand habitat is suspension feeders, other feeding types, including deposit feeders and scavengers, are represented.

Few publications on the productivity of sandy bottom areas exist. Lee[72] reported a lower fish food potential for sandy areas than silty sand areas. In terms of biomass, the surf clam (*Spisula*) population found within the sandy zone is the most highly productive faunal group known.

• Silty Sand Areas. The shifting sandy bottoms merge into the silty sand bottoms characterized by approximately 25 percent silt content and 2 percent organic matter. These silty sand sediments are usually covered by a thin organic layer at the surface. The benthic fauna of this silty sand habitat are usually diverse, productive, and stable because of reduced scouring by the bottom currents. Many tube-forming and burrow-making species, including amphipods and polychaetes, are found within this relatively stable bottom habitat; the tubes and burrows act to further stabilize the sediments. In this environment, a vertical faunal distribution exists with deposit-feeding and suspension-feeding species occupying different levels. The suspension feeders in general augment the food supply of the deposit feeders through biodeposition. The silty sand fauna are also highly productive in terms of fish food potential. The North Sea and southern New England fishing banks are examples of this habitat. Northern groundfish (cod, haddock, hake, yellowtail flounder) feed on benthic organisms in this area during the winter.

• Gravel Areas. The gravel faunal assemblage is characterized by an epibenthic group of organisms living on or in association with solid surfaces such as rocks, gravel, and shells. The sediment consists of a gravel and sand mixture in areas of relatively high current velocity. Relatively productive epibenthic assemblages are usually dominated by suspension feeders, although a diverse group of deposit feeders, predators, and browsers are found in mature epibenthic assemblages. The predominance of suspension feeders is believed to be the result of the role of relatively high water flow which increases the growth rate and biomass by supplying food and oxygen and by removing wastes. Few field studies of benthic populations in gravel areas of the continental shelf exist.[73]

Shellfish. Many species of shellfish are of commercial importance, especially in the New England and Gulf regions. The lobster is the most commercially valuable shellfish resource in the United States and is caught chiefly in the Atlantic north of Cape Cod. Sea scallops, surf clams, and ocean quahogs also support a $16 million industry from Cape Hatteras to the Gulf of Maine.[74] Oysters and oyster seedlings form a major industry on the Connecticut coast. For a detailed inventory of benthic organisms and shellfish on the North Atlantic continental shelf, a number of environmental inventories can be consulted.[75]

Potential Environmental Impacts. Unavoidable adverse effects of dredge mining on the benthos include the following: (1) disruption and loss of subtrate, (2) loss of biomass, and (3) burial of benthos. Burial of benthic organisms will largely depend upon the quantity of sediment disturbed, the rate of disposal, and the areal extent of settling. Since the impact of destruction and loss of substrate was treated in Section B.1 of this chapter, this discussion deals with the effects of deposition and burial.

Laboratory experiments[76] using commercially valuable shellfish from Massachusetts Bay have shown that in general adult forms are resistant to both short- and long-term exposure to fairly high levels of suspended solids. The levels of solids used were higher than those expected from a rain of fines. Larval stages of the shellfish show resistance to lower levels of solids but have not been tested at higher levels. This is consistent with a series of experiments conducted over several decades which have demonstrated that various types of shellfish, especially oysters, are resistant to high levels of solids,[77] probably because turbid waters constitute a typical environment for these filter feeders.

Experiments on the eastern lobster, *Homarus Americanus*, indicate that this organism in its adult stage is highly tolerant to siltation. However, experiments have shown that lobster larvae in certain developmental stages are sensitive to particular particle size ranges and/or concentrations of suspended solids.[78]

Smothering of these benthic forms which inhabit the shifting sand and gravel bottom is not expected to be a significant feature of dredge mining on a short- or long-term basis. Motile bivalves (scallops, surf clams) and crustacea (crabs, lobsters, shrimp) are well adapted to such conditions and consequently many will respond by fleeing the area during the mining operation. Commercial and recreational shellfishing may therefore not suffer a loss of these resources and may not be significantly altered by such effects on the benthos; however, some rescheduling and resiting of such mining activities, following initial permits, may be necessitated and may produce economic consequences over the short term.

The most significant ecological impact occurs when the rain of fines is sufficient to cause burial of the benthos. May[79] has reported 65-70 percent mortality for certain species, with population reestablishment over a period of 6 months to 2 years. However, the recovered colony is of a lower species diversity and as a result may have indirect impacts on consequent fish feeding patterns and productivity.

Impact on Finfish and Fisheries. Offshore mining of hard minerals may be expected to affect finfish and finfish fisheries in several ways:

1. Disruption of bottom sediments which are critical habitats
2. Disruption of feeding grounds
3. Suspension of solids in the water column which interfere with visual feeding
4. Alteration of physical-chemical environments
5. Potential loss of estuarine fish breeding grounds through filling and destruction of wetlands, arising from use of dredged materials

The potential effects of the sediment plume upon fisheries are primarily those of disruption of feeding grounds and destruction of spawning and nursery grounds. The latter are discussed in connection with dredge mining of the seafloor earlier in this chapter. The current discussion centers on the effects of the rain of fines on feeding and nursery grounds.

Effects on Juvenile Stages. Little is known regarding the effects of suspended solids on egg and larval development of any fish species. O'Connor and Sherk (unpublished data) exposed fertilized winter flounder (*Pseudopleuronectes americanua*) eggs to suspensions of kaolinite for the entire incubation period (6 to 8 days) and found no discernible effects of the suspension on hatching success, even though the demersal eggs of the flounder became covered with up to 3 millimeters of fine sediment.

Several researchers[80] have tested the effects of suspended solids on larval stages of striped bass and winter flounder. As yet no conclusive results are available from their studies, although concentrations of very fine solids up to 500 mg/l have been shown to have some (as yet undefinable) adverse effects on such fish larvae during a 96 hour exposure.

It is quite common for coastal fish communities to use estuaries as *nursery grounds* where young growth stages can take advantage of the physical protection and abundant food. The most productive, and hence most important, part of the nursery ground is the intertidal and adjacent shallow water zones. Two-thirds of all eastern seaboard commercial fisheries are based on marsh-dependent species.[81] Since fishermen usually harvest these species offshore, however, the importance of estuaries to marine fisheries is often not sufficiently emphasized. Unfortunately, the intertidal wetlands have been the target of human encroachment through landfill development and the construction of coastal facilities. If sea-mined aggregates are used to fill and destroy coastal wetlands for such developments, serious effects on fish and fisheries would follow.

Effects on Adult Fish. Direct impact of the rain of fines on adult finfish is unlikely, since they are not as dependent on specific areas and could avoid regions of suspended silt. However, there are certain fish, such as cod, winter flounder, sea robin, and sculpin, which are known to be attracted to this sort of turbid environment. The literature reporting on lethal concentrations of sediments to finfish is primarily based on tank experiments where the fish are subjected to prolonged exposure of very fine sediment.

Boehmer et al. experimented with 5 species of Massachusetts Bay fish—silverside, white flounder, yellowtail flounder, menhaden, and coho salmon—and found that solids concentrations of >30 g/l resulted in 100 percent mortality in 24 hours and that solids content of >20 g/l resulted in 100 percent mortality in 96 hours. Silverside and coho salmon were found to be more sensitive to chronic exposure than other species. Once again it should be noted that these were tank experiments in which solids concentrations appear unrealistically high in constrast to actual dispersion in coastal waters.

Boehmer et al. also confirmed the theory that the lethal aspects of fines on fisheries arise primarily from physical clogging of fish gills. Sherk et al.[81] observed physiological responses to abnormally high levels of suspended solids which include depression of oxygen transfer across gill tissues and reduction in tissue glycogen levels. These effects, if persistent, can result in increased mortality and impairment of reproductive ability.

Rogers[82] studied the effects of several types of suspended solids on marine and estuarine fishes and determined that the "toxicity" of the sediment was correlated inversely with particle size and directly with angularity and hardness of particles. Only fine particles, less than 1.0 microns, had any lethal effect on the experimental organisms and even then only at concentrations well in excess of 100 g/l.

Groundfish rely upon benthic organisms for food and generally spend the greater portion of their lifecycles at or near the mud-water interface. The potential effects of mining on these fish extend to redeposition of sediments and disruption of their food resources.

Redeposition of sediments to a depth of several millimeters would have no effect upon benthic fish like flounder and sole. The behavioral characteristics of these fishes, in fact, include patterns of fin and body movement which effect the burial of the fish when they are resting on the bottom.[83] Special morphobiological adaptations exist in many species to allow for irrigation of the gills when such fish are buried in the sediments. O'Connor and Sherk (unpublished data) have determined that of all species tested for the lethal effects of suspended solids, benthic forms (i.e., hogchokers, winter flounder, cusk eels) were among the most resistant to suspensions of fine particles at concentrations in excess of 100 g/l. Longterm exposure to suspensions of finely divided solids (0.2 microns) in their tests caused no detrimental sublethal effects in hogchokers after 4 days.[84]

Most groundfish consume considerable quantities of finely divided mud when feeding. Specific adaptations of fishes normally exposed to relatively high concentrations of solids due to habitat preference or feeding habit have been discussed by Neuman et al.[85] Their conclusions state that benthic fish and benthic feeding fish have been able to compensate for the potentially adverse effects of heavy concentrations of suspended solids, either through reduced metabolism or morphologic adaptations of gill structure. Because of their opportunistic feeding habits and low sensitivity to suspended solids, groundfish may concentrate in the vicinity of the mining operation to prey upon benthic invertebrates disturbed during the mining process.

It is quite possible that the rain of fines will prompt nonresistant species to leave the area subject to dredge mining, resulting in a shift in the ecosystem to domination by resistant species, which may become an unstable system if continued for any period of time. Various researchers[86] have dismissed this potential impact because they believe that mining dredges will operate intermittently and that the rain of fines will therefore be transient. However, this may not be the case if the sediments do not penetrate the pynocline or are delayed in penetrating it. Therefore, it is quite probable that the cloud of fines is more permanent than assumed. This potential environmental impact should not be dismissed until the dispersion patterns of the rain of fines and their effects have been determined.

It is obvious that in light of the dearth of data regarding the responses of marine organism to rains of fines, the potential environmental effects are very important issues facing marine mining. There is initially a need to quantify the amount of fines that would reach the water column so that further studies on biological responses can be designed. Before such data and findings are generated, extreme caution is advised, as the scope and rate of environmental impacts on marine organisms is highly significant ecologically and commercially.

C. EFFECTS OF PROCESSING FACILITIES

The previous sections have dealt with the environmental impacts of marine mining technologies for separating hard minerals from seafloor overburden and other unwanted sediments. It can be assumed that only limited processing will be done at sea, even if hopper dredges are employed and that there will be a need for onshore facilities for the processing and transshipment of the minerals. This section deals with the potential environmental impacts from such onshore facilities.

It is useful to again divide marine minerals into 2 classes: the high-value, low-bulk; and the low-value, high-bulk. Gold and other heavy minerals form the first class, for which separation of such minerals from the bulk will be accomplished through density or size differentiation. In such cases, mechanical separation will be the most commonly used technique, with virtually no use of chemical separation. Therefore, the resulting environmental issues will be similar in type to those arising from the separation of low-value, high-bulk minerals discussed later.

Of the low-value, high-bulk marine minerals expected to be in demand, sand and gravel, and shells for calcium carbonate are most likely to be exploited in the foreseeable future (see Chapter 3). As discussed earlier, such minerals can be used after separation without further treatment or extensive processing other than washing to produce graded aggregates and other marketable products.

The potential impacts of a shore-based sand and gravel processing plant, as the prototypical shore-based primary processing facility for most marine hard minerals, are now examined.

1. Scenario
It is useful to postulate alternative scenarios to envision the environmental impacts of an onshore aggregate processing plant since

no such plants for marine mining are currently in operation. Assume a marine miner with a trailing suction hopper dredge of 6,000 cubic yard (4,588 m^3) capacity, which is capable of working on the outer continental shelf, a capacity assumption in keeping with the most modern dredges in Britain. Its oceangoing capability enables such a dredge to work year round if economically necessary. It is also probable that such a dredge would work around the clock and bring in two loads a day, as in Britain. The total haul would then come to 12,000 yd^3 (9,175 m^3) per day. If one further assumes that the processing plant onshore will operate ten hours a day, the capacity of the processing plant would be 1,920 tons/hr. (1,743 m ton/hr.), equivalent to a normal capacity plant for a modern upland sand and gravel operation.[88] If the capacity of the average sand and gravel truck is assumed to be 15 tons, the amount of traffic to be expected is 128 trucks per hour. (Truck capacity is here estimated somewhat conservatively; in reality, such trucks frequently exceed legal limits and carry greater loads.)

Shore-based support facilities for such a dredge would include wharves, stockpiling areas, and the processing plant. The exact operational flowchart depends on the nature of the unloading technique, the processing required to produce marketable aggregates, and the required environmental control equipment. As will be shown, the unloading technique determines in large part the types and extent of the environmental impact.

Some dredges unload by reversing the dredging operation, using either the dredgepump on board, or shore-based pumps. The hopper is reflooded with water from a high pressure jet, and the slurry is pumped onshore. This is the method used by the hydrobarge *Ezra Sensibar*, the only dredge barge in the United States engaged primarily in sand and gravel mining.[88] The aggregates must then be separated from the transport water. This mode of operation enables the processing plant to be located inland and further allows the use of an existing sand and gravel processing plant. The distance inland is completely a function of how powerful the pumps and/or booster pumps are and the costs thereof.

An alternative method, dry unloading, is accomplished by use of clamshell grabs, belt conveyors, or scraperbuckets. Self-discharging by scraperbuckets, coupled with over-the-side conveyor belts, has been well received in Great Britain as the most efficient and economical system available. The aggregates are picked up by scraperbuckets traveling on rails and dumped into a hopper from which the aggregates are carried ashore by belt conveyors. This system does not involve the use of a transporting fluid and eliminates the need for a water separation system. However, it is not economical to convey aggregate a long distance on belt conveyors. Therefore, this system is usually used only where dockside processing is possible.

Sea-won aggregates are discharged at over 100 different landing points in Britain, and most points have a shoreside processing facility of some kind. The functions of these processing plants depend on market requirements and on the nature of the dredged materials. It is reasonable to conclude that such dockside processing plants for ocean-source aggregates resemble upland sand and gravel processing plants. Indeed, one can expect roughly the same machinery, albeit in different mixes. Because of the extensive resource of sand and gravel in the ocean, the marine miner with adequate exploration data may be able to find a deposit that meets almost exactly his product specifications, thus reducing though not eliminating, the need for onshore processing.

The usual operations at a sand and gravel processing facility are washing, crushing, screening, and grading. Excessively large stones are scalped off prior to screening and taken to a crushing plant. Processing involves washing to remove both fines and salt and passing the material over a series of mechanical vibrating screens to obtain materials of certain marketable sizes. The mode of transport usually consists of conveyor belts or bucket elevators.

Most plants in Great Britain wash the marine sand and gravel with recirculated water. Washed sand must be dewatered, either by air drying or rubber vibratory screens. Large settling tanks are also used in Britain to separate the silt and fines from the washwater before discharge or reuse.

2. Potential Environmental Impacts of the Processing Plant

Water Pollution.

Potential Problems. There are two types of potential water pollution problems from a shoreside sand and gravel processing plant—salt and fines, both of which accrue from the washing operation. The degree of washing required depends largely on the amount of fines present in the dredged materials, since aggregates with salt are quite acceptable for construction purposes. Any washing, other than with sea water, will quickly remove the salt. In upland operations, water requirements have varied from zero to 800 gallons of water per ton, with the mean at 70 gallons per ton.[89] It is unlikely that any ocean mining operation would extract materials of more than 2 percent to 5 percent fines, or a maximum amount of fine of 40-100 lb/ton. If 100 gallons of wash water are required per ton, then the wash water suspended solids concentration is 4,800-12,500 mg/l, a thick slurry.

If hydraulic unloading is used, there is a great deal of solid-liquid separation that must be performed at the processing plant. According to the Construction Aggregates Corporation, the pumped out slurry contains about 20 percent solids. Therefore, to discharge a load of 6,000 yd of aggregates, 6 million gallons of water would be required. For two loads a day, a treatment facility requiring 12.6 million gallons must be built, and this substantial amount is equivalent to the needs of a city with a population of 100,000. Settling basins must be provided to separate the valuable aggregates and to accomplish water reuse. Assuming that the settling basin would be 95 percent efficient, the 6.3 million gallons of water for each load would contain 480 tons of fines, which must be recycled or discarded. If discarded without further treatment, the overflow suspended solids concentration is 18,300 mg/l, clearly an unacceptable slurry. A series of settling ponds would be required before water of a reusable or dischargeable quality could be obtained.

Control Technology. It is difficult to transfer the experience of upland sand and gravel operations to a prospective shoreside processing plant. Information on upland sand and gravel operations generally lacks details concerning waste discharges or wastewater treatment systems. Monroe, in his study of wastewater treatment practices in the aggregates industry, could not find representative data. One reason may be that most upland operations have many diffuse points of discharge and generally use worked-out deposits as settling areas. Settling ponds, however common, are not entirely satisfactory because:

1. A certain amount of commercially valuable fine material is lost, together with the undesirable clays and silt.
2. In order to allow for adequate settling, large areas of land must be set aside, and the cost of immobilizing this area may be prohibitively high.
3. Since settling takes a long time, large volumes of water cannot be reused immediately. Thus the operator must maintain a large supply of clean water, which can entail additional investments for wells, ponds, and treatment facilities.

The inadequacies of settling ponds have prompted the use of hydrocyclones and chemical treatment to improve settling. Hydrocyclones use centrifugal force to separate the solids from the transporting fluid, with about 60–70 percent efficiency.[90] However, the use of a hydrocyclone does not create a completely closed system, as part of the overflow must be bled off to discharge. The use of coagulants, such as alum and lime, and coagulation aids such as synthetic long-chain organic polymers, are especially effective in removing clays and colloidal particles.[91] Their use has been extensively examined in the wastewater treatment field. Laboratory tests must be made to determine the proper coagulant and coagulant aid and their optimal dosages. With the use of coagulation, the sizes of settling tanks are dramatically reduced, and effluents of very high quality are produced.

The salt problem is different in nature. If it is desired to reduce the salt content in construction aggregates from 1.0 percent by weight to 0.1 percent by weight as required by the Greater London Council, fresh water must be used for washing. A dockside operation cannot build its own reservoirs to catch fresh water runoff as upland operations can and must therefore use municipal or ground water. If the demand for fresh wash water is large, this may cause undesirable secondary environmental impacts. The discharge of salty wash water back into the saline ocean should not be a problem if fines have been eliminated as suggested earlier. The salty wash water would probably not be recycled, since the costs of salt removal processes such as reverse osmosis, electrodialysis, and ion exchange are very high (about 30¢ to 50¢ per 1,000 gallons) and probably are not economical for a high-volume, low-margin industry such as sand and gravel.

Since technological means for controlling water pollution from sand and gravel processing plants exist, are economically feasible, and can be imposed by federal and state water quality officials, these plants should not be allowed to cause water pollution problems.

Air Pollution.

Potential Problem. Sand and gravel processing operations have a potential for air pollution in the form of dust. This problem has long made sand and gravel plants a community nuisance and has been the subjects of much state and local regulation.[92] Again, one can look to upland sand and gravel facilities for potential emission figures.

Sand and gravel entering the processing plant are usually moist enough to be nondusting. However, as new, dry surfaces are created in the crushers, dust emission may occur. At each successive crushing operation, the dust emission potential increases as the size of the particles decreases.

The Environmental Protection Agency has compiled a list of expected air emission factors for stone quarrying and processing plants, as shown in Table 5-3. Assuming a dockside processing plant to have only primary and secondary crushers and no other emissions, the uncontrolled emission is about 1 lb/ton. The plant with a capacity of about 2,000 tons/hour would produce dust emissions of about 2,000 lb/hour.

Control Technology. There are two methods for suppressing dust emission from a processing plant. One method is to keep the aggregates moist in all stages of processing. Wet dust suppression is a method which uses water moisture with or without a dust control chemical, which is usually a wetting agent. The dust control chemical, mixed in very small quantities with water, wets the dust and causes the dust particles to agglomerate, thereby preventing the dust from becoming airborne. This dust control mixture is usually applied with spray nozzles. Those who market this control technology claim that it is the most economical and effective method.[53] Experience of commercial sand and gravel vendors appears to confirm these claims.[54]

Table 5-3. Particulate Emission Factors for Rock-handling Processes—Emission Factor Rating: C-Low Reliability

Type of process	Uncontrolled total		Settled out in plant (percentage)	Suspended emission	
	lb/ton	kg/MT		lb/ton	kg/MT
Dry crushing operations					
Primary crushing	0.5	0.25	80	0.1	0.05
Secondary crushing and screening	1.5	0.75	60	0.6	0.3
Tertiary crushing and screening (if used)	6	3	40	3.6	1.8
Recrushing and screening	5	2.5	50	2.5	1.25
Fines mill	6	3	25	4.5	2.25
Miscellaneous operations					
Screening, conveying, and handling	2	1			
Storage pile losses	10	5			

Source: U.S. Environmental Protection Agency. 1973. *Compilation of Air Pollution Emission Factors,* 2nd ed.

Adding water in the manner just described tends to cause binding in the finer screens and to impede the already precarious flow of granular materials. By making smaller particles adhere together, it also reduces the amount of rock dust that can be sold as a by-product. Therefore, some firms prefer a completely dry process. For this case, a firm can install hoods and ducts to convey the dusty air to some kind of particulate removal device. The device usually preferred is a baghouse similar to a giant vacuum cleaner, for which design procedures can be found in Danielson.[95] Baghouses usually have a particulate removal efficiency of over 99.9 percent. While a cyclone may leave a visible plume as a result of the escape of extremely fine dust, a baghouse is so efficient that no plume can be detected. For the case of a sand and gravel plant, some type of cotton or nylon filter cloth can be used, and shaking or reverse air cleaning of the bags will be more than adequate. Rock dust collected by the filter can be sold as a plant by-product to recover the cost of the bag installation. This type of treatment is preferred if the entire processing plant is to be housed indoors.

Noise Pollution.

Potential Problem. In addition to the dust problem, upland sand and gravel plants have also been considered nuisances because of noise. Quarrying and other rock type operations sometimes use explosives, jackhammers, and crushers. In the case of a processing plant using sea-won aggregates, the only potential noise sources are the machinery and transport mechanisms. Botsford[96] has reported on typical noise levels in mining situations. He found the noise levels to be

- Primary crushers   88–91 dB (A)
- Secondary crushers   91–101 dB (A)
- Vibrating screens   98–109 dB (A)

Kolp[97] found similar data and included additional data for conveyors and feeders:

- Between two vibrating screens   104 dB (A)
- Head end of conveyor feeding screens   100 dB (A)

The noise levels are extremely high, with those from secondary crushers and vibrating screens approaching the noise level of a jet aircraft at 1,000 ft. It should be noted that the Occupational Safety and Health Administration (OSHA) would only allow worker exposure to 105 dB (A) for one hour each day.[98] However, Schreibeis and Schrenk showed that noise levels from sand and gravel plants dissipated rapidly with distance.[99] At 200 feet (61 m) from one plant, the noise level fell to 68 dB(A), roughly the level of a highway. In most inland sand and gravel facilities, the operator has acquired extensive lands around the plant to provide for a reserve of aggregates, and this land, whether used or not, serves as a buffer zone for noise to offsite receptors. Plants for marine minerals processing would lack the economic rationale (reserves) for such a buffer zone, and control technology would therefore assume more importance.

Control Technology. There are a number of means to reduce the very high noise levels at the plant.[100] Baffles can be built around noise-producing equipment by either of two methods. One method to prevent the generation of sound from vibrations uses resilient materials to block the vibrations or viscous material to absorb the vibrations. Once the noise has been generated, one can again block the noise by solid material or dampen the noise by porous material.

The second noise control method is to purchase quieter machinery. Buyers can insist that the manufacturer supply noise data and include maximum noise levels as part of the specifications. EPA noise standards have been developed for certain classes of equipment, and such federal limitations on equipment may be sufficient. Federal regulations are discussed in Chapter 7.

However, such noise abatement techniques may be inadequate for mechanical, esthetic, economic, or other reasons. For such cases, the only remaining alternatives are to employ hearing protective devices for personnel, such as ear muffs now used at airports; to purchase land around the facility as a buffer zone to protect offsite receptors; or to operate during specific hours when offsite impacts are acceptable to the neighboring communities.

Solid Waste. With sea-dredged aggregates, there is the possibility of creating solid wastes at the processing plant in the form of shells. Hess[101] describes in detail research now being conducted in Great Britain on the strength of concrete made with aggregate containing shells. Current data indicate that shell material in the sand fraction has no effect, but excessive amounts of hollow shell in the gravel fraction could adversely affect concrete strength.

Hess has also reported that some shell extractors have been employed in Great Britain but have met with little success. The need for such shell extractors in an operation on the U.S. coast would depend on two factors: (1) the amount of shells in the dredged material; and (2) the limits on shell content of sand and gravel in building codes and various other specifications. Should a shell extractor be installed, the operator would most certainly try to sell the by-product shells for their calcium carbonate content, as shells can be processed into cement.[102] Failing to do so, the extractor could crush the shells into sand; however, it may be cheaper to dispose of the shells at a landfill. If this solution is chosen, it represents an additional load for the local solid waste system. Since there are a number of methods to dispose of shell material, some profitable, this problem does not appear to be significant.

3. Potential Environmental Impacts of the Truck Fleet

In addition to potential environmental impacts from a processing facility, substantial environmental impacts may arise from operations of the truck fleet.

As indicated earlier, a 200 ton per hour processing facility could require the movement to and from the plant of 130 trucks each hour. These heavy, 15 ton Diesel trucks could cause severe local air and noise pollution and traffic congestion and safety problems.

Air Pollution.

Potential Problem. Heavy-duty, diesel-powered trucks are generally used in hauling sand and gravel. Diesel trucks emit pollutants from the same sources as gasoline-powered cars: exhaust, crankcase blow-by, and fuel evaporation. Blow-by is virtually eliminated in diesel trucks, since air is only in the cylinder during the compression stroke. The low volatility of diesel fuel, together with the use of closed injection systems, essentially eliminates evaporation losses in diesel trucks.

Exhaust emissions from diesel trucks have the same general characteristics as automobile exhausts, but concentrations of various pollutants do not occur in the same proportion. Since sulphur dioxide emissions are directly proportional to the sulphur content in the fuel, and since diesel fuels generally contain higher sulphur content (0.20 percent S) than gasoline, diesel trucks emit more SO_2 in the exhaust.[103]

Hydrocarbon and carbon monoxide emissions from diesel trucks are generally low. New fuel injection techniques on diesel trucks can reduce hydrocarbon emissions by as much as 50 percent, but the high temperatures and the large excesses of oxygen involved in diesel combustion cause higher nitrogen oxide emissions.

Particulate matter from diesel exhaust occurs in two major forms— black smoke and white smoke. White smoke, generally observed in cold starts, occurs when the fuel droplets are kept cool in an oxygen-rich environment. Black smoke, observed in road conditions, is emitted when the fuel droplets are subjected to high temperatures in an engine lacking in oxygen. A properly tuned diesel truck should show no visible "smoke."

Table 5-4 indicates typical emissions from diesel trucks. The air pollution in the vicinity of the processing plant will appear to depend on several factors: the length of time the truck is in the immediate area, the length of the truck queue, the condition of the truck fleet, the meteorological conditions, and the topography of the area.

Noise Pollution.

Potential Problem. Given the considerable truck traffic associated with a dockside processing plant, noise problems must also be considered. The Department of Transportation has made extensive studies of highway noise.[104] The relationship between highway

Table 5-4. Typical Emissions from Heavy-Duty, Diesel-Powered Trucks[a] — Reliability: Intermediate

Pollutant	Emissions			
	$lb/10^3$ *gal*	$kg/10^3$ *liter*	*g/mi*	*g/km*
Particulates	13	1.6	1.2	0.75
Sulfur Oxides[b] (SO_x as SO_2)	27	3.2	2.4	1.5
Carbon monoxide	225	27	20.4	12.7
Hydrocarbons	37	4.4	3.4	2.1
Nitrogen oxides (NO_x as NO_2)	370	44.0	34	21
Aldehydes (as HCHO)	3	0.4	0.3	0.2
Organic acids	3	0.4	0.3	0.2

Source: M.J. McGraw and D.S. Kircher. 1973. "Heavy-Duty, Diesel-Powered Vehicles," in U.S.E.P.A., *Compilation of Air Pollutant Emission Factors.* 2nd ed.
[a]Data based on weighting factors applied to actual tests conducted at various load and idle conditions with an average gross vehicle weight of 30 tons (27.2 MT) and fuel consumption of 5.0 mi/gal (2.2 km/1).
[b]Data based on fuel with average sulfur content of 0.2 percent.

traffic characteristics and the effective ambient noise level generated for a specific locale is extremely complex. The sounds produced at a particular highway depend on a number of factors which are functions of the vehicles on the highway, their speed, number, operation, acceleration, and age. The ambient sound level is also a function of topographical considerations such as location, orientation, shape, and reflectivity of obstacles in the surrounding area; by atmospheric and ground absorption; by micrometeorological conditions of varying wind speed and direction, temperature gradients, humidity; and by many other factors. Finally, sound levels can be considered to fluctuate randomly with time.

The noise output of trucks generally increases with age,[105] and the increase in noise generation with age is typically a function of truck maintenance. The major sources of noise from trucks are engines, exhaust pipes, cooling fans, transmission mechanisms, air intakes, tire noise, and aerodynamic noise. The dominant source of truck noise is the exhaust system, principally because of inadequate muffling of the exhaust gases. At speeds over 45 mph, however, tire noise may be dominant. Since sand and gravel trucks will probably travel at low speeds in or around the plant, tire and aerodynamic noises will probably not be important.

Control Technology. Advances in muffler technology in recent years have provided the capability for significantly reducing exhaust noise levels.[106] Noise reduction is achieved by increasing muffler volumes to obtain silencing and low back pressures. Also, acoustical wrapping or double wall construction of mufflers has significantly reduced noise produced by vibration of the muffler's outside walls.

Wesler has developed several methods of predicting highway noise. Using his nomograph approach and the following inputs

Vehicle speed	20 MPH
Percentage trucks	100 percent
Vehicle volume	130 per hour

the following noise levels would be obtained in the vicinity of the processing plant:

Distance to Observer (in feet)	*dB(A)*
50	85
100	82
500	74
1000	71

Figure 5-5 indicates typical community noise levels. It can be seen that the noise level 100 feet away from the trucks would be approximately that of a busy urban street. Since a sand and gravel plant

	Noise Level	*Response*	*Hearing Effects*	*Conversational Relationships*
Carrier deck jet operation	140			
		Painfully loud		
	130	Limit amplified speech		
Jet takeoff (200 feet)	120			
Discotheque				
Auto horn (3 feet)		Maximum vocal effort		
Riveting machine	110			
Jet takeoff (2,000 feet)				Shouting in ear
Garbage truck	100			
N.Y. subway station		Very annoying		
Heavy truck (50 feet)	90			Shouting at 2 feet
Pneumatic drill (50 feet)				Very loud conversation, 2 feet
	80	Annoying		
Alarm clock				
Freight train (50 feet)				Loud conversation, 2 feet
Freeway traffic (50 feet)	70	Telephone use difficult	↑ Contribution to hearing impairment begins	
		Intrusive		Loud conversation, 4 feet
Air conditioning unit (20 feet)	60			
Light auto traffic (100 feet)	50	Quiet		Normal conversation, 12 feet
Living room				
Bedroom	40			
Library				
Soft whisper (15 feet)	30	Very quiet		
Broadcasting studio	20			
	10	Just audible		
	0	Threshold of hearing		

Figure 5-5. Sound Levels and Human Response.

Source: Environmental Protection Agency. 1974 reprint. *Noise Pollution: Now Hear This*. Washington, D.C., Government Printing Office.

must, in fact, be designed and operated to meet the requirements of its community, the noise level produced by trucking may not be incompatible with the existing land use; but if combined with plant operation noise, unacceptable levels of noise may be the result. EPA standards for noise levels emitted by new motor vehicles, together with community ambient noise limitations, must be consulted before siting a processing plant.

4. Conclusions

For a processing facility receiving dry-unloaded aggregates from a dredge, the pollution problems are minimal. Current technology can control the potential water and air pollution problems. The technology for noise control is not as well developed, and the impact will fall mainly on the workers. The maximum sound levels in the plant may be in keeping with those for background-busy urban streets.

If hydraulic unloading is used, the processing plant can be recessed from the shoreline. However, the lack of a ready solution to the water pollution problem for such plants and unloading methods should create grave doubts about the viability of such a site plan. Even if the processing plant is 3 miles inland, the discharge of wastewater would still impinge upon the estuarine ecosystem. If the plant is located that far inland, the marine miner could lose any competitive edge which arose from proximity to the market. Potential impacts from air and noise pollution for the inland plant are the same as for the shoreline alternative.

The truck fleet traffic will be the same for dockside and inland locations, provided the plants are of the same throughput. Therefore, the potential air and noise impacts from trucking are the same for both sites. However, the dockside alternative may be superior: First, sea breeze may assist in the dispersion of gaseous pollutants and speed up the atmospheric renewal reactions. Moreover, a dockside facility would have a noise emission angle of only 180 degrees, whereas the inland facility may be surrounded by other uses.

NOTES

1. E.P. Odum, *Fundamentals of Ecology*, 3rd ed. (Philadelphia: Saunders, 1971).

2. J.H. Steele, *The Structure of Marine Ecosystems* (Cambridge: Harvard, 1974); H.T. Odum, *Environment, Power, and Society* (New York: Wiley, 1971).

3. This point was impressed on us by Dr. Robert Edwards, National Marine Fisheries Service, Woods Hole, MA.

4. For an interesting discussion of this phenomenon, see D.H. Meadows, D.L. Meadows, J. Randers, and W.W. Behrens, III, *The Limits to Growth* (New York: Potomac Associates, 1972), p. 37.

5. This section adapted from U.S. Bureau of Land Management, *Draft Environmental Statement for Proposed OCS Hard Minerals Mining Operating and Leasing Regulations* (Washington, D.C., 1974).

6. J.L. Goodier and S. Soehle, "Protecting the Environment during Marine Mining Operations," *Oceanology International* 6, 11 (1971): 25.

7. See, for example, S.B. Salia (compiler), *Coastal and Environmental*

Inventory, Cape Hatteras to Nantucket Shoals, 2 vols. (Kingston: University of Rhode Island, 1973); H.T. Odum, B.J. Copeland, and E.A. McMahan, eds., *Coastal Ecosystems of the United States,* 4 vols. (Washington, D.C.: The Conservation Foundation, 1974).

8. N. Yamakado and A. Yokota, "Fracture of Rock by High Speed Water Jet," *J. of Japan Society of Civil Engineers* 133 (1966).

9. M. Kondo, K. Fujii, and H. Shoji, "Excavation by Two-Phase Water Jets," Procedure of the 6th World Dredging Conference (San Pedro, Ca: WODCON, 1975, p. 565.

10. Current research at the Ports and Harbors Research Institute, Ministry of Transport, Kurihama, Japan, 1974.

11. R.R. Dickson and A.J. Lee, "Gravel Extraction Effects on Seabed Topography," *Offshore Services* 6 (1973): 32–39, 56–61.

12. Personal communications from M.S. Rolfe, Fisheries Laboratories, Ministry of Agriculture, Fisheries and Food, Burnham-on-Crouch, United Kingdom, to William Lee, August 1974.

13. Personal communications from John Baker, Connecticut Department of Agriculture, Milford, CT, to William Lee, February 1974.

14. W.H. Vesper, "Behavior of Beach Fill and Burrow Area at Prospect Beach, West Haven, Connecticut," U.S. Army Corps of Engineers Beach Erosion Board Tech. Memo No. 127 (1961).

15. C.E. Maguire Inc., Environmental Impact Statement, Proposed Dredge Project for Silver Sands State Park (Hartford: Connecticut Department of Public Works, 1973).

16. R.G.J. Shelton and M.S. Rolfe, "The Biological Implications of Aggregates Extraction: Recent Studies in the English Channel," ICES C.M. 1972/E:26 (1972).

17. See note 12, *supra,* and note 11, *supra,* at 48.

18. H.D. Hess, *Marine Sand and Gravel Mining Industry in the United Kingdom* (Tiburon, CA: NOAA Marine Minerals Technology Center, 1971).

19. This naraative primarily from I.P. Jolliffe, "Beach-Offshore Dredging: Some Environmental Consequences," *Preprints Offshore Technology Conference,* II-257 (1974).

20. Personal communications from John Edwards, Crown Estate Office, U.K., to William Lee, August, 1974.

21. U.S. Army Corps of Engineers, *Shore Protection Manual,* 3 vols. (Fort Belvoir: Coastal Envineering Research Center, 1973).

22. Personal communications from H. van der Tuin, North Sea Directorate, Public Works Department, Ministry of Transport and Public Works, the Netherlands, to William Lee, August 1974.

23. M.J. Crickmore, C.B. Waters, and W.A. Price, "The Measurement of Offshore Shingle Movement," *Proc. 13th Coastal Engineering Conference* (New York: American Society of Civil Engineers, 1972), p. 1005.

24. D.J.P. Swift, D.B. Duane, and O.H. Pilkey, eds., *Shelf Sediment Transport: Process and Pattern* (Stroudsburg, PA: Dowden, Hutchinson & Ross, 1972).

25. W. Harrison, M.P. Lynch and, A.G. Altschaeffl, "Sediments of Lower

Chesapeake Bay with Emphasis on Mass Properties," *J. of Sedimentary Petrology* 34, 727 (1964); S.B. Salia, S.D. Pratt, and T.T. Polgar, *Dredge Spoil Disposal in Rhode Island Sound* (Kingston: University of Rhode Island, 1972); L.S. Slotta, "Dredging Problems and Complications," in *Proc. 1973 Technical Conference on Estuaries of the Pacific Northwest* (Corvallis, OR: Oregon State University, 1973), p. 39.

26. R.R. Dickson, "A Review of Current European Research into the Effects of Offshore Mining on the Fisheries," *Preprints Offshore Technology Conference*, I-103 (1975).

27. D. Rhoads and D. Young, "The Influence of Deposit-Feeding Organisms on Sediment Stability and Community Trophic Structure," *J. of Marine Research* 28, 2 (1970).

28. H.L. Sanders, "Oceanography of Long Island Sound, 1952-1954, The Biology of Marine Bottom Communities," *Bingham Oceanographic Collection Bull.* 15, 345 (1956).

29. See Note 26, *supra;* R.G. Johnson, "Particulate Matter at the Sediment-Water Interface in Coastal Environments," *J. of Marine Research* 32, 313 (1974).

30. *Id.*

31. See Slotta, note 25, *supra.*

32. T. Fenchel, "The Ecology of Marine Microbenthos. IV. Structure and Function of the Benthic Ecosystem, Its Chemical and Physical Factors and the Microfaune Communities with Special Reference to the Ciliated Protozoa," *Ophelia* 6, 1 (1969); J.A. Servizi, R.W. Gordon, and D.W. Martens, "Marine Disposal of Sediments from Bellinham Harbor as Related to Sockeye and Pink Salmon Fisheries," International Pacific Salmon Fisheries Commission Progress Report no. 23 (1969).

33. P.I. Colby and L.L. Smith, Jr., "Survival of Walleye Eggs and Fry on Paper Fiber Sludge Deposits in Rainy River, Minnesota," *Trans. Am. Fisheries Soc.* 96, 279 (1967).

34. R. Boehmer, A. Westneat, H. Sleight, III, and D. Cook, "Effects of Suspended Marine Sediments on Selected Commercially-Valuable Fish and Shellfish of Massachusetts," *Preprints Offshore Technology Conference*, I-133 (1975).

35. *Id.*

36. J. Wang, "Mathematical Modelling of Near Coastal Circulation," (Ph.D. dissertation, M.I.T., 1975).

37. P.J. Sullivan, "The Penetration of a Density Interface by Heavy Vortex Rings," *Water, Air and Soil Pollution* 1, 322 (1972).

38. R.C.Y. Koh and Y.C. Chang, *Mathematical Model of Barged Ocean Disposal of Wastes* (Pasadena, CA: Tetra Tech, Inc. [NTIS PB 232 018], 1973).

39. G.C. Christodoulou, W.F. Leimkuhler, and A.T. Ippen, *Mathematical Model of the Massachusetts Bay. Part III: A Mathematical Model for the dispersion of Suspended Sediments in Coastal Waters* (Tech. Report No. 179, Ralph M. Parsons Laboratory for Water Resources and Hydrodynamics, MIT, Camb., Mass. 1974).

40. W.F. Leimkuhler, "A Two-Dimensional Finite Element Dispersion Model" (Civil Engineer thesis, M.I.T., 1974).

41. See note 20, *supra.*

42. B.H. Johnson, *Investigation of Mathematical Model for the Physical Fate of Prediction of Dredged Material* (Vicksburg, MS: Waterways Experiment Station, 1974).

43. R.B. Gordon, "Dispersion of Dredge Spoil Dumped in Near-shore Waters," *Estuarine and Coastal Marine Science* 2, 349 (1974).

44. See Salia, Pratt, and Polgar, note 25, *supra;* J. Mackin, "Canal Dredging and Silting in Louisiana Bays," *Publication of the U. of Texas Inst. of Mar. Sci.* 7, 262 (1962); E.B. May, *Environmental Effects of Hydraulic Dredging in Estuaries* (Dauphin Island: Alabama Marine Resources Lab. [NTIS COM-73-11271], 1973).

45. D.F. Westlake, "The Light Climate for Plants in Rivers," in R. Bainbridge, C.G. Evans, and O. Rackahm, eds., *Light as an Ecological Factor* (New York: Wiley, 1966), pp. 99-120.

46. J.A. Sherk, "The Effects of Suspended and Deposited Sediments on Estuarine Organisms (College Park: University of Maryland, 1971).

47. H.T. Odum and R.F. Wilson, "Further Studies on Reaeration and Metabolism of Texas Bays, 1958-1960," *Publication of the U. of Texas Inst. of Mar. Sci.* 8, 23 (1962).

48. D.A. Flemer, "Phytoplankton," in *Gross Physical and Biological Effects of Overboard Spoil Disposal in Upper Chesapeake Bay* (College Park: University of Maryland, 1970).

49. H.B. Moore, *Marine Ecology* (New York: Wiley, 1958).

50. National Marine Fisheries Service, *The Effects of Waste Disposal in the New York Bight*, Highland, N.J.: Sandy Hook Lab. [NTIS AD 743 936], 1972).

51. J.H. Ryther and W.M. Dunstan, "Nitrogen, Phosphorus and Eutrophication in the Coastal Marine Environment," *Science* 171, 1008 (1971).

52. Massachusetts Science and Technology Foundation, *Proc. First International Conference on ToxicDinoflagellate Blooms* (Cambridge: MIT Press, 1974).

53. For a discussion on the soluability of phosphorus under different conditions see Chapter 10 in W. Stumm and J.J. Morgan, *Aquatic Chemistry* (New York: Wiley, 1970).

54. For a summary, see G.F. Lee and R.H. Plumb, *Literature Review on Research Study for the Development of Dredge Material Disposal Criteria* (Dallas: U. of Texas [NTIS AD 780 755], 1974).

55. L.R. Pomeroy, E.E. Smith, and C.M. Grant, "The Exchange of Phosphate Between Estuarine Water and Sediments," *Limnology and Oceanography* 10, 167 (1965).

56. F.R. Hayes and J.E. Phillips, "Lake Water and Sediments IV. Radiophosphorus Equilibrium with Mud, Plants and Bacteria under Oxidized and Reduced Conditions," *Limnology and Oceanography* 3, 459 (1958).

57. D.L. Correll, M.A. Faust, and D.J. Severn, "Phosphorus Flux and Cycling in Estuaries," in L.E. Cronin, ed., *Estuarine Research* (New York: Academic, 1973).

58. H.L. Windom, "Processes Responsible for Water Quality Changes During Pipeline Dredging in Marine Environments," *Proc. Fifth World Dredging Conference* [Hamburg] (San Pedro, CA: World Dredging Assn., 1973).

59. See note 53, *supra.*

60. *Id.*, especially Chapter 6.

61. H.L. Windom, "Environmental Aspects of Dredging in Estuaries," *Proc. A.S.C.E.* 98, WW4 (1972): 475.

62. J.F. Gustafson, "Beneficial Effects of Dredging Turbidities," *World Dredging and Marine Construction* 8, 12 (1972): 44.

63. See note 54, *supra.*

64. See May, note 44, *supra.*

65. See *id.*, and note 46, *supra.*

66. See note 34, *supra.*

67. See *id.*, and J.A. Sherk, J.M. O'Connor, D.A. Neumann, R.D. Prince, and K.V. Wood, *Effects of Suspended and Deposited Sediments on Estuarine Organisms, Phase II* (Prince Frederick: University of Maryland, 1974).

68. J.E.G. Raymont, *Plankton and Productivity in the Ocean* (Oxford: Pergamon, 1963).

69. C.B. Jorgensen, *Biology of Suspension Feeding* (Oxford: Pergamon, 1966).

70. J. Caperon and J. Meyer, "Nitrogen-limited growth of Marine Phytoplankton II. Uptake Kinetics and their Role in Nutrient Limited Growth of Phytoplankton," *Deep Sea Research* 19, 619 (1972).

71. R.C. Harris, D.B. White, and R.B. MacFarlane, "Mercury-Compounds Reduce Photosynthesis by Plankton," *Science* 170, 736 (1970).

72. R.E. Lee, "A Quantitative Survey of the Invertebrate Fauna in Menemash Bight," *Biological Bull.* 86, 83 (1944).

73. See notes 26 and 16, *supra.*

74. R.L. Wigley and K.O. Emery, "Submarine Photos of Commercial Shellfish off Northeastern U.S., *Commercial Fisheries Rev.* 30, 3 (1968): 43.

75. See note 7, *supra.*

76. See note 34, *supra.*

77. R.G. Lunz, "Oyster Culture with Reference to Dredging Operations in South Carolina," A Report for the U.S. Army Corps of Engineers (1938).

78. D.A. Cobb, "Effects of Suspended Solids on Larval Survival of the Eastern Lobster," *Preprints VIII Marine Technology Society Conf.*, 395 (1975).

79. See May, note 44, *supra.*

80. J.R. Schubel, E. Scheimer, and G. Schmidt, "A Laboratory Apparatus for Maintaining Uniform Suspension of Fine-Grained Sediments," *Chesapeake Science* 13, 154 (1972).

81. See note 67, *supra.*

82. B.A. Rogers, "The Tolerance of Fish to Suspended Solids" (M.A. thesis, University of Rhode Island, 1969).

83. H. Kruuk, "Diurnal Periodicity in the Activity of the Common Sole, *Solea Vulgaris,*" *Neth. J. Sea Res.* 2, 1 (1963).

84. J.A. Sherk, J.M. O'Connor, and D.A. Neumann, "Effects of Suspended and Deposited Sediments on Estuarine Environments" (Paper presented at Second International Estuarine Research Conference, Myrtle Beach, S.C., 1974).

85. D.A. Neumann, J.M. O'Connor, J.A. Sherk, and K.V. Wood, "Respiratory and Hematological Responses of Oyster Toadfish (*Opsanus tau*) to Suspended Solids" (Unpublished manuscript, n.d.).

86. See note 34, *supra.*

87. F.F. Davis and J.R. Evans, "Mining Activity in California," *California Geology* 26, 291 (1973).

88. C.J. Poppe, "Hopper Dredges," *World Dredging and Marine Construction* 11, 12 (1975): 16.

89. R.G. Monroe, *Wastewater Treatment Studies in Aggregate and Concrete Production* (Lake Oswego, Oregon: Smith, Monroe and Grady Engineers [NTIS PB 219 670], 1973.

90. R.J. Lund, "Industrial Mineral Mining," in C.F. Gurnham, ed., *Industrial Wastewater Control* (New York: Academic, 1965).

91. J.A. Oleszkiewicz and P.A. Krenkel, "Principles of Sedimentation and Coagulation as Applied to the Clarification of Sand and Gravel Process Water," *National Sand and Gravel Association Circular No. 118* (1972).

92. A.D. Dawson, "Earth Removal and Environmental Protection," *Environmental Affairs* 3, 166 (1974).

93. M.J. Natale, "Dust Control. Technology and the Crushed Stone Producer," in K. Noll and J. Duncan, eds., *Industrial Air Pollution Control* (Ann Arbor, Michigan: Ann Arbor Science Publishers, 1973).

94. H.L. Harger, "An Update of Methods Los Angeles County Operators are Using to Meet Air Pollution Control District Requirements," *National Sand and Gravel Association Circular No. 115* (1972).

95. J.A. Danielson, ed., *Air Pollution Engineering Manual*, 2nd ed. (Los Angeles: Los Angeles County Air Pollution Control District, [NTIS PB 225 132], 1973).

96. J.M. Botsford, "Control of Mining Noise Exposure," *Mining Congress J.* 52, 8 (1967): 22.

97. R.J. Kolp, "Problem of Dust and Noise in Ready Mixed Concrete and Aggregate Operations in Realtion to OSHA and Bureau of Mines Regulations" (Paper presented at the National Sand and Gravel Association, Bel Harbor, Fl., 1973).

98. U.S. Department of Labor, Occupational Health and Safety Administration, *Noise—the Environmental Problem, A Guide to OSHA Standards* (Washington, D.C.: OSHA, 1972).

99. W.J. Schreibeis and H.H. Schrenk, "Evaluation of Dust and Noise Conditions at Typical Sand and Gravel Plants" (Unpublished Report for the National Sand and Gravel Association, 1961).

100. L.L. Beranek, ed., *Noise Reduction* (New York: McGraw-Hill, 1960).

101. See note 18, *supra*.

102. J. Mero, *Mineral Resources of the Sea* (New York: American Elsevier, 1965).

103. M.J. McGraw and D.S. Kircher, "Heavy-Duty Diesel-Powered Vehicles," in U.S.E.P.A., *Compilation of Air Pollutant Emission Factors*, 2nd ed. (Washington: EPA [NTIS PB 223 996], 1973).

104. J.E. Wesler, *Manual for Highway Noise Prediction* (Cambridge, Mass.: Transportation System Center, Department of Transportation [NTIS PB 226 086], 1972).

105. 38 Fed. Reg. 20059 (July 27, 1973).

106. 38 Fed. Reg. 20103 (July 27, 1973).

✳️ *Chapter 6*

Ownership and Regulatory Interests

INTRODUCTION

The logical beginning for legal analysis of a resource management subject is examination of resource ownership and the property rights that are involved. The next important step of analysis involves determination of the sources, nature, extent, and allocation of public regulatory authority that is directly applicable to the resources and to the lands and waters in which the resources are found.

Therefore, this chapter focuses on ownership, property rights, and regulatory authority applicable to the hard mineral resources of the offshore regions, as such resources may be subjected to the exploration and extraction activities discussed in earlier chapters. This is preceded, however, by a brief examination of the principles that delineate public from private interests, in order to provide a fuller view of property interests in coastal regions and to promote understanding of the interactions between ownership and regulation.

A. PRIVATE AND PUBLIC INTERESTS IN COASTAL LANDS AND RESOURCES

Common law principles traceable to Roman civil law origins generally establish the rules that divide coastal lands and resources between private and public ownership in the United States. The fundamental rule is that coastal and other lands lying beneath navigable waters are owned by the sovereign—the respective states in the case of inland waters and nearshore coastal waters which may be abutted by private riparian or littoral land.[1]

On the coast, where the shore is alternately covered and uncovered by tidal waters, the general rule is that the shore is land that lies beneath navigable waters of the state and is therefore in public rather than private ownership.[2] The division of private from public ownership under this approach is the mean high water line.[3] The general rule used to distinguish private from public lands in coastal regions is not, however, unvaried, and in no state are all property interests absolutely determined by the locus of the ownership interest.

Public ownership of the shore is burdened under common law principles by access and other rights of the littoral owner over adjacent shore land lying between the lines of high and low water.[4] Protection of these rights and encouragement of their exercise to promote trade and commerce led several colonial and state legislatures to go beyond the common law and grant title in the shore to littoral owners.[5] Still other legislative acts have granted either exclusive or preferential rights to littoral proprietors for the taking of sand and gravel, or other resources, from the shore.[6]

In other states, however, statutes and judicial decisions extend public property rights or interests inland from the mean high water line. Thus, in Texas, it is declared by statute that there is a legal presumption that littoral land ownership does not permit exclusion of public ingress and egress to public shore lands adjacent to coastal property and, further, that the beach seaward of the vegetation line is subject to a prescriptive easement protecting the public's right of ingress and egress.[7] And in Oregon, the state's highest court has ruled that the public's customary use of Oregon's coastal beaches has vested ownership in the public of the beach area all along the coast.[8]

In addition to being varied by judicial decision and legislation, the seemingly simple general rule delineating private from public ownership of coastal lands poses some difficult problems in its application. There has been controversy as to the criteria to be employed in determining the mean high water line,[9] and it is difficult to determine precise boundary lines for ownership and right of use purposes even with the use of accepted definitions or standards.[10] Further, individual colonial, legislative, and administrative grants and actions conveying specific title and other interests to particular littoral owners and municipalities create the potential for an inestimable number of private versus public disputes over ownership and rights of use.[11]

Public authority to regulate the use of private land at the state government level basically rests on the so-called "police power," the power to regulate both conduct and land use for the purpose of protecting public health, safety, or welfare.[12] This authority has come to be broadly interpreted by the courts to mean that state regulation is legitimate if it is for a "public purpose," but even regulation for the most unassailable public purpose is limited by the constitutional prohibition against taking private property without compensation by either eminent domain or the imposition of regulations that so far restrict the use of property as to preclude its reasonable use.[13] Wetlands fill and development,[14] and resource extraction[15] cases often raise these issues concerning the limits on public regulation of the uses of private property.

Private property interests in the coastal zone are also subject to some forms of federal regulation. Filling, dredging, and construction cannot be conducted unless a permit has been acquired from the Army Corps of Engineers;[16] and discharges into waters of the United States are subject to water pollution control regulations of the Environmental Protection Agency.[17]

From this brief survey of conflicting private and public interests in coastal lands emerges a framework of fundamental legal principles and a perspective on the multidimensional system of legal and institutional controls central to this study. Most significantly, the discussion makes it clear that land and resource ownership is not a source of absolute rights. Regulation from the perspective of a broader state or national public interest may severely limit and impinge on the value of property rights, whether such regulation is state or federal control of the use of private property or, as will be seen in the following discussion, federal control of the use of state-owned property.

B. STATE AND FEDERAL INTERESTS IN OFFSHORE LANDS AND RESOURCES

1. State and Federal Ownership Interests

From the founding of the republic to 1947, it was commonly assumed that the coastal states owned the submerged land and the resources therein from the mean high water line to the edge of the territorial sea, the so-called "three mile limit." Each state became a sovereign state as a result of the American Revolution and, as such, acquired and retained absolute rights to all navigable waters and the lands beneath them, excepting those rights surrendered to the federal government under the Constitution.[18] The Supreme Court has held that states other than the original states were admitted on equal terms, under which they acquired the same rights as original states in navigable waters and the lands below.[19]

These rights of the coastal states were repeatedly confirmed by the U.S. Supreme Court, but in 1947 the Court acted, in a suit brought by the United States against California concerning offshore oil and gas leasing, to establish federal "paramount rights and power" over offshore lands that "transcended the rights of a mere property owner," in this case the state of California.[20] The basis for ruling that all oil and gas leasing offshore was the subject of federal rather than state control was the existence of an exclusive federal interest in and power to conduct the international affairs of the United States.

The decision in *United States v. California* spawned a continuing struggle in Congress over legislation clarifying the state and federal interests in submerged lands lying within the historic three mile territorial limits of the United States. At the same time, litigation concerning the submerged lands interests of the Gulf Coast states came before the Supreme Court and was resolved on the same basis as the California litigation.[21]

Congress finally moved to resolve the controversy by enacting the Submerged Lands Act[22] and the Outer Continental Shelf Lands Act[23] in 1953. The first of these statutes delineates ownership and resource management interests as between the federal government and the coastal states with respect to all lands lying between the mean high water line and the outer limits of United States outer continental shelf jurisdiction. Further, the Submerged Lands Act defines federal regulatory interests and authority in the region committed to state ownership and control by the act.

The Outer Continental Shelf Lands Act serves primarily to establish a federal regulatory regime for the use of those lands and waters that were made the subject of exclusive federal ownership and control by the Submerged Lands Act. Together, the two statutes specifically define state and federal ownership of submerged lands and generally delineate federal and state regulatory authority with respect to all coastal lands and waters for all purposes, despite the fact that the specific context of their passage was the controversy over offshore oil and gas resources.

The Submerged Lands Act confirms and establishes the title of the states in lands beneath navigable waters within the boundaries of the state.[24] The act further declares:

§ *1312. Seaward Boundaries.*
The seaward boundary of each original coastal State is hereby approved

and confirmed as a line three geographical miles distant from the coast line. . . . Any state admitted subsequent to the formation of the Union . . . may extend its seaward boundary to a line three geographical miles distant from the coastline. . . . Nothing in this section is to be construed as questioning or in any manner prejudicing the existence of any State's seaward boundary beyond three geographical miles if it was so provided by its constitution or laws prior to or at the time such State became a member of the Union, or if it has been heretofore approved by Congress.

The term *boundaries* is defined by purposes of the Submerged Lands Act as follows:

§ 1301. Definitions.
(a). . .
(b) The term "boundaries includes the seaward boundaries of a State or its boundaries in the Gulf of Mexico or any of the Great Lakes as they existed at the time such State became a member of the Union, or heretofore approved by the Congress, or as extended or confirmed pursuant to Section 1312 of this title but in no event shall the term "boundaries" or the term "lands beneath navigable waters" be interpreted as extending from the coast line more than three geographical miles into the Atlantic Ocean or the Pacific Ocean, or more than three marine leagues into the Gulf of Mexico.

For purposes of establishing a baseline from which to measure seaward distance in the establishment of boundaries, the act defines the term *coast line* as the line of ordinary low water.[25]

Submerged lands lying on the continental shelf seaward of state boundaries were declared by Congress to be federally owned lands.[26] The outer limit of these federal lands was not specifically defined, except by reference to the provisions of the Geneva Convention on the Outer Continental Shelf, which creates a national option to elect between a limit defined by a depth of 200 meters or a depth established by the limits of resource exploitability.[27]

As in the case of private versus public ownership, the matter of division of state and federal submerged lands interests is not as simple as it may thus far appear. The Submerged Lands Act specifically recognizes that historical state boundaries in the Gulf of Mexico may extend beyond 3 miles up to 3 marine leagues (approximately 9 miles).[28] The Supreme Court has held that Texas and Florida, with respect to their Gulf Coasts, but not Alabama, Mississippi, or Louisiana, have adequately proven the existence of historical seaward state boundaries of 3 marine leagues.[29]

A second exception to the 3 mile limit of state ownership is provided by the exception for boundaries approved by Congress. One such boundary is the Connecticut and New York boundary line in Long Island Sound, which divides all of Long Island Sound into either Connecticut or New York, despite the fact that the body of water exceeds 6 miles in breadth at many points. This boundary line was approved by Congress in 1881[30] and is confirmed by § 1312 of the Submerged Lands Act.

More recently, the Supreme Court has had before it, as a matter of original jurisdiction, the claims of 12 Atlantic coast states in which the states asserted boundaries coextensive with the outer boundary limits claimed by the United States.[31] The foundation of these claims was argued to be in pre-American Revolution charters and patents and in the principle that the states, as postrevolution sovereigns, acquired and presently retain title and control to all coastal lands and water except for land or authority expressly relinquished under the Constitution or by individual conveyance. The special master appointed by the Supreme Court to take evidence and hear argument filed his decision ruling against the states on October 15, 1974, and on March 17, 1975, the Supreme Court adopted the report and findings of the special master in ruling for the United States.[31]

The Supreme Court rested its decision in *United States v. Maine* on, and refused to overrule, its earlier rulings that each state yielded sovereignty over submerged lands in accepting statehood and the Constitution; the grant of title to lands within the 3 miles limit through the Submerged Lands Act was viewed merely as the federal exercise of the paramount national authority over such lands.[33] Thus, the Court clearly ruled that state ownership of offshore submerged lands is a product of, and limited by the terms of, the 1953 legislation.

Still other points of controversy becloud the division of submerged lands into state and federal ownership. One such matter concerns the establishment of the baselines from which seaward distances are to be measured for the purpose of establishing the boundary between state and federal lands. This was the issue in a second case involving the United States and California,[34] and in recent years the federal government has been at odds with Massachusetts and Alaska with regard to the closing lines to be employed in, respectively, Nantucket Sound and Cook Inlet.[35]

2. State and Federal Regulatory Jurisdiction

The most significant feature of the Submerged Lands Act is not that it confirms the coastal states' title to submerged lands beneath territorial waters but that it also declares the states' authority to administer, develop, and lease these lands and their resources.[36] Ownership was arguably not divested by the Supreme Court decisions, but regulatory control, including leasing authority, was pre-empted because there were found to be "paramount rights and power" that transcended the states' interest in controlling the use of their offshore lands. Thus, the critical provision of the statute is its restoration of the basic right of the coastal states to control the use of their submerged lands.

The regulatory authority of the states over submerged lands was, however, made conditional rather than absolute by the Submerged Lands Act. It is subject to paramount federal authority to exercise constitutionally grounded jurisdiction to regulate and control navigation, commerce, national defense, international affairs, flood control, and power production within state boundaries.[37] The commerce power itself is, of course, extremely broad,[38] and coupled with the other federal constitutional powers, it gives the federal government wide-ranging authority effectively to override or limit the scope of state authority to administer, develop, and lease submerged lands and resources. Moreover, the exercise of such federal authority is regarded by the courts as an indirect taking of property without compensation in only the most extreme cases.[39]

The Outer Continental Shelf Lands Act complements the Submerged Lands Act by establishing that federal regulatory authority is exclusive with respect to submerged lands lying between the coastal states' outer boundaries and the farthest reach of United States outer continental shelf jurisdiction.[40] Management, including the power to lease, is vested by the act with the secretary of the interior.[41] The primary limitations on this authority to lease exploration and extraction rights in this area are several national security powers committed to exercise by the president[42] and the paramount status accorded any restrictions imposed by the Geneva Convention on the Outer Continental Shelf.[43]

Although Department of the Interior authority to manage the resources of the outer continental shelf is less encumbered than private control of owned land or state administration of submerged lands, that authority is itself not singular. As noted, the effect of the reservation of federal regulatory authority in the Submerged Lands Act is to subordinate state control of state submerged lands to a wide range of specific federal regulatory schemes, including, but not limited to, Army Corps of Engineers regulation for the purposes of protecting and improving navigation and for flood control, Environmental Protection Agency regulation of water and air quality,

Coast Guard regulation of navigation, Fish and Wildlife Service protection and enhancement of marine resources, and Bureau of Customs control over the use of foreign-built and foreign-registered vessels.

This regulatory overlay also generally applies with respect to federal outer continental shelf (OCS) activities through interagency consultation and general compliance requirements if not, in fact, by direct extension of these regulatory systems to federal leasing programs and lessees' activities.[44] In addition, the National Environmental Policy Act mandates the use of a consultative process in developing leasing impact statements.[45] This process involves all federal agencies having jurisdiction by law or special expertise concerning the subject matter. The act also mandates the circulation of completed impact statements and an ensuing commentary process that involves private interests and appropriate federal, state, and local government agencies.[46] This commentary process for draft environmental impact statements affords affected states, as well as groups and individuals, an opportunity to inject state regulatory and other interests into federal decision-making processes.

The influence of one regime of governmental regulatory interests on another is therefore not exclusively unidirectional. Further, consultation and comment are not the sole means by which state interests may affect federal administration of OCS lands mining. The Outer Continental Shelf Lands Act itself authorizes the Secretary of the Interior to cooperate with state conservation agencies adjacent to leased tracts in the enforcement of conservation laws and regulations in leased areas.[47] In addition, the act makes the laws of adjacent states applicable in the OCS to the extent that the states' laws are not inconsistent with federal law.[48]

State regulation also effects federal OCS leasing through the exercise of state controls on onshore land development and state administration of coastal water pollution control laws. Regulation of onshore facility siting and construction by the coastal state will be a particularly significant factor in determining the economic feasibility of high-bulk aggregate mining, since transportation costs from the processing facility site to port are a critical economic factor.[49] State water quality standards may, to the extent they are enforcible, also have significant effects on marine mining and the use of vessels employing onboard processing systems.[50] Finally, the Coastal Zone Management Act of 1972[51] directs that federal projects, federally funded activities, and federally licensed projects must be consistent to the maximum extent practicable or in compliance, in the case of licensing, with approved coastal land and water use management programs of affected states.[52]

This survey of state and federal ownership and regulatory interests demonstrates that the legal and institutional system regulating the use and extraction of offshore resources is highly complex and that it would be erroneous to assume that the intricacies inherent in on-shore land ownership, use, and control are absent or unnecessary in the offshore areas that are uninhabited by man and, by comparison to onshore lands, undeveloped.

C. NATIONAL AND INTERNATIONAL INTERESTS IN OFFSHORE LANDS AND RESOURCES

The final parameter to consider in the survey of ownership and regu-latory interests in submerged lands and their resources is that which defines national and international interests. Again, interjurisdictional ambiguities abound, and the competing interests themselves, as the recent history of the Caracas and Geneva sessions of the United Nations Law of the Sea Conference demonstrate, are by no means two-dimensional.

This section does not attempt to speculate on the ultimate success or results of the Law of the Sea Conference. Rather, its purpose is to take note of existing sources of law that are significant to this study, in particular: the Convention on the Outer Continental Shelf[53] as it pertains to the exploitation of OCS resources; the Convention on the Territorial Sea and the Contiguous Zone[54] as it relates to the exercise of national regulatory jurisdiction in coastal waters; and the 1972 Convention on the Prevention of Marine Pollution by Dumping of Wastes and Other Matter.[55]

The 1958 Geneva Convention on the Outer Continental Shelf primarily addresses the matter of exploitation of the OCS seabed and subsoil resources. It constituted an international community re-sponse to the Truman Doctrine, which had asserted jurisdiction over seabed resources to a depth of 600 meters.[56] The international con-vention, to which the United States acceded, sets the limit of national jurisdiction at the 200 meter isobath "or, beyond that limit, to where the depth of superadjacent waters admits the exploitation of the natural resources of said areas."[57] This rather ambiguous definition establishes the national limits of seabed and subsoil resources ownership and regulatory jurisdiction, which jurisdiction explicitly extends to, but only to, regulation of the conduct and effects of seabed and subsoil resource exploitation activities.[58]

The 1958 Geneva Convention on the Territorial Sea and the Con-tiguous Zone defines the national territorial sea as a 3 mile wide belt measured from the shore baseline;[59] it also authorizes the establishment of a contiguous zone, the outer limits of which are 12 miles measured from the same baseline.[60] National regulatory jurisdiction may be exercised in the contiguous zone, which is otherwise legally a part of the "high seas," for a nation to prevent "infringement of its customs, fiscal, immigration or sanitary regulations within the territorial sea."[61] Here it is important to note, as will become evident in later discussions of water pollution regulation, that exercise of national regulatory jurisdiction in the contiguous zone is allowed for the limited purpose of protecting the integrity of national sovereignty in adjacent territorial waters.

A third international convention, signed by the United States and ratified by the Senate in 1973, is also relevant to the exploration and extraction of OCS hard minerals. The 1972 Convention on the Prevention of Marine Pollution by Dumping of Wastes and other Matter requires signatory nations to adopt and enforce permit laws concerning waste disposal in the contiguous zone, prohibitions on the dumping of 7 classes of substances, and special permit laws for the disposal of certain other substances.[62]   However, the convention excludes disposal in connection with seabed mineral resources exploration, extraction, and related processing from its coverage.[63] This exception recognizes the existence of authority to regulate such disposal under the Convention on the Outer Continental Shelf as well as the Convention on the Territorial Sea and the Contiguous Zone and anticipates the establishment of a regulatory regime by the Law of the Sea Conference. The United States implemented the 1972 convention in enacting Title I ("Ocean Dumping") of the Marine Protection, Research and Sanctuaries Act of 1972.[64]

This review of interjurisdictional legal interests related to the exploration of offshore hard mineral resources indicates that national-international, as well as private-public and state-federal, interests are complex and in a state of dynamic tension. The influence of the international conventions on United States regulation of offshore mining and related activities is strongest, of course, with respect to federally administered OCS lands management. The conventions and implementing federal laws are not, however, without effect on states' administration of their submerged lands, a fact that is most evident in the area of pollution control regulation applicable to coastal waters.[65]

CONCLUSION

The objective in this chapter has been to introduce the complex and interactive private, state, national, and international interests in ownership, use, and control of offshore lands and hard mineral resources. A general overview approach has been followed, and the particulars of regulatory interests have been left for discussion in the chapters that follow.

The complex mosaic of laws and regulations is an expression of the subtle mix of economic and political interests that have been framed in legal terms, and this perspective is essential to a full comprehension and evaluation of the functional objectives of the specific laws discussed in the following chapters and, more important, to the development of regulatory alternatives.

NOTES

1. See generally, J. Sax, "The Public Trust Doctrine in Natural Resource Law: Effective Judicial Intervention," 68 *Mich. L. Rev.* 473, 475 (1970); Note, "The Public Trust Doctrine in Tidal Areas: A Sometime Submerged Traditional Doctrine," 79 *Yale L.J.* 762, 763 (1970).

2. Martin v. Waddell, 41 U.S. (16 Pet.) 367 (1842); Borax Consolidated, Ltd. v. City of Los Angeles, 296 U.S. 10 (1935).

3. See also Hughes v. State of Washington, 389 U.S. 290 (1967).

4. Marks v. Whitney, 6 Cal. 3d 251, 98 Cal. Reptr. 790, 491 P. 2d. 374 (1971); Michaelson v. Silver Beach Imp. Assn., Inc., 342 Mass. 251 (1961).

5. See Michaelson v. Silver Beach Improvement Assn., 342 Mass. 251, 173 N.E. 2d 273 (1961); Opinion of the Justices, 313 N.E. 2d 561 (1974); Sinford v. Watts, 123 Maine 230, 122 A. 573 (1923); Nudd v. Hobbs, 17 N.H. 524 (1845); Miller v. Commonwealth, 159 Va. 924, 166 S.E. 557 (1932).

6. See, e.g., Md. Code art. 27, §485; Va. Code §61.1-190, 62.1-193.

7. Vernon's Ann. Tex. Stat., art. 5415d. See generally, Luttes v. States, 159 Tex. 500, 324 S.W. 2d 167 (1958).

8. State *ex rel* Thornton v. Hay, 254 Ore. 584, 462 P.2d 671 (1969).

9. Hughes v. State of Washington, 389 U.S. 290 (1967); Borax Consolidated, Ltd. v. City of Los Angeles, 296 U.S. 10 (1935).

10. See generally Shalowtiz, "Boundary Problems Raised by the Submerged Lands Act," 54 *Colum. L. Rev.* 1021 (1954).

11. See, *e.g.*, Tappan v. Burnham, Mass. 65 (1864); Dolphin Lane Associates, Ltd. v. Town of Southampton, 72 Misc. 2d 868, 339 N.Y.S.2d 966 (1971).

12. Goldblatt v. Town of Hempstead, 369 U.S. 590 (1962); Commonwealth v. Tewksbury, 52 Mass. 55 (1846); Potomac Sand and Gravel Co. v. Mandel, 266 Md. 358, 293 A.2d 241, *cert. denied,* 409 U.S. 1040 (1972).

13. Pennsylvania Coal Co. v. Mahon, 260 U.S. 393 (1922); Goldblatt v. Town of Hempstead, 369 U.S. 590 (1962).

14. Commissioner of Natural Resources v. Volpe, 349 Mass. 104, 206 N.E. 2d 666 (1965); State of Maine v. Johnson, 265 A.2d 711 (1970).

15. Commonwealth v. Tewksbury, 52 Mass. 55 (1846); Potomac Sand and Gravel Co. v. Mandel, 266 Md.358, 293 A.2d 241, *cert denied,* 409 U.S. 1040 (1972).

16. 33 U.S.C.A. §404; 33 C.F.R. §209.120(b) (2) & (6). See generally Zabel

v. Tabb, 430 F.2d 199 (5th Cir. 1970); United States v. Stoeco Homes, 498 F.2d 597 (3rd Cir. 1974).

17. 33 U.S.C.A. §§ 1311, 1343, 86 Stat. 816 (1972).

18. Martin v. Waddell, 41 U.S. (16 Pet.) 367 (1842); Pollard's Lessee v. Hagan, 44 U. S. (3 How). 212 (1845).

19. Pollard's Lessee v. Hagan, 44 U.S. (3 How.) 212 (1845); Shively v. Bowlby, 152 U.S. 1 (1894).

20. United States v. California, 332 U.S. 19 (1947).

21. United States v. Louisiana, 339 U.S. 699 (1950); United States v. Texas, 339 U.S. 707 (1950).

22. 43 U.S.C.A. § 1301, 67 Stat. 29 (1953).

23. 43 U.S.C.A. § 1331, 67 Stat. 462 (1953).

24. 43 U.S.C.A. § 1311 (a) (1).

25. 43 U.S.C.A. § 1301(c).

26. 43 U.S.C.A. § 1312.

27. 1958 Convention on the Outer Continental Shelf, art. I, 15 *U.S. Treaties* 471, T.I.A.S. No. 5578, 499 U.N.T.S. 311.

28. 43 U.S.C.A. § 1301(a).

29. United States v. Louisiana, 363 U.S. 1 (1960).

30. 21 Stat. 351 (1881).

31. United States v. Maine, 420 U.S. 515 (1975).

32. *Id.*

33. *Id.*

34. United States v. California, 381 U.S. 139 (1965).

35. Litigation concerning United States efforts to quiet title to lands beneath Cook Inlet is reported in United States v. Alaska, 422 U.S. 184 (1975), *remand* 519 F.2d 1376 (9th Cir. 1975).

36. 43 U.S.C.A. § 1311(a).

37. 43 U.S.C.A. § 1311(d) and 1314(a). See also 43 U.S.C.A. § 1313.

38. See Katzenbach v. McClung, 379 U.S. 294 (1964); Heart of Atlanta Motel v. United States, 379 U.S. 241 (1964).

39. See Zabel v. Tabb, 430 F.2d 199 (5th Cir. 1970).

40. 43 U.S.C.A. § 1332.

41. 43 U.S.C.A. § 1334.

42. 43 U.S.C.A. § 1341.

43. See United States v. Ray, 423 F.2d 16 (5th Cir. 1970).

44. 43 U.S.C.A. § 1333(e) (1)-(3).

45. 42 U.S.C.A. § 4331, 83 Stat. 252 (1969).

46. 42 U.S.C.A. § 4332(2)(c).

47. 43 U.S.C.A. § 1344(a).

48. 43 U.S.C.A. § 1333(a).

49. See Chapter 1, note 26. See also pp. 4-5, 37.

50. It appears that state enforcement of stricter effluent limitations for vessels operating in territorial waters has been pre-empted. This question is discussed in detail in Chapter 8. However, the states have the authority to establish water quality (ambient) standards, without apparent federal limitations.

Indeed, such standards could force the promulgation of stricter federal effluent limitations. 33 U.S.C.A. § 1311(b) (1) (c).

51. 16 U.S.C.A. § 1451, 86 Stat. 1281 (1972).

52. 16 U.S.C.A. § 1457(c).

53. 15 U.S.T. 471, T.I.A.S. No. 5578 (1958).

54. 15 U.S.T. 1606, T.I.A.S. No. 5639 (1958).

55. 1972 Convention on the Prevention of Marine Pollution by Dumping of Wastes and Other Matters, T.I.A.S. No. 8165, 3 ELR 40329.

56. See Lettow, "Marine Pollution," in E. Dolgin & T. Guilbert, eds., *Federal Environmental Law* (St. Paul: West Publ. Co., 1974); pp. 596, 600.

57. 1958 Convention on the Outer Continental Shelf, art I, 15 *U.S. Treaties* 471, T.I.A.S. No. 5578, 499 U.N.T.S. 311.

58. *Id.* See also 43 U.S.C.A. § 1332.

59. *Id.*

60. *Id.*, art. 24.

61. *Id.*, art. 24(2).

62. See note 55, *supra* at 596, 662–70.

63. 1972 Convention on the Prevention of Marine Pollution by Dumping of Wastes and Other Matters, T.I.A.S. No. 8165, 3 ELR 40329.

64. 33 U.S.C.A. § 1401.

65. This subject is explored in detail in Chapters 8 and 9.

Chapter 7

Federal Laws and Regulations:
Outer Continental Shelf

INTRODUCTION

The federal interest in the regulation of exploration, extraction, and other activities associated with hard mineral resources of the outer continental shelf (OCS) is not singular. As a result, numerous federal agencies exercise jurisdiction that is of major significance for OCS mining activities. While basic management responsibility for the management of OCS lands and resources rests with the Department of the Interior under the provisions of the Outer Continental Shelf Lands Act,[1] that act itself vests other regulatory authority in the Coast Guard[2] and the Army Corps of Engineers.[3] In addition, the Environmental Protection Agency and several other federal agencies administer statutes, many recently enacted, that are of major importance with respect to possible mining of OCS hard mineral resources.

The diverse federal regulatory interests and authorities pertinent to OCS mining are reviewed in this chapter. It will be evident that the simplistic general rule locating both resource ownership and control in the United States is complex in its implementation. Thus, in an effort to delinate and describe clearly these diverse federal management and regulatory interests, the following sections separately examine discrete agency and functional interests, authorities, and procedures. The concluding section of the chapter draws upon this compartmentalized description in presenting an integrated view of federal legal and institutional controls over OCS hard mineral resources exploration and extraction.

A. LEASING AND LEASE SUPERVISION

1. OCS Tract Leasing

Existing Arrangements. The Bureau of Land Management (BLM) of the Department of the Interior administers OCS and other public lands. BLM authorization is required for private commercial mining or other exploitation of the lands and resources subject to its jurisdiction. Statutes and regulations establish legal and institutional controls for BLM approval of resource exploration and extraction in onshore and offshore BLM-administered lands.[4]
administered lands.[4]

The Outer Continental Shelf Lands Act provides that "The Secretary [of the Interior] shall administer the provisions of this subchapter relating to the leasing of the Outer Continental Shelf, and shall prescribe such rules and regulations as may be necessary to carry out such provisions."[5] This authority and responsibility is exercised within the Department of the Interior by the Bureau of Land Management.

At present, there are no existing BLM regulations concerning OCS hard mineral resources and their exploration and extraction. Oil, gas, sulphur, and salt leasing regulations[6] constitute the only Department of the Interior regulations which have been promulgated to implement the Outer Continental Shelf Lands Act.

The absence of a comprehensive regulatory program for the exploitation of OCS hard mineral resources should not be construed to mean that federal regulatory jursidiction or federal regulatory authority does not exist. Programmatic regulatory jurisdiction is made explicit by the act; and regulatory authority for development activities which may be proposed in the absence of programmatic regulations is implicit in the act[7] and explicit in an omnibus section of the oil, gas, sulphur, and salt leasing regulations.[8] The Department of the Interior has expressed the view that it may presently grant hard mineral resources leases under either the general jurisdictional provisions of the statute or the omnibus clause.[9] Such leases would not, of course, necessarily be governed in the strict sense by the provisions of the oil, gas, sulphur, and salt regulations.[10]

Geological, geochemical, and geophysical OCS explorations require authorization from the U.S. Geological Survey (USGS), another division of the Department of the Interior.[11] OCS lease operations are also supervised by the Geological Survey; in the case of oil, gas, sulphur, and salt exploration and extraction regulations, this jurisdictional bifurcation of leasing and operations supervision is implemented by separate but coordinated regulations of the Department of the Interior.[12]

Although the Department of the Interior asserts that it may lease OCS tracts for hard mineral mining before developing leasing regulations, no such leases have yet been granted. USGS, on the other hand, entertains applications for permits for OCS prospecting or exploration for hard mineral resources.[13] These permits are reported, however, to be quite limited with respect to the types of activities and methods authorized in exploring for deposits of OCS hard mineral resources.[14]

Proposed Leasing Regulations. On February 1, 1974, the Secretary of the Interior published proposed regulations, and also published a draft environmental impact statement (EIS), pursuant to the National Environmental Policy Act, concerning the establishment of a comprehensive regulatory system for commercial exploration for and extraction of OCS hard mineral resources. The proposed regulations vest leasing authority in the BLM[15] and supervision powers over lease working or operations in the USGS.[16] Promulgation of final regulations and publication of a final EIS was expected to occur shortly thereafter, but has not yet occurred, four years later.

Under the proposed leasing regulations, lease tract nominations may be made on the initiative of potential lessees, or in response to a call for nominations issued by the Bureau of Land Management.[17] All nominations would be required to be accompanied by a list of the principal minerals expected to be found in the nominated tracts and by a description of the nominator's preliminary plans for tract exploration and development.[18] The exploration and development plan description, including specification of exploration, anticipated mining, soil disposal, and transportation methods, would be augmented by a supply and demand analysis, a description of market conditions that warrant the proposed development, and a statement of possible environmental effects and planned environmental protection measures.[19] As to the environmental impact assessment elements of tract nominations, the basis for the nominator's evaluation of environmental effects must be indicated.

Final selection of tracts for leasing would be preceded by a full BLM evaluation, in consultation with other federal agencies, of "the potential effect of the leasing program on the total environment, aquatic resources, aesthetics, recreation, and other resources and competing activities in the entire area during exploration, development and operational phases."[20] The regulations specifically require that the Geological Survey submit its recommendations concerning tract selections and lease terms and conditions.[21] In his discretion, the director of the BLM may also hold public hearings and seek comments and suggestions from states, various organizations, industry, and individuals.[22] Final decisions on the selection of specific tracts and conditions for leasing would be made, upon the recommendation of BLM after completion of this process, by the Secretary of the Interior.

Notice of the offer to lease tracts selected for leasing would be published in the Federal Register at least 30 days prior to the proposed sale of leases.[23] The proposed regulations specify what would be required in the official notice: Among other things, it must indicate any environmental protection stipulations or conditions established by BLM as necessary terms of any lease.[24] In addition, the notice would state that no operations under any lease could commence until exploration, development, mining, and transportation plans have been submitted by the lessee and approved by the reviewing officer of the agency having jurisdiction over these matters.[25] Each such approval would be based, of course, upon satisfaction of environmental as well as other criteria employed by such agencies in their review processes.

The notice of lease offer would invite competitive, sealed, cash bonus bidding[26] on one or more of three classes of leases that may be specified in the notice. An *exploratory lease*, not exceeding 36 leasing blocks of not more than 5,760 acres each, would entitle a lessee to exclusive geophysical and other exploration rights for a term of 2 years.[27] A *2 year development lease*, acquired either through initial bidding or conversion from an exploratory lease, for not more than 9 lease blocks of not more than 5,760 acres each, would give the lessee "the right to conduct mining research, to collect bulk samples, and to develop mining systems, but shall permit only such production as necessary to verify the feasibility of systems."[28] *Production leases*, acquired either through initial bidding or conversion of an exploration or a development lease, would convey exclusive and renewable rights for 10 years in contiguous quarter blocks not exceeding a total 3 leasing blocks of 5,760 acres each.[29] Whether exploratory, development, or production leases are offered for sale depends upon whether, as between an exploratory or a development lease, valuable mineral deposits have yet been discovered on the lease tracts, and as between an exploratory or a development lease and a production lease, whether commercial feasibility of extraction of discovered mineral resources has been established.[30]

The proposed regulations are not specific concerning lease conditions except as to characterization of leases within the tripartite structure, length of term, rental, royalties, and minimum annual development expenditure requirements.[31] Other provisions of the proposed regulations focus on lease assignment,[32] suspension,[33] and relinquishment,[34] and environmental protection terms would be established primarily on the basis of special conditions or stipulations contained in the notice of lease order[35] and the lease development plans of nominators and bidders.[36] In addition, all leases would be subject to the authority of the Secretary of the Interior to make regulations concerning the prevention of waste, the conservation of natural resources, and the protection of correlative rights.[37]

The tripartite leasing system proposed in the OCS mining regulations for hard minerals differs from the existing oil, gas, sulphur, and salt leasing system. It substitutes the exploration and development leases for the exploration stage of the one lease system presently employed for such other minerals. Of particular note is the introduction of the intermediate development lease covering activities such as bulk sample collection, mining processes development, and mining system feasibility test production.

Marine mining leases for hard minerals would grant the right to mine or extract all minerals other than oil, gas, sulphur, and salt; but only those hard minerals specified by notice of the lease offering could be mined without first gaining specific approval from BLM.[38] Exploitation of mineral resources would be required to be conducted by the lessee or its assignee; however, production leases would be assigned in whole or, with approval, in part, except that no assignment of rights to mine separate mineral resources would be permitted.[39] Exploration and development leases are declared to be unassignable.[40]

Lease sales would be to the highest qualified cash bonus bidders.[41] Successful bidders would pay rentals at a rate of 10¢ per acre for exploratory leases, 25¢ per acre for development leases, and $1 per acre for production leases,[41] plus a royalty specified by the lease, but not less than 2 percent of the gross value of production, under production leases.[43] Royalties for minerals not identified in the original lease offering notice would be set by the Department of the Interior after a lessee's development plan for such other minerals has been submitted.[44]

2. Limitations on OCS Leasing: The Marine Protection, Research, and Sanctuaries Act

The previous chapter noted several specific limitations of the Outer Continental Shelf Lands Act on the leasing authority of the

Department of the Interior. More recently, the Marine Protection, Research and Sanctuaries Act of 1972[45] granted powers to the Secretary of Commerce that may further limit OCS leasing authority in areas designated as marine sanctuaries.

The act authorizes the Secretary of Commerce, to designate as "marine sanctuaries . . . those areas of ocean waters, as far seaward as the outer edge of the Continental Shelf, . . . [and] other waters where the tide ebbs and flows . . . which he determines necessary for the purpose of preserving or restoring such areas for their conservation, recreational, ecological or esthetic values."[46] The designation can be made, however, only after consultation, with an opportunity for review and comment, with heads of a number of affected federal agencies and upon the approval of the President.[47] Sanctuaries may be established in state waters or in waters above state offshore submerged lands, but only after consultation with officials of the state and subject to the authority of the governor of the state to certify that the designation is acceptable.[49]

The act further provides the Secretary of Commerce with authority to promulgate "necessary and reasonable regulations to control any activities permitted within the designated marine sanctuary."[49] These regulations are to be developed in consultation with interested federal agencies. After the regulations are promulgated, activities otherwise permitted by permit, license, or other authorization may not be undertaken unless the Secretary of Commerce certifies that the activity is consistent with the purposes of the act and permitted by the regulations.[50]

The legislative history of the marine sanctuaries law reveals substantial concern over the effects of mineral resources exploitation on the marine environment,[51] with some bills proposing moratoria on the exploitation of oil and gas extraction. However, the statute is silent with regard to any preferred, permissible, or unpermissible uses of mineral resources, nor does it articulate criteria, multiple use or otherwise, for regulations of the Secretary of Commerce. The statute is an apparent compromise struck between the alternatives of imposing statutory limitations on mineral resources extraction and legislative inaction. The express language of the Act making permits, licenses, and other authorizations for the conduct of activities in a sanctuary area invalid unless the Secretary of Commerce certifies the activity as appropriate omits any specific reference to leases. On the other hand, the regulatory authority is broadly stated, and the words "or other authorization" are so inclusive that there can be little doubt that marine sanctuary designations and regulations for the use of the sanctuary areas could substantially impinge on OCS lease tract sales and lease operations.

B. MINING OPERATIONS SUPERVISION

A companion set of proposed regulations for hard mineral lease operations was published along with the leasing regulations in February 1974. As in the case of oil, gas, sulphur, and sale lease operations, hard mineral lease operations would be subject to supervision by the Geological Survey of the Department of the Interior in general, and by USGS mining supervisors in particular.[51]

The proposed operating regulations govern activities conducted under all exploratory, development, and production leases for OCS hard mineral resources. The mining supervisor would enforce both lease terms and regulations and the USGS operating regulations. Thus, the proposed operating regulations broadly state that

> Subject to the supervisory authority of the Secretary [of the Interior] and the Director (of the Geological Survey), exploratory, development, mining, processing operations, handling and measurement of production, determination and collection of rental and royalty, and, in general, all other operations conducted on a lease by or on behalf of a lessee are subject to the regulations in this part and are under the jurisdiction of the mining supervisor for any region as delineated by the Director.[53]

The objectives of the mining supervisor's administration of all applicable laws, regulations, and lease terms are declared to be the conduct of operations "in a manner that will to the extent feasible protect the living and non-living natural resources of the Outer Continental Shelf and result in the maximum economic recovery of the mineral resources in a manner compatible with sound conservation, environmental and multiple use practices."[54]

Mining supervisors could exercise their regulatory authority by issuing OCS orders applicable to an entire region or a major portion of a region and approved by the chief, Conservation Division, Geological Survey.[55] Written and oral orders, the latter to be confirmed in writing, governing operations on specific leases are also authorized by the proposed regulations.[56] Among the orders authorized are emergency suspension orders for protection against "immediate and serious harm or damage" to the environment, leased deposits, or other valuable mineral resources.[57] Operations or production could be suspended in the interests of conservation on the initiative of the mining supervisor or at the request of the lessee.[58] Finally, the

Director of the Geological Survey, during the term of a lease, would be able to reduce the rental, minimum royalty, or royalty on the lease or any part of the lease if it is determined that the lease cannot be successfully operated under its terms and that such operation is necessary to increase the recovery of mineral resources or to fulfill conservation purposes.[59]

The responsibilities of the mining supervisor would begin with the granting of approval prior to any lease operations of exploration, development, or production plans.[60] Such plans must indicate the minerals that are the subject of the plan, and the site and methods for exploration, development, mining, processing, and transportation; and the plans must comply with all lease terms concerning "air, land and water pollution, interference with navigation, and damage to aquatic and wildlife species and other natural resources."[61] The supervisor could approve or suggest modifications to a lessee's plan, but no operations could be initiated until a plan is approved.[62] Approved plans could be modified by mutual consent; but exploration, development, or mining of minerals other than those specified in the original notice of lease offering must be approved by the BLM[63] and made the subject of a new operations plan which must itself be approved before such revised operations may be undertaken.[64]

The proposed regulations separately state the basic elements of exploration, mining, and development plans. The exploration plan would require identification of the exploratory operations to be conducted and the equipment to be employed and must include location maps; a description of air, land, and water pollution controls; damage prevention measures for aquatic wildlife and other natural resources; and safeguard measures for navigation and public health hazards that are to be implemented.[65] Mining and development plans must also describe environmental protection measures, and include a description of environmental conditions and species found in the area of operations; a description and maps of mineral deposits in the area; an explanation of the mining and development methods to be utilized; information concerning expected production rate and the method and location of processing operations; a description and maps detailing minerals transportation to the shore; and a description in detail of waste and refuse characteristics and the methods to be employed in their discharge and disposal.[66]

With respect to approved plan operations, the regulations would require the maintenance by operators of a log of all drill holes and bottom sampling, including a description of materials or geological forms, content analysis performed on any samples, and other information prescribed by the mining supervisor.[67] In addition, current and accurate scale maps of operations, showing geological conditions as well as excavations, must be maintained and submitted to the mining supervisor annually or as more frequently required.[68] Monthly operations reports for each lease describing activities during the period and the status of the operations are also required.[69]

Several operating regulations provisions concerning the critical matter of environmental protection have already been noted. The mining supervisor's regulatory authority in this area and environmental control elements of the required plans implement the broad directive that "the lessee shall not pollute the air, water, submerged and adjacent coast land, damage aquatic and wildlife species or cause any other unnecessary disturbance to the environment."[70] Waste disposal must conform to the approved exploration or mining and development plan,[71] and "spills or water pollution by hazardous substances" are made the subject of reporting and cleanup requirements."[72]

Other sections of the proposed regulations pertain to specific aspects of operations.[73] In particular, mining supervisors are provided authority to grant easements or rights of use for the construction and use of offshore platforms, floating structures, or fixed structures in connection with lease operations, whether the structure is on the lease site or on OCS lands near or adjacent to a lease.[74] Approval powers for easements or rights of use necessary to the construction, maintenance, and operation of pipelines and conveyers sited on OCS lands for the purposes of gathering, processing, storing, measuring, or delivery or production or for moving fluids or slurries necessary for lease operations are also vested in the mining supervisor.[75]

C. DREDGING OPERATIONS AND MATERIALS DISPOSAL

1. Dredging Authorization

The Rivers and Harbors Act of 1899[76] requires Corps of Engineers authorization of any dredging activity in the navigable waters of the United States. This regulatory authority has been implemented by Corps regulations establishing a permit system for such activities.[77] The meaning of the term "navigable waters" for purposes of dredging permit authorization limits Corps jurisdiction to lands lying beneath territorial waters.[78] The Corps regulations to specify and declare that Corps regulatory jurisdiction beyond the territorial sea exists only for special purposes defined by other statutes extending its jurisdiction for such purposes.[79] Thus, Corps of Engineers dredging permits are not required for OCS dredging but are necessary for dredging on states' submerged lands.

Dredge mining is technologically similar to channel dredging and other traditional applications of dredging; but, as discussed in Chapter 4, the economic feasibility of offshore dredge mining will probably depend on the employment of dredging equipment and procedures that are substantially more sophisticated than those employed in traditional channel and other dredging in the United States. Therefore, the issue that emerges is the extent to which dredging, employing such new equipment and techniques for the purpose of the commercial recovery of hard minerals, is subject to the provisions of the River and Harbors Act and the Corps' regulatory program.

Given the substantial functional similarity between economically feasible dredge mining and traditional dredging, the silence of the Act on the significance of commercial recovery of hard minerals which may be the result of dredging activity, and the history of Corps regulations under the Act of riverbed and harbor dredging for channel clearance and/or for the production of commercial aggregates or fill, it is reasonable to conclude that future offshore dredge mining on the submerged lands of the states will be subject to Corps authority under the act.[80] However, as discussed above, such Corps authority over dredging, and therefore over dredge mining, would not extend to such activities on the outer continental shelf. Corps dredging authorization is discussed further in Chapter 8.

2. Dredged Materials Disposal

Outline of Authority. The proposed regulations for OCS hard minerals leasing and mining operations acknowledge the parameters of minimizing injury to water quality and the marine environment.[81] In addition, the operations regulations specifically implement this goal in the description of the responsibilities of the mining supervisors[82] and of a specific antipollution section,[83] and in requiring exploration, development, and mining plans to detail potential environmental impacts, environmental protection measures, and dredged spoils disposal methods and effects.[84] This program is in accordance with the Convention on the Outer Continental Shelf, which affirmed national jurisdiction to regulate authorized activities and their effects involving seabed and subsoil resource exploitation.[85]

A second approach to the regulation of dredged materials disposal exists under the Federal Water Pollution Control Act (FWPCA)[86] and, for limited situations, the Marine Protection, Research and Sanctuaries Act (MPRSA).[87] The former regulates the discharge of "pollutants," including dredged materials,[88] in navigable, contiguous zone, and ocean waters.[89] The latter act controls transportation of material, including dredged material,[90] from the United States for the purpose of dumping or disposal in ocean waters, navigable waters, and waters of the contiguous zone;[91] and transportation of such material from outside the United States for the purpose of dumping in the territorial waters or the waters of the contiguous zone of the United States.[92] Finally, the MPRSA also provides for regulation of the transportation of such material from any location for the purpose of dumping in any waters of the territorial sea, contiguous zone, or ocean by any vessel of United States registry or flag or by any United States agency.[93]

The 1972 amendments to the Federal Water Pollution Control Act established a variety of water pollution control programs. The principal program is the National Pollution Discharge Elimination System (NPDES), a permit program that is designed to implement point source effluent limitations, performance standards, toxic pollutant discharge limitations, and ocean discharge provisions of the act.[94] NPDES applies to pollutant discharges into navigable waters, waters of the contiguous zone, and ocean waters to the edge of OCS jurisdiction.[95] In the case of dredged materials discharges into navigable waters, permits are to be issued by the Corps of Engineers in cooperation with the Environmental Protection Agency, rather than by the EPA.[96] NPDES permits for discharges into the territorial sea (a class of "navigable waters"),[97] waters of the contiguous zone, and ocean waters must meet the requirements of specifically applicable FWPCA sections and satisfy ocean discharge criteria established by the EPA.[98] Corps of Engineers, rather than Environmental Protection Agency NPDES, permits, must be obtained for the discharge of dredged materials into territorial waters,[99] but the EPA's ocean discharge criteria must be applied by the Corps in determining whether a permit should be granted or denied.[100]

The EPA ocean discharge criteria adopted for the purposes of the NPDES permit program are also established as the criteria to be applied in evaluating ocean dumping permit applications under the MPRSA.[101] Again, the Corps of Engineers is directed to apply the EPA criteria in permit cases in which it has jurisdiction over the transportation of dredged materials for purposes of disposal.[102]

Careful analysis of the two statutes and their implementing regulations indicates the permit jurisdiction concerning dredged materials disposal to be as depicted in Table 7-1. This division of jurisdiction reflects an accommodation reached in enacting both statutes to preserve traditional Corps of Engineers regulation of dredging and related dredged materials disposal in navigable waters of the United States, including the territorial sea, without either extending Corps jurisdiction or compromising the water pollution program goal of establishing a unitary set of criteria for discharge permits.

Examination of the combined FWPCA–MPRSA regulatory systems indicates therefore that OCS dredge mining discharges require an NPDES discharge permit from EPA. Neither Corps regulatory jurisdiction nor EPA ocean dumping permit requirements are applicable to dredge mining spoils or discharges with respect to OCS operations although, as discussed in Chapter 8, Corps jurisdiction pertains with respect to mining operations conducted in state submerged lands and superadjacent waters. Evaluation of applications for EPA permits will be governed by the combined application of standards implemented by the NPDES program and EPA's ocean discharge criteria published pursuant to § 403 of the FWPCA.[103]

Water Pollution Controls: Effluent Limitations. The 1972 FWPCA amendments established point source effluent limitations as the principal approach to water pollution control. This approach largely, but not totally, supplants earlier water pollution regulation, which was designed to achieve and maintain receiving water quality standards by defining acceptable pollutant levels for receiving waters and thereby establishing source limitations. Another way of describing this shift in emphasis is to characterize the new approach as one based primarily on available control technology rather than on the prescription of discharge requirements by extrapolation from local conditions.

All *existing point sources* must meet, in accordance with § 301 of the act, an interim level of effluent control by July 1977 and a

Table 7-1. Dredged Material Disposal Permit Authority

Activity	Agency	References
Disposal in navigable waters[a]	Corps of Engineers	FWPCA, § 404
Transportation from United States	Corps of Engineers	MPRSA, § 103(a)
Disposal in contiguous zone and oceans[b]	EPA	FWPCA, § 403

[a]Includes all such disposal, regardless of source of dredged material
[b]No substitution of Corps of Engineers regulation for general regulation by EPA

stricter level of control by July 1983.[104] The first is that attainable
by use of "the best practicable control technology currently available";[105] the second requires the application of "the best available
technology economically achievable."[106] More advanced levels of
control may be established by EPA for certain situations in which
competing water use needs require control.[107] Section 306 of the
act deals separately with *new point source* effluent controls by requiring that such sources must utilize "the best available demonstrated control technology."[108]

The EPA Administrator was directed by the act to promulgate
regulations for selected classes of point sources within these effluent
limitation categories. For *existing sources*, the elements of the regulatory program are to be based on findings as to relevant pollutants
and their effects and the degree of control attainable through use of
the mandated 1977 and 1983 criteria for control technologies, as
well as on other factors. After taking into account these considerations, the Administrator is required to determine control measures
and practices to be employed for different classes or categories
of point sources[109] and to implement controls through the NPDES
program. Similar regulatory requirements were also established for
new source standards of performance.[110]

OCS hard mineral mining will probably necessitate the design and
construction of *new* oceangoing hopper dredges as discussed in Chapter 4; therefore, the applicable effluent control limitations will really
be those to be promulgated as "new source" standards of performance
under § 306, although existing source limitations may also be
promulgated by EPA. The level of control that must be established
for such new sources will thus be "the best available demonstrated
control technology, processes, operating methods, or other alternatives, including, where practicable, a standard permitting no discharge of pollutants."[111]

At this time, there are no effluent limitations or standards of performance for commercial dredge mining vessels. Such vessels are not
included in the original list (in the statute) of point source categories to be controlled by EPA nor have such vessels been established
as a new point source category. However, the EPA Administrator has
recently taken first steps toward the development of some limitations which are applicable to marine mining, pursuant to § 306 and
other sections of the act.

1. *Addition of Mineral Mining to List of Categories of New Sources*
   to be controlled by means of effluent limitations and NPDES.
   (40 F.R. 48668, October 16, 1975).

2. *Promulgation of Interim Final Rules for Effluent Guidelines and Standards for the Mineral Mining and Processing Point Source Category*,[112] and the division of the category into 38 subcategories consisting of "specific mineral types or classes of minerals. In addition, within each subcategory a determination was made whether subparts required different effluent limitations based on type of ore, method of ore transport, type of processing."

    With regard to the development of applicable effluent limitations, EPA describes its methodology: For different "segments" of the category, existing "control and treatment" technologies were identified, including both in-plant and end-of-process technologies; the "chemical, physical and biological characteristics of pollutants" and "effluent levels resulting from the application of each . . . technology" were determined; the "limitations and reliability of each treatment and control technology. . . . The non-water quality environmental impact . . . the energy requirements . . . the cost of the application [were also determined, and] then evaluated in order to determine what levels of technology constitute 'the best, practicable control technology currently available.' "

    However, the resulting interim regulation reflects a concern clearly limited to land-based mining and processing activities only. The subcategories designated include "construction sand and gravel and crushed stone" and hard mineral resources found off shore; but no effluent limitations were specified, and the categories were "reserved" for future determination of such limitations. (40 F.R. 48652–67, October 16, 1975).

3. *Addition of Ore Mining and Dressing to List of Categories of New Sources* to be controlled by means of effluent limitations and NPDES. (40 F.R. 51748, November 6, 1975).

4. *Promulgation of Interim Effluent Limitations and Guidelines for the Ore Mining and Dressing Point Source Category*[113] which designate seven ore mining point source subcategories in these interim regulations. However, only the subcategories of "Base and Precious Metals" (40 C.F.R. 440.23–26) and "Titanium Ore" (40 C.F.R. 440.73–76) contain interim effluent limitations applicable to dredge mining activities in coastal or offshore regions.[114] For "base and precious metals," designated as gold, silver, tin, and platinum, the proposed effluent limitations apply to pollutants arising from the "mining of placer deposits, dredge mining and hydraulic mining operations." For "titanium ore," the proposed limitations apply to pollutants arising from "dredge mining of placer deposits of sands containing rutile, ilmenite, levcoxene, monazite, zircon and other heavy metals." In each

subcategory, the proposed limitations for existing and new sources are the same, reflecting the lack of working experience to date and the knowledge that such dredge mining will essentially constitute "new source" activities. (40 F.R. 51722-47, November 6, 1975).

These new interim regulations are expressly inapplicable at this time to sand and gravel dredge mining and onboard processing, but the regulations could possibly be broadened to cover offshore hard minerals and the extraction and processing activities associated with such minerals as OCS and other offshore mining comes nearer to realization.[116] New mineral and ore subcategories may be added, and existing categories can be further subdivided to include offshore mining and processing, to provide the effluent limitations and other regulatory controls appropriate for hopper dredge mining and other aspects of offshore minerals exploitation. It should also be noted that in cases where offshore mineral and associated extraction and processing activities coincide with an existing category, such as in the probably rare case of offshore shaft mining of a categorized mineral, the current, largely onshore regulations may be extended to such offshore activities.

Finally, the critical issue underlying the foregoing description of a new and rapidly evolving regulatory process must be highlighted—the extent to which EPA's promulgation of new source effluent limitations would manifest a true "technology-forcing" function by EPA. Since U.S. offshore mining experience has been decidedly limited to date and based on relatively crude channel dredging techniques, it would be inappropriate to use this background as the framework for establishing effluent limitations for the new, potentially large enterprise of offshore mining, particularly where sophisticated foreign technologies and techniques have been proven feasible and economic. The extent to which EPA would consider such foreign developments in promulgating further effluent limitations for offshore mining of U.S. hard mineral resources would therefore be critical to the fulfillment of EPA's role of water pollution control and other aspects of environmental protection.

Water Pollution Control: Ocean Discharge Criteria. As noted earlier, new source standards establish effluent limitations that are implemented under the NPDES permit program. But in cases involving point source discharges into coastal waters, no NPDES permit may be issued unless the proposed pollutant discharge also satisfies the ocean discharge criteria established by the EPA pursuant to the directives of § 403 of the FWPCA.[117]

The published § 403 FWPCA ocean discharge criteria for dredged materials permits classify dredged materials as (1) unpolluted and (2) polluted dredged materials. Material that is not classifiable as unpolluted is polluted; "unpolluted dredged material" is defined as material that satisfies 1 of 3 standards or sets of conditions. In the case of OCS mining in areas not used for waste disposal, the first standard may be satisfied: "The dredged material is composed essentially of sand and/or gravel, or of other naturally occurring sedimentary materials with particle sizes larger than silts and clays"[118] For areas where waste disposal or other contamination has occurred, it will be necessary to demonstrate that the water quality at or near the site for disposal is adequate for fish, shellfish, and wildlife propagation and that the biota associated with the material to be dredged are "typical of a healthy ecosystem"[119] or that the dredged material produces in tests "a standard eluriate in which the concentration of no major constituent is more than 1.5 times the concentration of the same constituent in the water from the proposed disposal site used for testing."[120]

The above definition of "unpolluted dredged material" might be erroneously read to suggest that the fine sediment discharged in the operation of, for example, a hopper dredge engaged in OCS sand and gravel mining is not "dredged material." This is not the case; the general definition of "dredged material" in the EPA regulations concerning Corps of Engineers regulation of discharges into navigable waters defines such materials as "any material . . . excavated or dredged from navigable waters, including without limitation, runoff or overflow which occurs during a dredging operation.[121] The NPDES regulations do not define the term, but the regulation quoted above was promulgated for the purpose of defining Corps regulation of activities exempted from the NPDES program by § 404 of the FWPCA: thus it is safe to assume that the same definition will be applied for purposes of Corps regulation of dredged material discharges in navigable waters and of EPA control under NPDES of such discharges beyond the seaward limit of the territorial waters.

Offshore dredge mining that involves onboard processing and onsite disposal will most likely satisfy at least 1 of the 3 "unpolluted dredge materials" standards. Such material may be discharged or dumped "at any site which has been approved for the dumping of settleable solid wastes of natural origin."[122] Polluted dredged materials disposal is subject to more stringent conditions.[123]

A potentially critical problem arises from the focus of the statutes and the EPA regulations on the identification by EPA of disposal "sites" and the designation of a particular site from among approved sites for disposal or dumping under individual permits. Whether or not a lease tract operation location may be specially classified as a disposal site, where the emphasis of the Act and regulations is on the designation of approved sites for disposal or discharges, is unclear; but accommodation of this probably unconsidered question will no doubt be possible at least in cases involving unpolluted dredged materials.

In summary, OCS mining and its immediate externalities of polluted effluents and dredged spoils for disposal are subject to regulatory jurisdiction currently divided among hte BLM, USGS, and EPA. As a practical matter, EPA regulation which is now evolving will ultimately be controlling by virtue of the specific terms of the MPRSA,[124] the absolute prohibition by the FWPCA of any pollutant discharge without acquiring any necessary NPDES permit,[125] and the precedence given the position of the EPA in any EPA-Corps disagreement.[126] Further, the proposed Department of Interior regulations for OCS hard mineral resources mining effectively defer to any applicable water pollution control law requirements.[127]

D. RELATED FEDERAL REGULATIONS

1. OCS Structures

The authority of the Army Corps of Engineers to protect against navigation obstruction in navigable waters is specifically extended by the Outer Continental Shelf Lands Act to cover OCS artificial islands and fixed structures.[128] The basic authority of the Corps rests in the Rivers and Harbors Act of 1899[129] and is elaborated in Corps of Engineers published regulations.[130]

The Rivers and Harbors Act prohibition against the construction of any structure in waters subject to Corps jurisdiction without prior authorization by the Corps has been implemented by a permit system established in Corps of Engineers regulations. These regulations specifically limit Corps evaluation of proposed construction projects associated with leasing programs to their effects on navigation and national security, since Department of the Interior leasing regulations indicate that the Department, in consultation with other federal agencies, will assess the total environmental impact of any OCS lease development.[131]

2. Operations Safety

Several federal laws relating to safety and health apply to OCS lease operations. The proposed OCS hard mineral lease operating regulations, to be administered by the USGS, direct that lessees shall conduct operations so as to prevent accidents, fires, and malfunction; perform operations with a view to protection of the health and safety of persons; and correct unsafe or hazardous conditions immediately.[132] The regulations make applicable to OCS operations the provisions of the Longshoremen's and Harbor Workers' Compensation Act,[133] but not with respect to the master or crew members of a vessel, since such persons are protected under the provisions of the Jones Act.[134] In addition, the Occupational Safety and Health Act of 1970,[135] which establishes a program of work environment safety regulation under the Department of Labor, broadly applies to employment activities on the OCS, without exemption for dredge or other vessels. Thus, occupational safety and health standards could be promulgated for offshore mining operations.[136]

Navigational safety regulation is the subject of Coast Guard and Department of Transportation authority.[137] The Outer Continental Shelf Lands Act authorizes Department of Transportation promulgation and enforcement of regulations covering warning lights and devices, safety equipment, and other navigation safety matters for the protection of life and property on OCS artificial islands and structures.[138] More broadly, and most significant for hard mineral mining by dredging, the Coast Guard has general authority, and has promulgated regulations, concerning vessel safety.[139] These latter regulations pertain to safety of construction, emergency equipment, safety appliances, firefighting equipment, and emergency operation features, and they establish regular inspection requirements.[140] The Coast Guard has also promulgated navigation safety rules specifically applicable to safety zones around OCS structures[141] as well as navigation safety rules of general application.[142] Special requirements for lights on dredging vessels have also been set out by Coast Guard regulations.[143]

Since these regulations have not been promulgated in contemplation of hopper dredge and other methods of large-scale, continuous-operation marine mining, the Coast Guard and the Department of Labor will undoubtedly consider the unique features of marine mining as it becomes more imminent, for purposes of promulgating regulations, "finely tuned" to the needs and issues which may arise.

3. Mined Materials Transportation

As noted earlier, the Outer Continental Shelf Lands Act, and the proposed leasing and operations regulations, authorize the Department of the Interior to grant easements or rights of use in OCS lands for pipelines, conveyers, or other devices used to transport mined resources to facilities at which transfer to a transportation company occurs.[144] Although pipeline transport is a possibility for nearshore mined resources, vessel or barge transportation of mined OCS resources to shore is the most probable transportation mode; and here again, Coast Guard regulatory jurisdiction pertains as to transportation safety and navigation rules[145] and enforcement of any applicable water pollution control or other laws.[146] Pipeline transport in nearshore areas would also be subject to state regulation as to siting, safety, and design and to Corps of Engineers authority as such pipelines are facilities in navigable waters subject to the provisions of the River and Harbor Act and implementing regulations.

4. Foreign Vessel Restrictions

Customs restrictions on the commercial use of foreign-built and foreign-registered dredging vessels in United States waters are of particular significance to offshore hard mineral exploration and extraction. European technology and other features of offshore mining systems are far ahead of the United States state of the art for offshore hard minerals exploitation.[148] United States law declares, however, that "A foreign-built dredge shall not, under penalty of forfeiture, engage in dredging in the United States unless documented as a vessel of the United States.[148] Whether operations in OCS waters, outside of the territorial waters of the United States, for purposes of extracting seabed and subsoil resources that do belong to the United States is "dredging *in the United states*" [emphasis added] is a presently unresolved question. Neither the Convention on the Outer Continental Shelf, the Submerged Lands Act, nor the Outer Continental Shelf Lands Act purports to extend national sovereignty over ocean waters beyond the territorial sea;[149] rather, the sovereignty is over the resources of the OCS and the regulation of exploration and exploitation.[150]

The historical basis for the prohibition, which was enacted in 1906, was a need to protect domestic shipyards, dredging firms, and labor against foreign competition in river and harbor dredging.[151] The locus and the activity involved in 1906 differ from those of today, but the protective considerations are likely to be given the same weight today as they were in 1906. There is good reason to question the characterization of proposed dredge mining operations as "dredging" merely because advanced dredging technology is employed in this context of economic regulation, as distinct from the earlier context of navigation regulation discussed in part C.1 of this chapter. There is stronger reason to question the applicability of the 1906 statute to operations outside territorial waters; it is arguably not within the category of federal laws made applicable to OCS operations by the Outer Continental Shelf Lands Act;[152] and, as noted above, any such extension may be inconsistent with international conventions.

A similar set of issues exists concerning the transportation of mined materials to shore by such vessels. Another federal law regulating coastal transportation and commerce provides that for such vessels "No merchandise shall be transported by water, or by land and water, on penalty of forfeiture, between points in the United States, including Districts, Territories, and possessions thereof embraced within the coastwide laws."[153]

Here the issues are whether the OCS is a point "in the United States" and whether the transportation could be considered to be "embraced within the coastwise laws" which are laws of domestic maritime trade.[154] The difficulty in both instances is that the common distinction drawn is that between domestic and foreign commerce; the activities which would be undertaken do not fit well into either category, given the background and language of the international conventions and the Outer Continental Shelf Lands Act.

5. Onshore Processing Facilities and Operations

Regulation for the siting of onshore facilities is principally a matter of state jurisdiction. However, several federal regulatory interests exist in this area despite the general preeminence of state and local authority in land use matters.

Army Corps of Engineers authorization would be required for any dredging in harbors or channels necessary for providing or improving offloading vessel access to onshore facilities.[155] A Corps permit must also be obtained for the construction of any pipeline, wharf, or pier or any filling or bulkheading at such a facility or site.[156]

Corps jurisdiction was not exercised until recent years in areas landward of established harborlines or, alternatively, mean low water. Regulatory control was then extended to the mean high water line,[157] and since the enactment of the 1972 FWPCA, further landward extension to include additional areas has been urged by the EPA and environmental groups. Litigation instituted to compel such an extension, consistent with the intent of Congress in enacting the FWPCA to exercise water pollution control to the fullest extent permitted by the Constitution, resulted in a court order directing the revision of Corps regulations and their definition of the term "navigable waters" to reflect that intent.[158]

The revised Corps regulations extend regulatory jurisdiction beyond the traditional agency definition of "navigable waters" to cover all coastal tidal waters shoreward to the mean high water mark (mean higher high water on the Pacific coast) and to all contiguous or adjacent wetlands, swamps, and mudflats that are subject to periodic salt or fresh water inundation and are characterized by the presence of salt water vegetation or vegetation that requires saturated soil conditions.[159] These regulations, which also substantially broaden Corps regulatory jurisdiction over inland fresh waters and wetlands, were structured for implementation in three phases over a two year period. Coastal waters and contiguous or adjacent wetland areas are all subject to regulation in Phase I.[160]

In anticipation of an increased permit processing load, the Corps also concerned itself with procedural aspects of implementing broader regulatory jurisdiction. The revised procedures require applicants to obtain state water quality and coastal zone management program certification and overall approval by a designated state agency for proposed dredge or fill materials disposal in areas covered by the extension of jurisdiction before Corps permit processing begins.[161] Issuance of necessary state approvals will lead to Corps permit approval in the absence of any overriding national interest, provided that the certifying agency has followed and considered the requirements, concerns, policies, and goals of NEPA, the FWPCA, the Fish and Wildlife Coordination Act, the National Historic Preservation Act, the Endangered Species Act, and the Coastal Zone Management Act.[162] Further streamlining of procedures is envisioned for joint processing of permits by the Corps and qualified states.[163] These Corps regulations will directly affect the siting of most onshore processing facilities. They are also applicable to the method, manner, and place for disposal of tailings and other residuals where, for example, disposal in low-lying wetland areas or other "navigable waters" is planned for residual sediments produced when sand and gravel is washed, crushed, screened, and graded at an onshore facility. However, disposal of such residual material into ocean waters, including territorial waters, will be subject to EPA regulation under either the FWPCA or the MPRSA permit programs. These systems, and their application to onshore processing plant waste disposal, are considered in detail in Chapter 8.

Potential air pollution resulting from dust and other air pollutants produced in the processing of mined materials at an onshore facility is also subject to federal regulation. First, federal air pollution control laws require states to develop plans to achieve implementation of federally established primary and secondary ambient air quality standards.[164] State plans may employ a variety of control techniques, including emission limitations for point sources of air pollutants such as onshore processing plants.[165] Second, the EPA has been directed to identify classes or categories of new stationary sources and to promulgate standards of performance that require the use of "the best system of emission reduction which (taking into account the cost of achieving such reduction) the Administrator determines has been adequately demonstrated" by such sources subject to the standards.[166] To date, no specific standards for sources likely to be constructed or operated as a direct result of offshore hard mineral extraction have been promulgated by EPA, but general regulations and guidelines that apply to all new source construction and operation have been published.[167]

In another perspective, an onshore processing facility may be viewed as an indirect or "complex" source of air pollution or one inducing air pollution as it is produced by emissions from mobile sources (vehicles) serving or otherwise associated with the facility —which in the case of a gravel facility would consist of large, heavy-duty diesel trucks. Although such vehicles may each satisfy applicable vehicle emissions control standards as established by EPA, pollutant concentrations in the vicinity of the plant may, depending upon the ambient air quality for the area and the nature and extent of air pollution by existing sources in the area, cause applicable ambient air quality standards to be exceeded. This would not be permissible;[168] and, in this regard, air quality control regulations have the potential to become significant determinants of major siting and land use decisions.[169] Many uncertainties currently beset EPA and state implementation of transportation control plans and programs for the preconstruction review of new "complex" sources: EPA ability to enforce such plans against the states, state discretion in implementing alternative air quality control techniques preceding and subsequent to achievement of ambient quality standards, numerous bills to modify EPA authority as it would influence land use, and the extent to which high air quality regions can be degraded without breaching primary and secondary ambient standards. Therefore, to a considerable extent, the regulatory framework for air pollution control for onshore facilities necessary to process the minerals to be extracted from offshore deposits is incomplete, and this condition of uncertainty may inhibit offshore developments.

Noise pollution control regulations concerning expected high noise levels offsite, from construction and operation of sand and gravel and other processing plants, may also be prescribed by EPA when such construction and operation involves the use of new equipment subject to EPA regulation under the 1972 Noise Pollution Control Act.[170] Such regulations may therefore be developed for application to categories of equipment, and thereby to categories of facilities, irrespective of the noise effects of operations in the area where the plant is located. Additional regulations are required to be promulgated by EPA for truck and rail equipment[171] and by OSHA for the purpose of protecting plant employees' health and safety.[172] Finally, state and local governments may continue to establish and enforce regulations governing ambient noise levels, except as limited by provisions of the Noise Act and judicial decisions construing the extent of federal preemption intended by Congress.

Once again, the rapidly evolving nature of noise control regulations by EPA and other levels of government makes for current uncertainties as to the ability to site, construct, and operate the onshore facilities which may be essential for the realization of offshore mining.

6. Marine Resources Protection

Protection of fish and wildlife resources and of the marine environment is the subject of a variety of statutes and regulations. These are of two types, the first of which requires consultation in connection with federal projects and license or permit actions with agencies having expertise concerning the effects of the proposed action on fish, wildlife, and marine resources;[173] the second requires developmental or permitting agencies themselves to evaluate the effect of any proposed action on such resources.[174] There is, however, no direct fisheries regulation authority vested in any federal agency that is of relevance to offshore hard mineral resources exploration and extraction. The closest approximation of such jurisdiction is that of the Department of Commerce for the establishment and regulation of marine sanctuaries[175] and that of EPA for regulating ocean dumping and prohibiting such dumping in areas of critical environmental concern.[176]

Primary responsibility for the protection of marine fisheries and resources in the case of OCS hard mineral mining lies, therefore, with the Department of the Interior as the leasing and operations-supervising agency. The proposed leasing and operations regulations recognize this responsibility in sections that are concerned with various environmental impacts of offshore hard mineral exploration, development, and production.[177] These regulations also specifically acknowledge the consultative roles of federal agencies with expertise in the area.[178]

Presumably, if marine mining for hard minerals becomes imminent, the Fish and Wildlife Service of the Department of the Interior will promulgate regulations or guidelines similar to those it has recently established for offshore oil and gas exploration and development.[179]

CONCLUSIONS

Table 7-2 presents an integrated perspective on the regulation of activities related to outer continental shelf submerged lands.

Table 7-2.   Regulation of Activities Related to OCS Mining

Agency	Exploration	Extraction and off-shore processing	Transport to shore	Processing on-shore	Transport for sale, use
Dept. Interior and Dept. Transportation	Overall authority for structures, including pipeline easements			—	—
USGS	Authorization Supervision			—	—
BLM	—	Authorization		—	—
Fish and Wildlife	General concern and recommendations concerning fish and wildlife				
Dept. Commerce	Protection of marine sanctuaries			—	—
Bureau of Customs	—	Restrictions on foreign-built or registered ships		—	—
Coast Guard	Regulation of navigational safety			—	—
Army Corps of Engineers	Authorization of dredging activities in navigable waters Authorization of dredge spoil disposal in navigable waters Authorization of structures (including pipelines) on navigational merits				
EPA	Effluent limits and NPDES permits Dredge spoil disposal in ocean	Air pollution regulation Equipment noise pollution regulation		Effluent limits and NPDES spoil disposal in ocean	—
OSHA	Worker health and safety regulation				
State and local authorities	—	—	—	Siting Regulation of ambient noise, safety, and amenities Implementation of EPA air and water pollution programs and OSHA programs	

NOTES

1. 43 U.S.C.A. § 1334.

2. 43 U.S.C.A. § 1333(e) (2).

3. 43 U.S.C.A. § 1333(e) (f).

4. See 40 C.F.R. § 3100; 40 C.F.R. § 3300 (proposed).

5. 43 U.S.C.A. § 1334.

6. 40 C.F.R. § 3100.

7. By way of contrast, the act explicitly requires that oil and gas leasing be conducted pursuant to regulations promulgated before further leasing of tracts. See 43 U.S.C.A. § 1337.

8. 43 C.F.R. § 3307.4–5.

9. U.S. Department of the Interior, Draft Environmental Impact Statement, Proposed Outer Continental Shelf Hard Mineral Mining Operating and Leasing Regulations 251 (1974).

10. *Id.* at 252.

11. 43 U.S.C.A. § 1440. See also 39 Fed. Reg. 43562 (December 16, 1974).

12. 30 C.F.R. § 250.

13. See generally, J. Goodier, *U.S. Federal and Seacoastal State Offshore Mining Laws* (1972), p. 12.

14. *Id.*

15. 39 Fed. Reg. 4105 (February 1, 1974); 43 C.F.R. § 3300 (proposed).

16. 39 Fed. Reg. 4105 (February 1, 1974); 30 C.F.R. § 260 (proposed).

17. 43 C.F.R. § 3301.3–1 (proposed).

18. 43 C.F.R. § 3301.3–2 (proposed).

19. *Id.*

20. 43 C.F.R. § 3301.4 (proposed).

21. *Id.*

22. *Id.*

23. 43 C.F.R. § 3304.5 (proposed).

24. *Id.*

25. *Id.*

26. 43 C.F.R. § 3302.1, 3302.1–2(c) (proposed).

27. 43 C.F.R. § 3302.1–2(d) (proposed).

28. 43 C.F.R. § 3302.1–2(e) (proposed).

29. 43 C.F.R. § 3302.1–2 (f) (proposed).

30. 43 C.F.R. §§ 3302.2, 3303.1, 3303.2, 3303.4 (proposed).

31. 43 C.R.F. § 3305.1 (proposed).

32. 43 C.F.R. § 3305.a4 (proposed).

33. 43 C.R.F. § 3306.1 (proposed).

34. 43 C.F.R. § 3301.5 (proposed).

35. *Id.*

36. 43 C.F.R. § 3302.2(f) (proposed). See also 43 U.S.C.A. § 1334(a) (1).

37. *Id.*

38. 43 C.F.R. § 3301.5 (proposed).

39. 43 C.F.R. § 3305.1 (proposed).

40. 43 C.F.R. § 3305.1(b) (proposed).

41. 43 C.F.R. § 3302.1-2(e) (proposed).
42. 43 C.F.R. § 3303.1 (proposed).
43. 43 C.F.R. § 3303.2(b) (proposed).
44. *Id.*
45. 33 U.S.C.A. § 1401; 86 Stat. 1052 (1972).
46. 16 U.S.C.A. § 1432; 86 Stat. 1061 (1972).
47. 16 U.S.C.A. § 1432(a).
48. 16 U.S.C.A. § 1432(b).
49. 16 U.S.C.A. § 1432(f).
50. *Id.*
51. M. Lynch, M. Patton, and T. Smolen, "A Policy Study of Marine and Estuarine Sanctuaries: Background Information" (Proceedings of the National Workshop on Sanctuaries, 1973), pp. 3, 11.
52. 30 C.F.R. § 260 (proposed).
53. 30 C.F.R. § 260.10 (proposed).
54. 30 C.F.R. § 260.11 (proposed).
55. 30 C.F.R. § 260.12 (proposed).
56. *Id.*
57. 30 C.F.R. § 260.12(c) (proposed).
58. 30 C.F.R. § 260.12(d) (proposed).
59. 30 C.F.R. § 260.12(e) (proposed).
60. 30 C.F.R. §§ 260.11, 260.33 (proposed).
61. 30 C.F.R. § 260.33 (proposed).
62. 30 C.F.R. § 260.33(a) (proposed).
63. *Id.* See also 43 C.F.R. § 3301.5 (proposed).
64. 30 C.F.R. § 260.33(d) (2) (proposed).
65. 30 C.F.R. § 260.33(b) (proposed).
66. 30 C.F.R. § 260.33(c) (proposed).
67. 30 C.F.R. § 260.34 (proposed).
68. 30 C.F.R. § 260.35 (proposed).
69. 30 C.F.R. § 260.80 (proposed).
70. 30 C.F.R. § 260.36(a) (proposed).
71. *Id.*
72. 30 C.F.R. § 260.36(b)-(c) (proposed).
73. 30 C.F.R. § 260.17 (proposed).
74. 30 C.F.R. § 260.16(c) (proposed).
75. *Id.*
76. 33 U.S.C.A. § 403; 30 Stat. 1151 (1899).
77. 33 C.F.R. § 209.120(b) (2) & (b).
78. 33 C.F.R. § 209.260(k).
79. 33 C.F.R. § 209.120(d) (1)-(2) and § 209.260(k) (1).
80. Discussion of the regulations of the Corps of Engineers is therefore deferred to Chapter 8.
81. 32 C.F.R. § 3301.4 (proposed); 30 C.F.R. §§ 260.11, 260.30 (proposed).
82. 30 C.F.R. §§ 260.11, 260.12 (proposed).
83. 30 C.F.R. § 260.36 (proposed).
84. 30 C.F.R. § 260.33 (proposed).

85. 1958 Convention on the Outer Continental Shelf, art. 1. 15 U.S. Treaties 471, T.I.A.S. No. 5578, 499 U.N.T.S. 311.

86. 33 U.S.C.A. §§1251-1376; 86 Stat. 816 (1972).

87. 33 U.S.C.A. §§1401-1444; 86 Stat. 1052 (1972).

88. 33 U.S.C.A. §1344.

89. 33 U.S.C.A. §§1251(a) (6), 1343.

90. 33 U.S.C.A. §1402(c).

91. 33 U.S.C.A. §1411.

92. *Id.*

93. 33 U.S.C.A. §1342.

94. *Id.*

95. 33 U.S.C.A. §1344.

96. 33 U.S.C.A. §1362(7). See also 33 C.F.R. §209.120(d) (1) & (2) and §209.260(k) (1).

97. 33 U.S.C.A. §1343.

98. 33 U.S.C.A. §1344(a).

99. 33 U.S.C.A. §1344(b).

100. 40 C.F.R. §227.

101. 33 U.S.C.A. §1413.

102. 33 U.S.C.A. §1412.

103. 33 U.S.C.A. §1311.

104. 33 U.S.C.A. §1311(b) (1) (A).

105. 33 U.S.C.A. §1311(b) (2) (A).

106. 33 U.S.C.A. §1312.

107. 33 U.S.C.A. §1316.

108. 33 U.S.C.A. §1314(b). Although the statute does not specify classes or categories of existing sources, legislative history indicates that "the Administrator will concentrate on, but not be limited to, those classes . . . enumerated in Section 306(b) (1) (A)" (the 27 categories of new sources for which performance standards are required expressly in the act). H.R.Rep. No. 92-911, 92d Cong., 2d sess. 107 (1972). See note 109 *infra.*

109. 33 U.S.C.A. §1316(b) (1) (B). Offshore or marine mining is not listed among the 27 categories of new sources designated in the act. However, the administrator is not limited to the 27 categories and has the discretion to add new categories. See text.

110. *Id.*

111. In accordance with the order of the U.S. District Court for the District of Columbia in NRDC v. Train, (CV. No. 1609-73).

112. *Id.*

113. The other subcategories are designated as iron ore; bauxite, ferroalloy ores; mercury ores; and uranium, radium, and vanadium ores.

114. 40 C.F.R. 440.

115. 40 C.F.R. §436.30.

116. Legal or interagency challenge to EPA regulation of such activity under §301, §304, and §306 might result from any extension of EPA regulation to marine mining, the argument being that §404 vests the corps, subject to EPA guidelines, with exclusive regulatory authority. See EPA final rule-making for

Mineral Mining and Processing Point Source Category, 40 C.F.R. §436, Appendix A (42 F. Reg. 35843, July 12, 1977) which provides in part that: "dredge water discharges from land-based construction sand and gravel plants are not regulated by the Corps of Engineers pursuant to section 404 of the [Water] Act and are not subject to these regulations."

116. 40 C.F.R. §227.

117. 40 C.F.R. §227.61(a); and 40 Fed. Reg. 19794 (May 6, 1975) 40 C.F.R. §230.4-1(a) (2) (proposed).

118. 40 C.F.R. §227.61(b) and 40 C.F.R. §230.4-(a) (2) (proposed).

119. 40 C.F.R. §227.61(c) and 40 C.F.R. §230.4-1(b) (proposed).

120. 40 C.F.R. §230.2(d) (proposed). See also Corps of Engineers regulations, 33 C.F.R. §209.120(d) (1)-(2).

121. 40 C.F.R. §227.62.

122. 40 C.F.R. §227.64.

123. 33 U.S.C.A. §1416(a) & (d).

124. 33 U.S.C.A. §1343(a).

125. 33 U.S.C.A. §1344(c); 33 U.S.C.A. §1413(c).

126. See generally 43 C.F.R. §3301.4 (proposed).

127. 43 U.S.C.A. §1333(e) (3).

128. 33 U.S.C.A. §403; 30 Stat. 1151 (1899).

129. 33 C.F.R. §209.120(b) (2).

130. 33 C.F.R. §209.120(f) (1).

131. 43 U.S.C.A. §1333(e).

132. 43 U.S.C.A. §1333(c).

133. *Id.*

134. 29 U.S.C.A. §§651, 655 (1975).

135. The act does not require that safety regulations be promulgated for all occupations. Rather, the act merely grants authority to make regulations deemed to be necessary. See also activity authorized to the Mining Enforcement and Safety Administration.

136. 14 U.S.C.A. §§2, 81.

137. 43 U.S.C.A. §1333(e).

138. 43 U.S.C. §1333(3).

139. 43 U.S.C. §1333.

140. 43 U.S.C. §1333(e) (1). See also 33 C.F.R. §147.01-1.

141. 33 C.F.R. §178.

142. 33 C.F.R. §178e.

143. 30 C.F.R. §260.16 (proposed).

144. See text accompanying notes 130-136, *supra*.

145. See, *e.g.*, 33 U.S.C.A. §1417(c).

146. See discussion in Chapter 4.

147. 46 U.S.C.A. §292.

148. To the contrary, the Convention on the Outer Continental Shelf, art. 3, declares that waters above the OCS are "high seas."

149. Convention on the Outer Continental Shelf, art. 2(1).

150. House Report No. 1341, 59th Cong., 1st sess. (1906); U.S. Code and Admin. News (1953).

151. See 43 U.S.C.A. §1332.

152. 46 U.S.C.A. §883.

153. See Opinion of the Attorney General, August 7, 1963, concerning the applicability of 46 U.S.C.A. §292 to dredging operations in the Virgin Islands, to which the navigation and coastwise laws are, by statute, not applicable.

154. 33 U.S.C.A. §565; 32 Stat. 371 (1902). See also 33 C.F.R. §209.120(b) (2) & (4).

155. 33 U.S.C.A. §407; 30 Stat. 1152 (1899). See also 33 C.F.R. §209.120.

156. See, *e.g.*, NRDC v. Callaway, 392 F. Supp. 685 (D.D.C. 1975); United States v. Holland, 373 F. Supp. 665 (D. Fla. 1974); United States v. Stoeco Homes, Inc., 498 F.2d 597 (3d Cir. 1974), *cert. denied*, 420 U.S. 927.

157. 33 C.F.R. §209.120(d)(2). See also C.F.R. §209.260.

158. 33 C.F.R. §209.120(e)(2)(i)(a).

159. 33 C.F.R. §209.120(f)(3)(iii). See also 33 C.F.R. §209.260.

160. 33 C.F.R. §209.120(e)(2)(a).

161. 33 C.F.R. §209.120(f)(3)(v).

162. 42 U.S.C.A. §1857c.2 to 1857c.5; 84 State. 1713 (1970).

163. 42 U.S.C.A. 1857c.5.

164. 42 U.S.C.A. 1857c.6.

165. See 40 C.F.R. §60 for all EPA-promulgated New Source Performance Standards adopted pursuant to 42 U.S.C.A. §1857c–6.

166. 42 U.S.C.A. §1857c.5.

167. 42 U.S.C.A. §1857c.5(a)(2)(B).

168. 42 U.S.C.A. §4901; 86 State. 1234 (1972).

169. 42 U.S.C.A. §4916, 4917.

170. 29 U.S.C.A. §651.

171. 16 U.S.C.A. §661.

172. See, e.g., 33 U.S.C.A. §1343(c); 33 U.S.C.A. §1412(a), 42 U.S.C.A. §4321 et seq.

173. 16 U.S.C.A. §1432; 86 Stat. 1061 (1972).

174. 33 U.S.C.A. §1343(c); 22 U.S.C.A. 1412.

175. 43 C.F.R. §3301.4; 30 C.F.R. §260.11 & 260.33(a).

176. 43 C.F.R. §3301.4; 30 C.F.R. § 260.33(a).

177. Guidelines for Oil and Gas Exploration and Development Activities in Territorial and Inland Navigable Waters and Wetlands, 40 F.R. 30020–30023 (July 16, 1975).

178. *Id.*

179. *Id.*

 *Chapter 8*

Federal Laws and Regulations: State Submerged Lands

INTRODUCTION

State ownership and management of submerged lands and the hard mineral resources therein lying beneath territorial waters is expressly subjected to paramount federal regulatory authorities by the Submerged Lands Act.[1] This chapter examines federal agencies' regulatory jurisdiction and authority to which state authorized submerged lands mining is subject. Thus, this chapter presents a description of a federal regulatory system that is an overlay on all state programs, regardless of differences among such states' programs themselves.

A. CORPS OF ENGINEERS DREDGE AND FILL PERMITS

As noted in Chapter 7, the Rivers and Harbors Act of 1899[2] provides the Corps of Engineers with authority to control dredge and fill activities in navigable waters of the United States, including the territorial waters superadjacent to state submerged lands. Thus any dredging or filling activities in these areas are subject to Corps of Engineers permit regulations implementing the Rivers and Harbors Act.[3] Also as discussed in Chapter 7, to the extent dredge mining, the most likely form of marine mining to be employed, would be construed as dredging, it would be subject to Corps authority over dredging activities. Because of substantial technical and functional similarities between dredging and dredge mining and because dredge mining has implications for navigability, this form of marine mining may be subject to Corps authority as discussed in this section on dredge permits.

Past practice of the Corps to receive, process, and act on permit applications for dredge and fill activities only after the applicant obtained all necessary state permits, licenses, or other authorizations has been modified: Now applications are received and processed by the Corps while state action is pending, but no final determination is made until such state clearances, certification of compliance with applicable water quality control requirements, and other necessary approvals have been obtained.[4] In addition, the applicant for a permit must now certify that the proposed work is in compliance with a state's federally approved coastal zone management program,[5] discussed in Chapter 10.

Applications to the Corps for dredge or fill permits must include a complete description of the proposed work, its location, maps, work schedule, purpose, and necessary state and federal approvals.[6] Dredging applications must further describe the "type, composition and quantity of the material to be dredged, the method of dredging, and the site and disposal of the dredged material"[7] and be approved with respect to dredged materials transportation and disposal pursuant to the FWPCA. Application fees for projects involving the dredging of more than 2,500 cubic yards of material are $100; the fee for smaller projects is $10.[9]

The general method for determining whether an application will be granted or denied by the Corps involves a benefit-cost analysis that includes evaluation of many factors, including "conservation, economics, esthetics, general environmental concerns, historic values, fish and wildlife values, flood damage prevention, land use classifications, navigation, recreation, water supply, water quality and, in general, the needs and welfare of the people."[10] If the analysis indicates that permit issuance is in the public interest, as required by Corps regulations, the permit will be provided. The many arbitrary aspects of such analyses and their limitations as tools for decision making are noted, but are not dealt with herein.

The criteria employed in evaluating permit applications include "the relative extent of the private and public need for the proposed work, the desirability of using appropriate alternative locations and methods, the extent and permanence of the beneficial and/or detrimental effects . . . on the public and private uses to which the area is suited, [and] the probable impact of each proposal in relation to the cumulative effect created by other existing and anticipated structures or work in the area."[11] These general guidelines are particularized in the regulations with respect to effects on adjacent properties and other water resources,[12] impacts on wetlands,[13] damage to fish and wildlife resources,[14] and effects on water quality[15] as well as in terms of common types of activities or projects.[16]

These general and particular factors and criteria are applied by the Corps, in cooperation and consultation with other federal agencies, state agencies, and the public, in order to fulfill the process required by the National Environmental Policy Act (NEPA), which mandates the preparation of an environmental impact statement for each "major federal action."[17] Permit approval for large-scale commercial dredge mining would undoubtedly be considered a "major federal action," since such activity would clearly be of the type that would "significantly affect the quality of the human environment,"[18] and the Corps would bear this NEPA responsibility since it would be the preeminent federal decision maker on dredge mining in the territorial waters—as distinguished from dredge mining on the outer continental shelf, where the Department of the Interior would be characterized as the "lead" agency with NEPA duties, as discussed in Chapters 7 and 10.

The EIS preparation procedure necessitates circulation of the draft EIS on a proposed project to agencies having jurisdiction or special expertise in the matter.[19] Consultation with such agencies may also occur during the preparation of the draft EIS. In any event, input from such agencies is effectively obtained prior to any final action and the publication of the final EIS considered in taking that action. The EIS process and NEPA are discussed further in Chapter 10.

Corps regulations, which reflect statutory directives as well as administrative policies, also call for consultation with and varying degrees of yielding to the views of other federal and state agencies having jurisdiction or expertise concerning specific proposed activities.[20] In particular, water quality control and fish and wildlife protection considerations are the subject of mandatory interagency jurisdiction and consultation.

Dredging activities must comply with applicable water quality control laws and regulations. This previously required state agency certification of compliance with water quality standards.[21] Under the 1972 FWPCA amendments, however, dredging operations are exempted from EPA's NPDES and states' SPDES permit programs, and the Corps of Engineers is vested with jurisdiction to determine whether to issue or deny a Corps FWPCA permit under the EPA's ocean discharge criteria.[22] Corps regulations, despite the apparent FWPCA exclusion of state permit authority, nevertheless require state water quality certification pursuant to § 401 of the FWPCA, which establishes a general certification requirement that must be met before federal agency permits or licenses may be granted.[23] It appears that § 401 was meant to apply only as to non-FWPCA federal permits or licenses; thus, the Corps regulation may be open to legal challenge, despite the fact that omission of the certification requirement for activities subject to the MPRSA avoids the clear pre-emption of state veto power contained in that statute.

However, this analysis of Corps authority to issue FWPCA permits on dredge or fill activities associated with marine mining may have been overtaken by recent events. The promulgation by EPA of interim regulations for the newly established "mineral mining" and "ore mining and dressing" categories of point sources subject to EPA authority to limit effluents and grant NPDES permits and to EPA-approved state authority to grant SPDES permits (as discussed in Chapter 7). These recent regulatory developments suggest the possible development in the future of an EPA regulatory program that may supplant or supplement Corps permit authority, and are discussed in part B.1 of this chapter.

Protection of fish and wildlife in territorial waters and on state submerged lands is dealt with through a notice and consultation process mandated by the Fish and Wildlife Coordination Act,[24] which requires the Corps to solicit the views of the Fish and Wildlife Service, National Marine Fisheries Service, and appropriate state agencies concerning the effects of the proposed work on fish and wildlife. Although it was strongly argued in a leading case on Corps jurisdiction that no dredge or fill permit could be denied under the Rivers and Harbors Act except for adverse effects on navigation, the court held that the Corps may deny such a permit because the work would adversely affect fish and wildlife.[25] Indeed, it is clear from court decisions that the Corps must take any such effects into account in deciding whether to grant or deny a dredge or fill permit.[26]

Another important consideration in Corps dredge and fill permit decisions is the effect of the proposed work on beach and shoreline stability.[27] Guidelines developed by the Corps as a result of its national shoreline study indicate that dredge mining of aggregate or other hard mineral resources should be limited in nearshore areas in order to prevent beach and shoreline erosion.

In addition to consideration of federal and state agency inputs, public inputs, particularly the views of any persons who may be directly affected by proposed work, are solicited and considered by the Corps in decision making on dredge or fill permits.[28] Notices of permit applications are sent upon receipt to organizations, adjacent property owners, and persons known to be interested, as well as to public agencies and officials. Copies of the notice are also posted in appropriate public locations.[29] If a matter is believed by the district engineer to be likely to evoke a substantial public interest, newspaper notice may also be employed at the expense of the applicant.[30] Public hearings are afforded as a matter of law when a person who may be directly affected by the work requests a hearing or a neighboring state objects on water quality grounds and requests a hearing;[31] public hearings are held in other cases, at the discretion of the district engineer, when warranted by public interest in the matter.[32] Responses to mailed and posted notices and the transcript of public hearings become a part of the record on which the Corps' determinations are ultimately made.

The district engineer may grant or deny a permit application, or grant it subject to special conditions.[33] Where the district engineer is unable to reach a decision, the matter is reviewed and decided by the divisional office of the Corps[34] or in unusual cases that are highly controversial or that involve high level state or federal opposition to a decision made by the district or division, by the chief of engineers.[35]

Operations under a Corps permit to dredge or fill are supervised by the district engineer. Regular and unannounced inspections conducted at the expense of the permittee are authorized, as is surveillance by reconnaissance.[36] Permit modifications, suspensions, and revocations in cases of noncompliance with permit conditions, changed circumstances, or significant objections to the work which were not previously considered are dealt with by the regulations.[37] Emphasis is placed upon renegotiation between the district engineer and the permittee; suspension orders are issued after consultation with the division engineer, and formal hearing procedures are also provided for in the regulations.[38] Permit revocations are reviewed and subject to final action by the chief of engineers.[39] In any event, enforcement of Corps orders issued in such proceedings is through judicial action instituted by the U.S. attorney for the district, at the request of the district engineer.[40]

B. WATER POLLUTION CONTROL

1. Mining Operations

The FWPCA generally preserved the state-federal cooperation mode for implementing water pollution control regulations that had prevailed under prior laws, by providing that the NPDES program could be administered by states whose SPDES programs receive EPA approval.[41] The principal exception made with respect to at least other than dredged materials discharges is that the EPA administrator may not waive, for any discharges into the territorial sea, the otherwise waiveable requirement that state SPDES permits be transmitted to and subject to veto by the EPA.[42]

While the FWPCA authorized the delegation of EPA permit authority to the states, no such authority is granted either the EPA or the Corps of Engineers concerning dredged or fill material discharges into navigable waters over which the Corps, rather than the EPA, has permit authority. States are specifically authorized, on the other hand, to adopt water quality standards and to force the promulgation by EPA or the adoption by state officials of more stringent effluent or other limitations or standards of performance than those established by EPA under the FWPCA.[43] This reservation of state power is consistent with the veto power over NPDES permits that is effectively granted to states in other sections.[44] Whether or not the reserved state authority also saves state regulatory jurisdiction over dredge and fill permits for the Corps, despite the nontransferability of Corps FWPCA permit authority, is an interesting point to debate; such debate, however, may be moot, in that the Corps of Engineers regulations on dredged materials discharges into navigable waters condition permit approval on state water quality certification for discharges into territorial waters.[45] That requirement is presumably applicable, however, only to dredged materials discharges regulated by § 404 of the FWPCA, since the ocean dumping system of regulation of the MPRSA, which governs transportation of materials dredged from navigable (territorial) waters for the purpose of dumping in ocean (including "navigable") waters, expressly preempts state exercise of regulatory control.[46]

The critical factor in determining whether the FWPCA or the MPRSA Corps of Engineers permit system, and thus whether state certification is or is not an enforceable Corps requirement, is whether the activity for which a permit is sought involves transportation for the purpose of disposal of the materials excavated or dredged from navigable waters. Commercial mining operations with hopper dredges that would involve overflow disposal in connection with dredge mining does not involve transportation of dredged materials for the purpose of disposal or dumping in the usual sense. Therefore, the Corps of Engineers FWPCA permit system, and the Corp's regulatory requirement of state certification, should apply to dredge mining activities conducted in state submerged lands that lie beneath territorial waters—unless the following analysis, based on recent EPA regulatory developments, proves correct.

As discussed in Chapter 7 and noted earlier in this chapter, EPA has recently established "mineral mining" and "ore mining and dressing" as categories of point sources to be regulated by means of effluent limitations which are to be contained in permits for both existing and new point sources under EPA's NPDES and EPA-approved state SPDES programs. And as noted earlier, several of the subcategories of minerals and ores cover dredge mining of such minerals and ores (gold, silver, tin, etc.). However, the dredge mining of sand and gravel from navigable waters is expressly excluded, the EPA regulations indicating that regulation of such activity, including onboard processing of dredged material, will remain subject to Corps permit jurisdiction.[47] Nevertheless, the EPA regulations suggest a significant alternative to Corps regulation in the event that large-scale commercial dredge mining, an activity that does not fit neatly into existing project-oriented Corps regulation, develops in the future. To the extent that these evolving EPA regulations could possibly be extended to cover dredge mining, and to the extent such regulations withstand any legal or interagency challenges,[48] they could constitute a substantial limitation on the authority of the Corps under the FWPCA to issue permits for future dredge mining operations. This EPA regulatory framework, if extended to the dredge mining of sand, gravel, phosphorus, calcium carbonate, and other likely candidates for offshore mining, could become a substantial limitation on or supplement to the role of the Corps in regard to governing the water quality aspects of marine mining.

If the potential realized through EPA extension of its regulations is one of limitation on the Corps, the Corps authority under the FWPCA will limited to nonresource recovery dredging that is, conventional channel, construction, and navigation-related dredging. EPA, and through EPA the states, would thereby become responsible for NPDES and SPDES permits, respectively, applicable to marine mining in the coastal and territorial waters overlying the submerged lands of the states.

2. Onshore Processing Facilities and Operations

Difficult jurisdictional questions exist concerning disposal in ocean waters, including territorial waters, of sediment-laden water used in onshore processing facility operations and disposal or dumping offshore of any such sediment removed from water by settling or other processes. The central issue concerns whether the FWPCA-NPDES permit program or the MPRSA ocean dumping permit system governs either or both disposal methods. Resolution of this issue is determinative of whether the disposal is subject to both federal and state regulatory control or to only federal regulation, since the FWPCA expressly preserves state jurisdiction[49] while the MPRSA explicitly preempts any other regulatory control, federal or state, over matters governed by the MPRSA.[50]

In the absence of the MPRSA, the NPDES permit program established by the FWPCA would apply to either type of disposal method, since the residual materials would not retain their classification as "dredged materials" subject to Corps of Engineers permit regulations.[51] Under the NPDES program, an effluent standard or a new source standard of performance would govern the first disposal method,[52] but any discharge would also be evaluated under the EPA's ocean discharge criteria in determining if an NPDES permit would be granted,[53] while the second method might well be governed by only the ocean discharge criteria.

Administration of these regulations will normally be delegated to the states under SPDES programs,[54] although any permits for discharges into territorial waters would remain subject to the exercise of nonwaiveable EPA review and veto.[55] Most significant, however, is that the FWPCA authorizes states to impose more stringent standards than those promulgated in EPA regulations.[56]

Once again, however, attention must be paid to the newly evolving EPA regulations governing the recently established mineral mining and ore mining and dressing point source categories. These categories cover onshore processing associated with such minerals and ores, and include effluent limitations applicable to such processing activities, irrespective of the source or site of or the mining techniques used to "win" such minerals. As this new regulatory framework is expanded, EPA will be armed with environmental knowledge and specific limitations sufficient to control the effluents of onshore processing facilities and activities through application of its NPDES permit program, and the states with EPA approval will be able to implement the same or stricter limitations through their SPDES permit programs. State input into administration of the MPRSA program is confined, on the other hand, to being consulted concerning permit applications and the statutory assurance that applicable receiving water quality standards will not be violated.[57]

This differential treatment of similar, and at times the same, discharges and their control is a consequence of the FWPCA and the MPRSA originating in different committees in Congress and proceeding almost simultaneously to enactment, without resolving conflicts created by somewhat different approaches to the ocean discharge regulation problem. The EPA's regulations attempt to coordinate the two systems, but debate continues over the question of whether the MPRSA pre-empts the NPDES program with respect to materials transported by vessel from the United States for discharge or disposal in territorial waters, since the MPRSA was signed into law five days later than the FWPCA. The EPA regulations establish ocean discharge criteria that apply alike to FWPCA and MPRSA permit applications.[58] There is therefore no likely problem of differential standards being applied under federal law. The regulations also seek to resolve the preemption quandry by preserving SPDES implementation of other than vessel discharges in such waters, and requiring a § 401 FWPCA state certification for vessel discharges that so require an MPRSA permit.[59] The effort was quite clearly to retain some state role without breaching the § 106 MPRSA prohibitions against state adoption or enforcement of any regulation concerning matters regulated by the MPRSA or involving the states by their issuance of any permit that might be declared void in accordance with the MPRSA. The accommodation does not seem unreasonable, nor in serious conflict with the preemption provision or the purposes of the MPRSA, so long as state certification is limited to water quality rather than other considerations ordinarily permitted by § 401 of the FWPCA.[60] Ultimate resolution remains, however, a matter for either the courts or Congress.

C. OTHER POLLUTION CONTROL

Air and noise pollution control authority and regulations of the Environmental Protection Agency are applicable to the coastal processing facilities associated with marine mining, irrespective of whether such mining is conducted in a state's submerged lands or on the outer continental shelf. Since such federal authority has already been discussed in Chapter 7 as it would apply to coastal facilities associated with OCS mining, it will not be repeated here for the case of state submerged lands mining.

D. MARINE SANCTUARIES

Marine sanctuaries in territorial waters superadjacent to state submerged lands may be established by the National Oceanographic and Atmospheric Administration (NOAA), Department of Commerce, with the concurrence of the governor of the affected state.[61] Once established, a marine sanctuary is managed by NOAA in accordance with a statement of purpose, guidelines and regulations, and management program published for the sanctuary at the time of its designation.[62]

The statement of purpose in the designation of a marine sanctuary will be based upon classification of the sanctuary as a habitat, species, research, recreational and esthetic, or unique area.[63] Multiple use will be permitted where the desired uses are compatible with the primary purpose(s) or use classification, but no state or federal permit, license, or authorization of another agency will be valid unless NOAA certifies that the authorized activity is permissible.[64] Thus, state permits, licenses, or leases for submerged lands mining in a marine sanctuary would require approval or certification by NOAA, as well as any other necessary state and federal authorizations.

CONCLUSIONS

Table 8-1 represents an attempt at presenting an integrated perspec-

Table 8-1. Regulation of Activities Related to State Submerged Lands Mining

Agency	Exploration	Extraction and offshore processing	Transport to shore	Processing onshore	Transport for sale, use
Fish and Wildlife	General concern and recommendations concerning fish and wildlife				
Dept. Commerce	Protection of marine sanctuaries			—	—
Bureau of Customs	—	Restrictions on foreign-built or registered ships		—	—
Coast Guard	Regulations of navigational safety			—	—
OSHA	Worker health and safety regulation				
State and local authorities	See Chapter 9 re authority in detail: Siting Regulation of ambient noise safety and amenities (general police powers) Implementation of EPA air and water pollution programs and of OSHA programs				
Army Corps of Engineers	Authorization of dredging activities in navigable waters Authorization of dredge spoil disposal in navigable waters Authorization of structures in navigable waters				
EPA	Effluent limits and NPDES permits Dredge spoil disposal in ocean Air pollution regulation Equipment noise pollution regulation			Effluent limits and NPDES spoil disposal in ocean	

tive on the *regulation of activities related to mining the state submerged lands,* and follows the format used in Table 7-2. The agencies and functions identified herein have been discussed in this chapter and in Chapter 7.

NOTES

1. 43 U.S.C.A. §1311(d).
2. 33 U.S.C.A. §403, 30 Stat. 1151 (1899).
3. 33 C.F.R. §209.120.
4. 33 C.F.R. §209.120(f)(2).
5. 33 C.F.R. §§209.120(c)(2) and 209.120(g)(18)(i).
6. 33 C.F.R. §209.120(h)(2)(ii).
7. 33 C.F.R. §209.120(h)(2)(i).
8. 33 C.F.R. §209.120(h)(2)(ii).
9. *Id.*
10. 33 C.F.R. §209.120(f)(1).
11. 33 C.F.R. §209.120(f)(2).
12. 33 C.F.R. §209.120(g)(1).
13. 33 C.F.R. §209.120(g)(3).
14. 33 C.F.R. §209.120(g)(4).
15. 33 C.F.R. §209.120(g)(5).
16. 33 C.F.R. §209.120(g)(6)-(18).
17. 42 U.S.C.A. §4332(2)(C).
18. *Id.* See generally, Council on Environmental Quality, Guidelines for Preparation of Environmental Impact Statements, 40 C.F.R. §1500.5; and Corps of Engineers Regulations on Environmental Imapct Statements, 33 C.F.R. §209.410.
19. 42 U.S.C.A. §4332(2)(C); 40 C.F.R. §1500.9; 33 C.F.R. §209.410(k).
20. 33 C.F.R. §§209.120(c), 209.120(f)(4), and 209.120(i).
21. 33 C.F.R. §§209.120(c) and 209.120(g)(5).
22. 33 U.S.C.A. §§1342, 1343, 1344.
23. 33 C.F.R. §209.120(c)(1), 209.120(f)(3)(iii), and 209.120 (g)(5).
24. 16 U.S.C.A. §661.
25. Zabel v. Tabb, 430 F.2d 199 (5th Cir. 1970).
26. *Id.* See also 33 C.F.R. §209.120(f).
27. 33 C.F.R. §209.120(g)(1) & (2).
28. 33 C.F.R. §209.120(i).
29. 33 C.F.R. §209.120(i)(1)(ii).
30. 33 C.F.R. §209.120(i)(1)(ii).
31. 33 C.F.R. §209.120(i)(1)(iv).
32. *Id.* See also 33 C.F.R. §209.120(k).
33. 33 C.F.R. §209.120(p)(2).
34. 33 C.F.R. §209.120(p)(2)(ii).
35. 33 C.F.R. §209.120(q)(3).
36. 33 C.F.R. §209.120(o).
37. 33 C.F.R. §209.120(o)(3).

38. 33 C.F.R. §209.120(o)(4).

39. *Id.*

40. *Id.*

41. 33 U.S.C.A. §413 and §1342(b) & (c).

42. 33 U.S.C.A. §1343(b).

43. 33 U.S.C.A. §1370; 86 Stat. 893.

44. 33 U.S.C.A. §1341; 86 Stat. 877.

45. 33 C.F.R. §§209.120(c)(1) and 209.120(g)(5).

46. 33 U.S.C.A. §1416(a) & (d).

47. 40 C.F.R. §436.30.

48. Such challenges would be based on an argument that §404 vests exclusive jurisdiction, subject to EPA guidelines, in the Corps and that §301, §304, and §306 are not applicable to dredge mining in navigable waters. See footnote 116 of Chapter 7 for EPA exclusion, "at this time," of such extended regulatory jurisdiction, made in July 1977.

49. See text accompanying notes 41, 43, and 44, *supra.*

50. 33 U.S.C.A. §1416(a) & (d).

51. See 40 C.F.R. §230.2(d)(proposed).

52. 33 U.S.C.A. §§1311 and 1316.

53. 33 U.S.C.A. §1343.

54. 33 U.S.C.A. §1343(b) & (c).

55. 33 U.S.C.A. §§1342(d)(3) and 1343(b).

56. 33 U.S.C.A. §1370.

57. 33 U.S.C.A. §1412.

58. 40 C.F.R. §227.

59. 40 C.F.R. §225.

60. 33 U.S.C.A. §1341(a)(3).

61. 16 U.S.C.A. §1432(b).

62. 15 C.F.R. §922.10.

63. 16 U.S.C.A. §1432(f).

Chapter 9

State Laws and Regulations

INTRODUCTION

This chapter examines the legal and regulatory frameworks
of six coastal states with respect to the management of
their offshore mineral resources and the control of offshore mining
operations and related onshore activities. This introduction sets
forth the analytical approach used in the examination of each state
and discusses some of the relevant federal laws implemented by the
states.

The six states to be considered—Alaska, California, Connecticut,
New Jersey, New York, and Texas—were chosen from among the 30
coastal states of the United States on the basis of several criteria.
These criteria included (1) the availability of offshore minerals
of different types likely to be subject to pressures for exploitation;
(2) differences in values and behavior toward offshore mineral exploitation; (3) relevant history or experience; and (4) differences
in institutional structures and regulatory approaches. Application
of these criteria resulted in the selection of states quite representative of the diversity of authority, attitudes, and resources now found
among the coastal states of this nation.

The laws, regulations, and institutional structure of each state
are examined in the following sequence: (1) state authorization of
offshore exploration and extraction; (2) other state laws affecting
offshore operations; (3) state laws affecting onshore facilities and
operations; and (4) state impact assessment and resource management laws. In each category, primary emphasis is placed upon spe-

cific state, rather than federal, laws and administrative regulations. Yet no attempt is made to catalogue every state law and regulation which may have some indirect effect on the offshore mining industry. Instead, discussion is limited to resource management authorizations and to permit or license requirements and other action-forcing regulations of most interest to those concerned with, and concerned about, the exploration and extraction of hard minerals of the submerged lands under state jurisdiction.

In addition to obligations which arise solely from state law, the potential offshore miner is also subject to various federal requirements which are implemented by the states, most of which are discussed previously, particularly in Chapter 8. For example, the Federal Water Pollution Control Act[1] is administered in part by the states through the issuance of water quality certifications and SPDES permits; the federal Coastal Zone Management Act of 1972[2] (CZMA) is implemented by the states through their coastal zone management programs. These federal laws are discussed in this introduction generally and are included in the analysis of each state only insofar as the implementation procedures differ among the states. Further general discussion of the FWPCA is presented in Chapters 7 and 8; and of the CZMA in Chapter 10.

1. State Authorization of Offshore Exploration and Extraction

State authorization of offshore mining may take a number of forms, e.g., a mining license (New York), a mineral lease (California), a permit to remove materials (Texas). In the case of each of the six states, the steps in the application process and the mechanics of decision making are detailed in subsequent parts of this chapter. Particular emphasis is placed upon the degree of formal legal control exercised by the state over its offshore hard mineral resources, the extent of the authorizing body's discretion, the type of institutional structure involved, and the degree of public participation in the decision-making process of the authorizing body.

Furthermore, current policies of the state regulatory agencies toward offshore mining activity had been elicited and are described in subsequent parts of this chapter. These policies are sometimes recorded in statutory purposes, administrative regulations, or agency resolutions. More commonly, however, operational policies are determined by the personal attitudes of various state decision makers and those interests which influence decision-making attitudes, and both are likely to be unrecorded. Therefore, interviews with state officials in the six states have been conducted in order to determine their attitudes toward new or increased offshore mining activity, the relative importance of economic growth and environmental considerations, and the degree and modes of co-operation between environmental and development-oriented agencies.

Finally, a brief description of the offshore mining activity currently taking place in each state's waters is given: for example, the purposes of current dredging activities (navigational, resource recovery, or both); the types of resources extracted; their location; and the royalty or other compensatory rates levied by the state.

2. Other State Laws Affecting Offshore Mining Operations

The remaining state legal controls over offshore mining may be grouped into the categories of monitoring of operations, sanctions, water quality control, and authority over the marine environment. Most of these regulations are largely a matter of state discretion and vary widely from state to state, as described subsequently.

State water quality control of dredging operations, however, has its source in federal law. Under the Federal Water Pollution Control Act, the discharge of dredged material is prohibited without a permit from the Army Corps of Engineers.[3] The Corps regulations, in turn, define "dredged material" as including any "runoff or overflow which occurs during a dredging operation."[4] Since current dredge mining technology involves some runoff of sediment at the dredge site or en route to shore facilities, the dredge mining operations themselves are subject to the Corps permit requirement of the FWPCA discussed in the preceding chapters. It should be noted that the Corps permit preempts any state level water quality permit, including the SPDES permit. Attention must, however, be paid to EPA's proposed regulations for mineral and ore mining point sources, discussed in the preceding chapters, which could eventually lead to substantially greater roles for states with EPA-approved SPDES programs (see discussion in Chapter 7 and 8).

To the extent that dredge mining remains subject to Corps FWPCA permit authority, however, the states can play a key role in regulating dredge residuals. Under Corps regulations, no dredge discharge permit will be issued without a certification by the state that the discharge will comply with water quality standards and effluent limitations established by the state and approved by the federal Environmental Protection Agency.[5] In effect, the states hold the power of veto over the Corps discharge permit through the certification requirement. The states have established widely different procedures for issuing the water quality certification. The discussion of each state examines these various procedures for current state water quality control of offshore dredge mining operations.

3. State Laws Affecting Onshore Facilities and Operations

Land-based facilities and operations related to offshore mining include pipelines for transporting materials to and along the shore, wharves and docking structures for receiving materials transported by barge, plants for processing and refining the mined material, and road and rail transportation systems for distribution of the refined minerals. The states have employed a variety of legal controls to site and regulate such activities in their coastal zones, and those controls of most relevance are briefly discussed in each of the state studies.

For example, the states may regulate the siting of shoreline facilities through traditional zoning ordinances, wetlands restrictions, and facilities siting laws. The latter two types of land use controls typically require the landowner to obtain a permit from a state or local agency before constructing the facility in certain locations. Some states have adopted a complete prohibition upon construction in ecologically sensitive areas such as coastal wetlands.

States exercise further control over such land-based operations in the form of water, air, and noise pollution control laws. Because the refining of mined material will result in effluent discharges, and because the loading and transporting of the minerals will produce a significant amount of noise, state water and noise pollution control laws will certainly be invoked in each of the six states. Air pollution from refining and processing operations is not expected to be as significant a problem. Discussion of federal authority to control air, water, and noise pollution arising from such facilities and operations on state lands is briefly presented in Chapter 8; and understanding of such federal authority is necessary for determining the scope of state pollution control authority.

4. State Impact Assessment and Resource Management Laws

Environmental Impact Assessment. The passage of the National Environmental Policy Act in 1969[6] prompted several states to enact similar legislation requiring state agencies to prepare environmental impact statements before commencing environmentally significant projects. Some state environmental protection acts limit the EIS requirement to activities undertaken by state agencies. Other states extend the requirement to private developments which require a permit or funds from a state or local agency. The latter type of EIS requirement is of greater significance to offshore mining, since marine mining activities will probably be conducted by private commercial ventures subject to federal and state agency approvals.

Resource Management. One of the more significant legal developments affecting the management of mineral resources in state waters is the establishment of state coastal zone management programs developed pursuant to the Coastal Zone Management Act of 1972.[7] Under the CZMA, states are encouraged through federal funding to develop programs to manage their coastal land and water resources, giving "full consideration to ecological, cultural, historic, and esthetic values as well as to needs for economic development." The CZMA, administered by the Department of Commerce, provides federal funding for two-thirds of the cost of developing a state management program for up to 3 years.[8] The act also authorizes subsequent federal administrative grants for two-thirds of the cost of state administering of its program.[9]

As part of the development of a coastal zone management program eligible for federal support, a state must formulate policy and regulations enabling multiple uses of its coastal region. The extraction of hard minerals from coastal waters would be a prime candidate for multiple use consideration by those states with offshore deposits of commercial significance. A state management program must include a definition of permissible land and water uses which have a significant impact on coastal waters,[10] broad guidelines on priority of uses in particular areas,[11] and an inventory of areas of particular concern.[12] Insofar as offshore mining has a significant impact on coastal waters and may occur in areas of special concern to the state, these planning tasks arguably entail some degree of policymaking by the state on the desirability of mineral extraction in coastal waters.

The thrust of the CZMA is to encourage more coherent state and regional control over coastal resources, which have historically been left to private sector development under the fragmented and inadequate control of local units of government. Statewide control in the coastal management program may take the form of direct planning and decision making from a central state office or may be indirect through state promulgation of standards and procedures for local implementation or through state administrative review of the decisions of local or regional units of government on coastal projects proposed by the private sector.[13]

Ultimately, in order to remain eligible for federal funding, the state must administer its coastal zone management program in accordance with the broad national goals and specific objectives expressed in the CZMA.[14] Therefore, state policies on offshore mining will be formulated and applied in the context of larger frameworks for coastal zone management, resulting in more coherent consideration of environmental and economic factors.

The CZMA further provides coastal states with veto power over Corps of Engineers dredge and fill permits and other actions of federal agencies. Section 307 of the act prohibits the issuance of a license or permit by a federal agency without a certification by the coastal state that the proposed activity complies with the state's coastal zone management program.[15] This provision considerably expands state control over federal permit decision making. State authority to prevent favorable federal actions on permits is not absolute, however: Section 307 also allows the Secretary of Commerce to order federal permit issuance despite a state's disapproval, upon certain findings. The limits of the Secretary's power in this regard have not yet been tested, nor have the implications of this federal authority for facility-siting and other activities in state coastal regions been determined.

Most coastal states are now in the process of developing coastal management programs, but few have established clear policies on the use of their offshore resources. A few states, New Jersey and California among them, enacted legislation prior to the CZMA which provided greater state control over coastal zone development. These states are now in the process of conforming the earlier legislation to the requirements of the CZMA in order to become eligible for federal funding.

State consideration of marine mining as a result of the passage of the Coastal Zone Management Act differs from state to state and is discussed for each of the six states in the following parts of this chapter. Further discussion of the CZMA is also presented in Chapter 10, as CZMA would afford a framework for harmonized federal-state decision making on marine mining.

A. ALASKA

Although relatively little exploration has been conducted on the vast mainland territory and offshore submerged lands of our largest state, experts have agreed that the state contains major reserves of numerous hard minerals and that these minerals will be increasingly exploited to meet commercial and governmental needs—particularly as continental U.S. reserves are depleted and foreign sources become inaccessible or uneconomical. Some of the minerals, such as gold and barite, are currently being exploited by a number of small, even part-time and weekend, enterprises. Other minerals, including a number of comparatively rare and strategic minerals, are known to exist but have not been economically studied or exploited to date. Alaska is pregnant with hard mineral exploitation possibilities on a large scale.

This condition of imminent exploitability is enhanced by the widespread values within the state favoring economic and population growth, values similar to those which earlier prevailed in bringing about large-scale exploitation of minerals in the lower western states. As a result, the state of Alaska has no comprehensive set of laws and regulations governing its resources and environmental quality, no carefully structured program for the stewardship of its mineral riches, and the state is largely dependent on the federal agencies which control much of its land. The balancing of environmental and economic factors which has thus far been conducted to govern exploitation activities has been marked by the relatively low significance placed on environmental quality criteria, and the state remains ripe for exploitation without proper safeguards.

1. Authorization of Offshore Exploration and Extraction

Laws and Institutional Structure. In Alaska, offshore mining for sand and gravel is not governed by mineral leasing or licensing, but instead is subject to the material sale regulations of the Department of Natural Resources (DNR), Division of Lands.[16] In order to purchase offshore sand and gravel from the state, an applicant must apply for a contract of sale of the state-owned materials. Two types of sales contracts are possible, competitive and noncompetitive (or negotiated). If the appraised value of the material to be sold is $2,500 or less, the material may be sold by negotiated sale when the director of the Division of Lands determines that a competitive interest does not exist. Sand, gravel, and other materials whose appraised value exceeds $2,500 may be sold only by competitive sale, i.e., at public auction or by sealed bid. Before any competitive sale can be made, public notice of the proposed sale, including a description of the type and quantity of material to be sold, must be published in a local newspaper. The notice must also contain an announcement of the time and place where the auction will be held or bids received. The director of the Division of Lands will execute a contract of sale to the highest bidder, unless he chooses to reject all bids. After the contract is awarded, the buyer may enter the lands specified and extract the material.

In certain cases, the Division of Lands may not award a contract without the approval of other agencies.[17] For example, if the proposed removal of the offshore materials will affect navigation in any way, the Corps of Engineers must provide prior approval before the contract may be executed. If the extraction of the materials will change, obstruct, or pollute the natural flow of any state waters, the purchaser must obtain the approval of the state Department of Fish and Game before commencing operations.

The terms of such sales, including the price of the offshore materials and duration of the contract, will of course vary. However, all contracts must stipulate that the unit price of the materials is subject to adjustment by the director at 2-year intervals.[18] Contracts may be extended upon request of the purchaser and at the discretion of the director. In all contracts, the director may require the purchaser to provide a corporate or a personal surety bond.

This constitutes the regulatory system governing "material lands," or public lands, including submerged lands, valuable for sand, gravel, stone, pumice, pumicite, cinders, and clay. However, a different system of regulation (mineral leasing) applies to lands valuable for coal, phosphate, oil shale, sodium, potassium, oil, gas, or geothermal resources. This discussion has been restricted to the first category —"materials"—on the assumption that such minerals fall within the scope of this study.

Alaska is one of the few places in the world where geological conditions are favorable for finding noble metals, i.e., gold and platinum, in the offshore area and has thus developed a relatively comprehensive set of statutes and regulations regarding offshore mining for such minerals.

To locate such valuable minerals, one must obtain a prospecting permit from the director of the Division of Lands, Department of Natural Resources.[19] This permit is valid for up to 10 years and may cover up to 2,560 acres. The prospecting permit may be converted to a noncompetitive lease if the permittee shows to the satisfaction of the director that the land contains "workable mineral deposits."[20] Such leases are valid for up to 55 years and renewable.[21] Rental payments are required for both the permit and the lease. The director may also offer areas with known mineral deposits for competitive leasing with similar rates.[22]

Once a lease has been issued, the responsibility of supervising mining operations falls on the director of the Division of Lands. The practice has been to require a detailed plan of operation which is reviewed by the Division of Lands, the Department of Fish and Game, and the Department of Environmental Conservation. There is no formal public participation in either the leasing stage or the operations supervision stage, although there are public announcements of actions taken.

Although there is no severance tax on minerals, miners must pay a "Mining License Tax".[23] This tax is administered by the Department of Revenue. The Mining License Tax, on net income and with depletion allowance, is as follows:

Income:	Tax:
$40,000–$50,000	3%
$50,000–$100,000	$1,500 + 5% of excess over $50,000
over $100,000	$4,000 + 7% of excess over $100,000

Depletion allowance for metals is 15 percent, but this tax is exempted for the first 3.5 years of production.

Policies of State Agencies. Alaskan attitudes can be characterized as in favor of resource development, in light of the state's "frontier" condition and orientation toward growth, both demographic and economic. Irrespective of statewide attitudes, there is considerable federal interest in the mineral resources of the state, an interest which has been manifest in the Department of the Interior's program for the development of Alaskan oil. In addition to oil, Alaska is believed to be extremely rich in diverse, important hard minerals. In *An Assessment of Mineral Resources in Alaska*,[24] prepared by the USGS, BLM, and Bureau of Mines of the Department of the Interior, Alaska is described as containing "great unexplored areas geologically favorable for the discovery of valuable mineral deposits. Indeed, compared to the 'lower 48' states, Alaska is yet in the early stages of the development of its mineral industry. Exploration and commercial development of ore deposits in Alaska have been restricted by economic conditions that require any deposit mined in the state to be of relatively higher value than are mineable in the 'lower 48' states."

The federal interest, which will undoubtedly influence Alaskan policy and converge with and reinforce favorable Alaskan attitudes toward resource development and growth, is succinctly expressed in the report.

The value of Alaska's undeveloped minerals and mineral fuels has been enhanced by long-term trends and by recent world events. Increasing national demands for minerals and fuels have resulted in an increasing reliance on imports. Many nations supplying raw materials to the United States are either developing their own uses of these materials or are combining to demand higher prices. Foreign nationalization of American mining interests; the threat of being subjected to unilateral decisions of foreign producers, as for instance the recent reduction of fuel shipments from the Middle East, and the growing world-wide competition for mineral commodities with resulting price increases all will increasingly affect our supply position. To remain in a strong industrial and political position, the United States must develop alternative raw material sources independent of foreign control. Alaska can provide a domestic source of minerals and mineral fuels.

Alaskan mineral production potential may be inferred by comparison with similar areas in Canada and the western United States. A remarkable similarity exists in the geology of Alaska and the geology of the Yukon Territory, British Columbia, and the western United States. Because the western Canadian mining industry is in the very early stages of development, comparison with the advanced mining industry of the western United States may be more meaningful. Recognizing the difference in the marketing conditions between Alaska and the Western States and the uncertainties involved in evaluating mineral potential, the remarkable geological similarity still makes it valid to draw rough comparison. The average mineral production of the 11 Western States up to 1970 totaled $120,000 per square mile. At today's prices, the value probably would be closer to $300,000 per square mile. This includes only minerals for which historical data are readily available—petroleum, copper, gold, lead, silver, and zinc. Alaska should be capable of equal production.

Mining Experience to Date. The existence of offshore gold in the vicinity of Nome has been known for some time. Mining of that gold by manual methods was done as far back as the nineteenth century. Since that time, some 5 million troy ounces of gold have been obtained from the beaches at Nome. Current efforts are underway to extract more gold from those beaches.

Platinum is known to occur in the offshore areas of Goodnews Bay, but no mining offshore has taken place. The estuarine areas have yielded 500,000 troy ounces of platinum. Finally, as discussed in earlier chapters, Barite has been extracted from offshore regions.

2. Other Laws Affecting Offshore Operations

Monitoring of Operations; Sanctions. In all sales contracts, the director of the Division of Lands may require the purchaser to submit periodic reports of the quantity of materials extracted and the disposition made of all materials removed.[25] If the purchaser defaults in the performance of any of the contract terms or of any regulations of the DNR, the director may take appropriate legal action including an action for forfeiture of contract.[26]

Water Quality Control. The Department of Environmental Conservation (DEC) has developed procedures for issuing water quality certification.[27] The applicant must first submit a detailed report of the chemical and physical properties of any effluent to be discharged to state waters and a description of the quantity and type of dredge material to be removed. The DEC then prepares a public notice of the application and forwards it to the applicant with instructions to publish at his expense. The notice must be published in a local newspaper and sent to other interested parties. If the DEC determines that there is sufficient public interest in the application, a public hearing will be held. The DEC will grant the certification if the applicant provides assurance that the proposed operations will not adversely affect the aquatic environment and will be in compliance with all applicable water quality standards, water quality control plans, and waste discharge requirements. DEC promulgation of ambient water quality standards and implementation of effluent limitations for offshore mining activities set by EPA and eventually by the state, or alternatively by the Corps for dredge mining, constitutes the federal regulatory framework which now governs state water quality efforts.

Authority over the Marine Environment. The Department of Fish and Game administers the state's program for conservation and development of commercial fisheries and sport fishing. Whenever the extraction of materials such as sand and gravel will "utilize . . . waters of the state or materials" from any river, lake, or stream bed, or tide or submerged lands, the purchaser must notify and obtain the approval of the commissioner of the Department of Fish and Game before commencing operations.[28] This requirement provides the Department of Fish and Game with a veto over proposed marine mining projects.

Failure to obtain the approval of the Department of Fish and Game can result in cancellation of the sales contract. Furthermore, it is a misdemeanor to fail to notify the Department of any construction which caused material damage to or interferes with the migration or spawning of anadromous fish.[29]

3. Laws Affecting Onshore Facilities and Operations

Shore Land Use Controls. Alaska has no statewide program of regulating land uses in the coastal region, such as a facilities siting law or wetlands act; however, any onshore construction which would interfere with marine life must be approved by the Department of Fish and Game before being commenced.[30]

Water Quality Control. Before any commercial or industrial operation is permitted to discharge solid or liquid wastes into state waters, a waste discharge permit must be obtained from the Department of Environmental Conservation.[31] The statutory definition of *waste* is broad enough to include any solid or liquid runoff from the processing of dredged materials, but excludes runoff from materials extracted for the purpose of mining precious metals.[32]

An applicant for a waste discharge permit must specify in detail the nature of any effluent into state waters, the sources of all industrial wastes, and a description of any treatment of disposal methods proposed.[33] The DEC prepares and publishes public notice of the application in a newspaper of general circulation within the area of the proposed discharge. Copies are also sent to, and comments solicited from, the Departments of Fish and Game, Natural Resources, Economic Development, and Health and Social Services. Thirty days after publication of public notice, the DEC may issue, deny, or grant a permit subject to conditions. No permit may be issued for a term longer than 5 years. Similar procedures are followed for the acquisition of NPDES[34] permits, which have been discussed in previous chapters.

4. Impact Assessment and Resource Management Laws

Alaska has no statewide requirement for preparing environmental impact statements on major actions of state agencies. Although there has been no recent legislation in the state regarding coastal resource management, the Division of Marine and Coastal Zone Management of the DEC is now preparing a management program to qualify for funding under the Coastal Zone Management Act. The DEC anticipates that state legislation will be introduced in the near future to authorize such coastal management policies.[35] Given the legislative and policy vacuum which presently exists in Alaska in regard to the management of marine hard mineral resources, the formulation and enactment of the state's coastal management program will assume considerable significance for marine mining of the state's submerged lands.

B. CALIFORNIA

California, as in so many other aspects of its social and legal system, encompasses extremes in values and laws relating to the use of its coastal and marine resources. The state has grown rapidly by economic and developmental measures, and this is attributable to an earlier frontier mentality of opportunism and exploitation. The state has also recently and rapidly changed its objectives and now fosters preservation of its amenities and imposes restrictions on future development which are substantial. Both sets of values and objectives are now incorporated into its legal and institutional framework, and a steady state condition for responsible balancing of economic and environmental factors in decision making on resource use has not yet been achieved.

Confusion and risk therefore beset the future of coastal and marine mining in California, and this has had a chilling effect on industrial interest in exploiting marine minerals. Clearly, the state's marine minerals, such as sand, gravel, and phosphorite, represent valuable resources capable of meeting growing demands, and the state has allowed a number of small-scale operations to proceed. Just as clearly, the California Coastal Act[36] rigorously defends coastal and marine areas against degradation of environmental quality and dislocation of established interests which range from recreation, tourism, and community amenities to shipping, military, and industrial activities. The trend is markedly toward increasing care in the use of coastal and marine resources, and the future of marine mining on state submerged lands will be determined by the strength of this trend and the state's willingness to accommodate further economic development.

1. Authorization of Offshore Exploration and Extraction

Laws and Institutional Structure. There are two methods of obtaining rights to hard mineral resources on submerged lands owned by the state of California: One may proceed either by obtaining a mineral lease through competitive bidding or by obtaining a prospecting permit which may later be converted into a preferential mineral lease. Both of these procedures involve application to the State Lands Commission (SLC), which has jurisdiction over all tide and submerged lands, bays, and estuaries owned by the state.[37]

Lands known to contain commercially valuable deposits of minerals, not subject to a preferential lease under a prospecting permit, may be leased by the SLC through competitive bidding.[38] Before the competitive leasing may formally begin, the SLC must design the bid package, i.e., the lands to be offered and the conditions to be attached to the leasing. The SLC's decision on the bid package generally follows the recommendation of the State Lands Division staff. The staff's action, in turn, begins when a prospective lessee applies for a lease of submerged mineral lands, up to a limitation of 5,760 acres per lease.

Once the staff determines that the state is the owner of the lands in question, the applicant is asked to furnish an environmental data statement (EDS), pursuant to the California Environmental Quality Act (see discussion *infra* of this legislation). The staff then recasts the EDS into an environmental impact report, which is subject to review for 60 days by local, state, and federal agencies as well as by private interests.

These public and private groups submit comments to the staff, which then holds working meetings to resolve differences of opinion on the proposed leasing. The staff then prepares a recommendation, and if positive, a bid package for the commission. The commission meets in open session to determine whether a lease sale (competitive bidding on the bid package) will be approved. The commission nearly always abides by the (nonbinding) recommendation of the staff.

Once the lease sale is approved, the SLC publishes a notice of intention to receive bids for the lease. The notice, which is published in a newspaper of general circulation in the county in which the lands are situated, describes the lands to be leased and states the form of the bidding. The bidding may be based on either the highest cash bonus or highest royalty rate. Since there has been no lease sale for sand and gravel to date, no typical royalty figure is available. The commission reserves the right to reject all bids; in that event, the commission may call for new bids or may refuse to receive new bids until a new application is made. Normally, however, the commission can award the lease to the highest qualified bidder, who must pay the first rental or other consideration within 15 days after the award. Mineral leases to be issued in this manner will generally run for terms not exceeding 20 years, with options for the lessees to renew for terms not exceeding an additional 10 years. The entire process of applying for and obtaining the lease takes 6 to 9 months.

The second method for obtaining mineral rights on submerged state lands is through a prospecting permit and preferential lease.[39]

The SLC may issue a prospecting permit for lands which are not definitely known to contain valuable mineral deposits. The permit entitles the holder to prospect for and extract minerals on the tract. An applicant for a prospecting permit must furnish a description of the lands involved, a statement of the use proposed, and a statement of the nature of the mineral deposits proposed to be developed. The permit may be issued for a term not exceeding 2 years, with extensions possible for a total term not exceeding 3 years. The cost of the permit is $1 per acre.

At any time during the life of a prospecting permit, the permittee may apply for a preferential mineral lease upon the discovery of a commercially valuable deposit of minerals within the permit area. Once the permittee establishes to the commission's satisfaction that land contains valuable deposits, he is entitled to a lease at a royalty rate determined previously at the time of issuance of the prospecting permit. Until the permittee obtains a lease, he must pay a royalty of 20 percent of his profit for any minerals sold.

It is the responsibility of the prospecting permittee or, in the case of competitive bidding, of the successful bidder to obtain any other permits which are required, e.g., permits from the Corps of Engineers and from the California Coastal Zone Conservation Commission (see detailed discussion *infra*).

Policies of State Agencies. The policy of the State Lands Commission is to favor development with suitable environmental protection.[40] One high official in the SLC has stated that if environmental safeguards can be demonstrated for offshore sand and gravel mining, the commission will probably approve such projects.[41]

The Fish and Game Department, which may exert influence on the SLC and other permit-granting agencies, is not unalterably opposed to dredging.[42] The chief concern of the Department is the protection of the marine and wildlife resources of the state. If the effects of dredging could be mitigated—e.g., through reestablishment of like habitat and/or replacement in kind of species—the Department might not oppose an offshore mining project. However, no filling of marshes or wetlands will be permitted. An official of the Fish and Game Department has stated that he would examine in detail the effect of any proposed dredging activity on the local habitat before giving approval.[43] In particular, the Department would be concerned with the possibility of turbidity plumes and possible adverse impacts on shellfish. As for mining in San Francisco Bay, the Department fears that toxic substances already in bay sediments might be resuspended by dredging operations.

A state agency which may have a great influence on the development of an offshore hard mineral industry in California is the California Coastal Commission (CCC). The CCC is the successor to the Coastal Zone Conservation Commission, the interim regulatory and coastal zone management plan development agency created by an initiative measure in 1972. The California Coastal Act of 1976, which created the CCC, adopted the plan that was developed by the interim agency and the regional commissions established by the 1972 measure, including provisions significant to offshore hard mineral resources mining. The recent coastal resources management legislation and its significance are separately discussed following the treatment of other specific laws related to offshore and onshore operations.

Mining Experience to Date. Four mining operations have been performed to date for sand extraction in Monterey Bay, totaling 250,000 cubic yards per year.[44] The cost of mining is about 40¢ per cubic yard, while the selling prices of the sand for glass making have ranged from $10 to $20 per cubic yard.

In San Francisco Bay, mining for both shells and sand and gravel has been permitted.[45] The largest sand and gravel operations account for 350,000 cubic yards per year; royalties range from 5¢ to 10¢ per cubic yard. Shell mining has been conducted for the calcium carbonate content of the shells, which is later processed into cement. One mining company has extracted 40 million tons of shells since 1930, but has now ceased operations. It is estimated that 60 million tons remain.

2. Other Laws Affecting Offshore Operations

Monitoring of Operations; Sanctions. Persons holding mineral leases from the State Lands Commission must furnish the SLC with monthly statements on the amount, quality, and value of all minerals produced, shipped, or sold during the preceding month.[46] Holders of prospecting permits must furnish similar statements quarterly. Lessees and permittees are required to keep accurate books and records of the mining operations, and inspectors of the State Lands Division have the right to inspect the records of account at any time.

Both lessees and permittees must idemnify the state against any loss or damage arising from their use of the land.[47] In the case of a prospecting permit, the SLC may, upon 30 days notice, terminate the permit for failure to perform any conditions specified in the permit.

Water Quality Control. Water quality certification for dredging projects is administered by the nine California regional water quality control boards. The regional boards are the implementing units of the state Water Resources Control Board, which acts as a level of appeal and a policymaking body.[48]

The San Francisco Bay Regional Board has the greatest experience with dredging projects, since most dredging in California has been navigational and taken place in San Francisco Bay.[49] When a dredging operation is proposed by a private group, the regional board must act upon the request for certification pursuant to § 401 of the Federal Water Pollution Control Act. The regional board asks each applicant to perform sediment analysis, and the results are circulated to several agencies, including the State Fish and Game Department, the (San Francisco) Bay Conservation and Development Commission, the Bureau of Sport Fisheries, the National Marine Fisheries Service, and the permits branch of the Environmental Protection Agency. These bodies comment on the dredging proposal and suggest disposal sites, but the comments are not binding on the regional board. If it is clear to the regional board that no conditions need be imposed to maintain water quality, then the staff of the board so notifies the state board, which issues the official certification. When conditions are to be imposed, the regional board itself issues appropriate orders, which act as the certification.

It should be noted that all these agencies, including the regional board itself, have a second opportunity to submit comments when the Corps of Engineers considers the application for a Corps permit on the same dredging proposal. The agencies often hedge on their initial comments to the regional board but take a more stringent view of the project in the second commenting period. Consequently, some projects have been substantially curtailed in proceedings before the Corps.

The Los Angeles Regional Board follows a less formal procedure in issuing water quality certifications since there is little dredging activity in the Los Angeles area.[50] The certification process is handled by the staff only, without consultation with the board members.

Authority over the Marine Environment. The California Fish and Game Department has general authority over the protection of the state's living marine resources.[51] The Department's role in controlling dredging activities stems from commenting on dredging proposals from the State Lands Commission, on Corps of Engineers permits, and on water quality certifications and Coastal Zone Conservation

Commission permits. There is no formal public participation in the formulation of these comments.

The Fish and Game Department also has specific authority over the use of certain dredging equipment in inland waters: It is unlawful to use a vacuum or suction dredge in any river, stream, or lake without a permit from the Department.[52]

3. Laws Affecting Onshore Facilities and Operations

Shore Land Use Controls: *Wetlands Legislation.* California has enacted legislation which restricts the rights of landowners to fill wetlands in the San Francisco Bay region.[53] In order to fill, dredge, or alter such wetlands, the owner must obtain a permit from the San Francisco Bay Conservation and Development Commission (BCDC). The BCDC's authority and its denial of a permit to fill wetlands in the bay were recently upheld in an important state court of appeals decision.[54]

Restrictions on Shoreline Construction. The erection of structures on state-owned shore or tidelands must have the approval of the State Lands Commission. An application to the SLC for such construction or for removal or deposition of materials of tidelands must be submitted to the Department of Parks and Recreation for examination. The SLC may deny the application if the proposed work would unreasonably interfere with recreational activities or the protection of shorelands.[55]

Before constructing any wharf or pier on lands bordering a navigable bay, lake, or inlet, one must receive the approval of the board of supervisors of the county where the lands are located.[56] The applicant must publish notice of his proposed structures in local newspapers before the board will act on the matter. Maximum length allowed for such structures is 1,000 feet along the shoreline, with a maximum width of 75 feet.

The authority of state and regional Coastal Zone Conservation Commissions with regard to coastal construction is discussed below.

Water Quality Control. It is apparent that materials discharged from dredging and refining operations will be subject to state regulation under the Porter-Cologne Act,[57] which grants authority to 9 regional water quality control boards to control the discharge of "waste" into state waters. Waste is defined in the statute as any waste substance from "any producing, manufacturing, or processing operation of whatever nature"[58] and has been specifically interpreted to include "changes in the physical or chemical characteristics of receiving waters caused by the extraction of sand, gravel or other materials from a streambed."[59]

Under the Porter-Cologne Act, anyone proposing to discharge waste which "could affect" the quality of the receiving waters must file a report of the discharge to the regional board.[60] The board then sets effluent limitations on the discharge or may prohibit it altogether. The regional board usually places heavy self-monitoring obligations on the discharger and may inspect his facilities to see if the board's standards are being met. At any time, should the discharger not file a discharge report, not abide by the effluent limitations, or fail to furnish a monitoring report, the regional board may request the state attorney general to act. In each case, the violator is guilty of a misdemeanor, and the statute also provides for a civil fine up to $6,000 per day.

Any person aggrieved by action or inaction of the regional board may appeal first to the state Water Resources Control Board, the parent body of the regional boards, and then to the courts.[61] In addition, the state board may review regional board decisions on its own initiative.

The state board, which consists of 5 appointed members, also acts as a policymaking body on water quality and water rights. The board members usually initiate a general policy, which is then developed in detail by the staff. This policy is reviewed at public meetings of the board for adoption. No statewide policy has yet been formulated for dredging and dredged spoils, however.

It should be noted that California's state and regional water boards are well-staffed, powerful regulatory units.

4. Impact Assessment and Resource Management Laws

Environmental Impact Assessment. With the passage of the state Environmental Quality Act (CEQA),[62] California became the first state to require the preparation of environmental impact reports (EIR) similar to the environmental impact statements required under NEPA. All state agencies, boards, and commissions must prepare an EIR on any project they plan to approve which may have a significant effect on the environment. In 1972, the California Supreme Court ruled that the EIR requirement applied to the issuance of leases, permits, and other approvals for private applicants by state and substate agencies.[63] Shortly afterward, the California legislature amended CEQA specifically to confirm the court's decision.[64] Therefore, as California law now stands, the leasing of submerged state lands for public or private mineral development cannot proceed without the preparation of an EIR.

The contents of the EIR, like the EIS under NEPA, include the unavoidable adverse impacts of the project and alternatives to the proposed action. The agency preparing the EIR is required to consult with all other agencies which have jurisdiction over the project before completing the report. The final EIR becomes a public document and is part of the project report used in the existing review and budgetary process. A federal EIS on the same project may be submitted in lieu of the EIR.

Although the public agency is responsible for the ultimate completion of the EIR, the law provides that the initial burden of collecting data may be placed on the private party applying for a permit or lease.[65] The State Lands Commission, for example, requires an applicant for a mineral lease to submit an environmental data statment (EDS), a detailed account of the purpose, physical description, environmental impacts, and alternatives to the proposed project. The commission recasts the EDS into a draft EIR, which it then circulates for comments.

The State Lands Commission allows 60 days for review of draft EIRs by public agencies and the general public and 21 days for review of a final EIR before a decision is rendered on an application for a permit or lease.[66] The commission charges the applicant a fee of at least $200 to defray the expense of completing the EIR.

California Coastal Act of 1976.   The California Coastal Act (CCA) requires a permit for any development in the coastal zone,[67] a region extending from the outer seaward limit of state jurisdiction to 1,000 yards inland of the mean high tide line.[68] Development is broadly defined and includes dredging, mineral extraction, discharge or disposal of dredged materials, and the placement or erection of any structures.[69] Permits for onshore developments are to be obtained from local government where a local coastal program has been certified to be in conformity with the California Coastal Conservation Plan policies adopted by the CCA or by the appropriate regional commission or the CCC.[70] Offshore development permits are, consistent with general exercise of state-level control of activities in state waters, obtainable from the appropriate regional commission or the CCC if no regional commission exists or an appeal is taken from a decision of a regional commission.[71]

The adopted policies that govern local coastal program development and nonlocal permit application decisions emphasize public access and recreational use of onshore areas,[72] including location of new onshore development within or proximate to existing developed areas,[73] protection of environmentally sensitive habitat areas,[74] and control of dredging and other marine activities for protection of the marine environment and in furtherance of policies of protecting environmentally sensitive habitat areas.[75] Specifically, dredge mining for sand and gravel or other mineral resources is permitted, except in areas designated as environmentally sensitive areas, "where there is no feasible less environmentally damaging alternative, and where feasible mitigation measures have been provided to minimize adverse environmental effects."[76]

Onshore development related to marine mining might be classified as coastal-dependent[77] and therefore encouraged within the bounds of public use and environmental policy restrictions. Emphasis is given to expansion or location within existing sites or developed areas; siting in other areas will be allowed, however, where no other alternatives are feasible, or when less environmentally damaging and environmental effects are mitigated to the maximum extent feasible.[78] Onshore development in "urban land areas," including areas zoned and developed for commercial or industrial use prior to January 1977, are excluded from the CCA permit requirements where the CCC finds that locally permitted development will consist of infilling a replacement in conformity with the scale, size, and character of the surrounding community and there is no potential for individual or cumulative adverse effects on public access to the coast or to coastal resources from such development.[79]

Jurisdiction and authority of other state agencies, including State Lands Commission, Water Resources Control Board, and Department of Fish and Game, are preserved intact by the CCA.[80] These agencies are directed to carry out their functions in conformity with the provisions and policies of the CCA,[81] but the CCA specifically provides that no state agency authorities are increased, decreased, or superseded by the act and prohibits the CCC and regional commissions from setting standards or adopting regulations that duplicate existing state agency regulatory controls.[82]

C. CONNECTICUT

The Connecticut coastal region is heavily populated and serves a variety of established interests ranging from recreation and tourism to shellfishing, manufacturing industry, and the military. Proposals for major new developments such as oil refineries which would significantly alter the existing allocation of coastal resources have failed, and it is likely that other major developments such as the growth of a marine mining industry will face a hostile political environment.

Marine mining of the submerged land of Long Island Sound, which is owned by Connecticut and New York, has been under study for some time.[83] The sound is shallow, rich in sand, and can easily be mined using relatively primitive dredge mining techniques. Further, significant markets for marine sand are believed to exist along the Connecticut coast and in the New York metropolitan region.

The state has felt little pressure thus far from potential marine miners and has not developed regulations for exploration and extraction. However, in response to other pressures, the state has established an impressive array of laws and agencies to protect its coastal environment. As a result, environmental agencies and criteria play a significant role in decision making on dredging and other developmental activity proposed for the coastal region, in contrast to other states where commercial and developmental agencies and criteria may be of greater significance. Further, in Connecticut environmental protection of the coastal region coincides with important economic interests such as shellfishing, recreation, sports, tourism, and the property values of affluent coastal communities. If the development of marine mining in this context is sanctioned, it will be stringently regulated, scheduled, and sited to ensure that it does not affect these well-established interests.

1. Authorization of Offshore Exploration and Extraction

Laws and Institutional Structure. The Department of Environmental Protection (DEP) has regulatory powers over the removal of sand, gravel, or other materials from lands under tidal and coastal waters. In regulating the extraction of these materials from submerged state lands, the Commissioner of Environmental Protection is required to give due regard to the prevention of shore erosion, the protection of fish habitats and shellfish grounds, the development of adjoining uplands, the rights of riparian property owners, and the need for coastal and inland navigation.[84]

Removal of sand, gravel, or other materials is prohibited without a permit from the Commissioner.[85] However, DEP has never entertained an application for the express purpose of mining sand and gravel or other marine minerals, and the department has formulated no administrative regulations governing the issuance of marine mining permits. It is likely that such an application process would follow the procedures established to govern the issuance of wetlands and dredging permits. A description of these procedures follows.[86]

An application for a dredging permit must be submitted by the dredger to DEP's Division of Water and Related Resources. The application must include the location of the proposed dredging, a plan for disposal of materials, a description of the materials to be extracted, and an analysis of possible changes in the water caused by the dredging. The application is circulated for review by several offices within DEP: water compliance, wildlife, transportation, land acquisition, and the marine regional office. Comments are also solicited from the Aquaculture Division of the Department of Agriculture. Although it is not statutorily required, the Division of Water and Related Resources, as a matter of discretion, grants these reviewing agencies a veto power over the proposed work.

Before a dredging permit can be granted, a public hearing is mandatory[87] and is arranged by the Division of Water and Related Resources. Such a hearing is similar to the hearings on wetlands permits: Notice is sent to interested parties and is published in a newspaper of general circulation. Public hearings on matters with environmental implications in Connecticut have attracted massive attendance, and anyone who wishes to speak at such hearings is entitled to do so.

After the hearing, the Division of Water and Related Resources and the Commissioner make the decision on the application. A permit may be granted subject to stated conditions, including the posting of a bond.[88] The royalty rate anticipated for sand mining may range from 35 to 45¢ per cubic yard.[89] Any person who is aggrieved by an order of the Commissioner relating to a dredging permit may appeal to the Superior Court within 15 days of the issuance of the order.[90]

Policies of State Agencies. The Division of Water and Related Resources generally discourages any dredging activity in Long Island Sound by means of strict regulation. This position has been taken to stem wetlands destruction in Connecticut, which has a long and inglorious history, and is reinforced by the belief that the sound is covered with a layer of polluted sludge. Agency officials fear that a disturbance of the sludge layer may release organics, toxins, and heavy metals into the surrounding waters, damage shellfishing, and endanger health.[91] DEP's Division of Water (pollution) Compliance, which has the task of water quality control, has a different view—that offshore dredging does not necessarily present significant environmental problems, especially if conducted far out in the sound.[92] The Aquaculture Division of the Department of Agriculture, which is in charge of leasing submerged lands for shellfish cultivation, has voiced no objection to dredging further out in Long Island Sound.[93] In the past, aquaculture officials have demonstrated a spirit of coexistence with dredging activities, once the dredgers consulted with them and adjusted their plans accordingly. With the advent of marine mining, continued coexistence would depend on the careful siting of leases for shellfishing and mining, at the least.

Mining Experience to Date. Connecticut has not yet entertained any applications for mining permits, although the Division of Water and Related Resources has allowed the sale of dredged spoils as aggregates. If the experience with regulated activities in wetlands is any guide, public hearings are likely to be heavily attended, with opponents of the proposed activity in the majority.

2. Other Laws Affecting Offshore Operations

Monitoring of Operations; Sanctions. The Division of Water and Related Resources is charged with enforcing the conditions contained in dredging permits, has the power to issue cease and desist orders for violations of permit conditions, and may also bring suit for environmental damages. As a practical matter, however, the monitoring and enforcement capabilities of the division are quite limited. Division administrators themselves inspect the worksites, but the agency lacks the manpower sufficient to do a thorough job of monitoring.[94]

Water Quality Control. The Division of Water Compliance has responsibility over water quality management in Connecticut, including the issuance of water quality certifications. Since this office is not opposed to most dredging activities and has encountered few dredging proposals, the division has not found it necessary to develop detailed procedures for issuing water quality certifications. At present, the Division's views are effectively expressed in its initial review of dredging permit applications, which are circulated by the Division of Water and Related Resources. The Division of Water Compliance is accorded a veto power over any proposed dredging operations.

Authority over the Marine Environment. The Aquaculture Division of the Department of Agriculture has authority over the leasing and protection of the substantial shellfish grounds in Long Island Sound. Fines and other penalties are provided for damage to shellfish grounds, including damage resulting from dumping mud or other substances in shellfish areas.[95]

3. Laws Affecting Onshore Facilities and Operations

Shore Land Use Controls: *Wetlands Act.* Connecticut's Tidal Wetlands Act[96] lists several activities which may not be conducted in tidal wetlands without a permit from the Commissioner of Environmental Protection. Among the regulated activities are dredging, excavating, filling, or dumping any sand, gravel, mud, or aggregate of any type.[97] When an application for a permit is made, the Commissioner notifies local authorities, and a public hearing is held within 60 days unless the Commissioner finds that the proposed activity will not have a significant effect on the wetlands.[98] The Commissioner may grant, deny, or attach conditions to a permit, and any party aggrieved by the Commissioner's order may appeal to the Court of Common Pleas of Hartford County.[99]

Regulation of Structures in Coastal Waters. The Commissioner of Environmental Protection has authority to regulate the erection of structures in tidal and coastal waters of the state, with regard to the prevention of shoreline erosion, the development of adjoining lands, and the improvement of navigation.[100] Specifically, it is prohibited to place any obstruction or to carry out dredging operations in coastal waters without a permit from the Commissioner, who may attach conditions to such work.[101] The Commissioner also considers the views of the Commissioner of Transportation and of the planning and zoning commissions of the town where the work is proposed.[102]

Water Quality Control. Discharges of any kind into state waters are prohibited without a permit from the Commissioner of Environmental Protection.[103] A public hearing on an application for a permit must be held within 60 days. The Commissioner may grant, deny, or attach conditions to permits, which are issued for 5 year terms;[104] may periodically investigate sources of discharge; and may issue orders to abate unauthorized discharge.[105] Any person aggrieved by an abatement order may request a public hearing and has the right of court appeal.[106] Any violation of these provisions is punishable by civil and criminal fines.[107]

Other Pollution Controls. Without prior hearing, the Commissioner of Environmental Protection may issue a cease and desist order to anyone who is engaged in an activity which is likely to result in "imminent and substantial" damage to the environment.[108] He may also bring an action in Superior Court for declaratory and equitable relief against any person for protection of the public trust in the state's natural resources.[109]

4. Impact Assessment and Resource Management Laws

The Connecticut legislature has adopted statewide requirements for the filing of environmental impact statements,[110] and the state is also developing a coastal zone management program pursuant to the federal Coastal Zone Management Act. The Connecticut statutes also provide that the Commissioner of Environmental Protection shall formulate a statewide plan for the management and protection of the state's natural resources.[111] These resource management plans are still in early formative stages, but will eventually provide the planning framework within which marine mining possibilities will be determined.

D. NEW JERSEY

1. Authorization of Offshore Exploration and Extraction

The marine mineral resources of the state of New Jersey consist of sand and gravel deposits lying along the state's heavily used coast. New Jersey also contains extensive dredging interests whose activities are associated with shipping in New York Harbor, and the state has been markedly committed to construction and economic development with resultant environmental costs now apparent. Nevertheless, the state has recently moved to protect its coastal resources and shorelands and in the process has developed a relatively centralized and responsible approach to potential development of its marine sand and gravel resources. This approach also affords substantial assurance that citizen participation will be an integral part of decision making on uses of its marine resources.

Laws and Institutional Structure. The Natural Resources Council within the Department of Environmental Protection is empowered to grant mining licenses for marine sand and gravel.[112] The Council generally follows the recommendations of the Bureau of Marine Lands Management and other agencies within DEP but may grant a license over the objections of these agencies.

Submarine mining permits are issued on an individual job basis. Application is made by the job owner to the Bureau of Marine Lands Management (BMLM) and must state the location of the proposed work, the amount of material to be removed, and the predicted environmental effects.[113] Following submission of an application, a notice describing the proposed work and soliciting public comments is published in a newspaper of general circulation. At the same time, the application is circulated among various agencies within DEP, including the Division of Fish, Game, and Shellfish, the Bureau of Water Pollution Control, the Bureau of Stream Encroachment, and the enforcement and monitoring staff. Each of these agencies studies the application and submits comments to BMLM, which then evaluates and summarizes the agency and public comments and submits its recommendation to the Natural Resources Council. The council is composed of 12 citizens representing a broad cross-section of society and interests.

The Natural Resources Council then considers the application, BMLM's recommendations, and the comments of individual citizens who are again encouraged to present their views. Ordinarily, the council follows the recommendation of BMLM.[114] If the application is approved by the Council, it is sent to the commissioner of DEP, who usually approves the Council's action. The governor has a final, though infrequently exercised, veto power over the application. Upon successful completion of this regulatory process, which may run for 6 months, a permit will be granted to the applicant, typically at a royalty rate of 35¢ per cubic yard for sand and gravel.[115]

Policies of State Agencies. The Natural Resources Council has expressed its views that marine sand and gravel is a nonrenewable resource that belongs to the people of New Jersey and that these minerals should be used only for public interest projects and not for commercial exploitation.[116] These views became manifest in a "Coastal Moratorium Resolution" passed by the Natural Resources Council in 1969.[117] Except for active permits, this moratorium essentially prohibited private dredging for sand and gravel in the waters of New Jersey. The moratorium has been somewhat relaxed but still serves to discourage private marine mining ventures for private gain.

Mining Experience to Date. While there have been expressions of interest in sand and gravel mining off New Jersey and extensive dredging of the estuarine areas, there has been to date no actual marine mining off New Jersey. The construction industry in New Jersey uses large amounts of sand mined from the submerged lands of New York.

Other Laws Affecting Offshore Operations

Monitoring of Operations; Sanctions. Once a contractor has been granted a permit, the dredge operator hired by the contractor is subject to the supervision of the Tom's Run Field Office of DEP.[118] The staff of this office has authority to monitor the dredging operations and enforce the terms of the permit. If violations are discovered, the field officer can send a stop order instructing the violator to halt operations within 5 days. If the dredging continues, an injunction may be sought.

Water Quality Control. The Department of Environmental Protection uses an informal procedure for issuing water quality certifications for proposed offshore mining projects.[119] The applicant describes his project in letter form, complete with maps and drawings, to the Bureau of Water Pollution Control, and his application is then circulated to other agencies within DEP for clearances. Water quality tests and further information on other issues may be required. A letter certification is sent if the application is subsequently approved, and the Department may also impose discharge and monitoring conditions upon the applicant.

In addition, a permit may be required from DEP pursuant to New Jersey's Clean Ocean Act of 1971.[120] The act empowers the Commissioner of Environmental Protection to require a permit from anyone who plans to dispose of materials of any composition at sea, and dredged spoils are among the substances specifically enumerated in the act as potentially harmful to the marine environment. Issuance of a permit is conditioned upon compliance with DEP regulations promulgated to control the loading and handling of materials which may have an adverse effect on the waters of the state.

Authority over the Marine Environment. In addition to permit-granting power under the Clean Ocean Act, DEP has general regulatory authority for the protection of marine life.[121] State law forbids the discharge of any substance into the ocean or other state waters destructive to aquatic life and provides that proof of a violation does not require a showing that the polluting substances have actually caused fish to die.[122] The department has the power to seek injunctive relief or civil or criminal penalties for such pollution.

3. Laws Affecting Onshore Facilities and Operations

Shore Land Use Controls: *Regulation of the Siting of Facilities.* Under the Coastal Area Facility Review Act of 1973,[123] certain types of facilities may not be constructed in New Jersey's coastal zone unless a permit has been issued by the Commissioner of Environmental Protection. Mineral processing plants are among the regulated facilities. Application for a permit must include a detailed environmental impact statement and becomes the subject of a public hearing. The Commissioner may issue a permit only if the proposed facility would conform with all applicable air and water quality standards and would result in "minimum feasible interference" with the natural environment and "minimum practicable degradation" of esthetic or cultural qualities of the surrounding area.[124] The Commissioner may attach conditions to the permit that are determined to be necessary to protect wildlife, marine fisheries, and the natural environment. The applicant may appeal the Commissioner's decision to a 3 member review board, which has the power to affirm, reverse, or modify the action of the Commissioner.

Wetlands and Meadowlands Acts. Under the Wetlands Act of 1970,[125] no one may erect structures in, dredge or remove material from, or deposit waste in coastal wetlands without a permit from the Commissioner of Environmental Protection. In granting, denying, or conditioning any permit, the Commissioner considers the effect of the proposed work on wildlife, marine fisheries, flood protection, and public health and welfare. A public hearing is held before any decision on a permit is made.

New Jersey's meadowlands are also regulated by the Department of Environmental Protection.[126] Any lease, conveyance, or use of meadowlands for facilities requires the approval of the Natural Resources Council. Before making its decision, the Council solicits recommendations from state, local, and regional governmental agencies. The environmental impact of the proposed work must be considered by the Council.

Regulation of Wharves and Harbor Facilities. DEP's Division of Navigation has general jurisdiction over harbor facilities, waterfront development, and power vessels.[127] Anyone wishing to construct a wharf or other shipping facilities will be subject to the regulations of the state Division of Navigation and of the municipality which owns the waterfront land in question. The municipality will grant, deny, or condition a construction permit after a public hearing.[128]

Water Quality Control. Discharge of wastes from onshore facilities is regulated by DEP, pursuant to the Federal Water Pollution Control Act. DEP administers the issuance of SPDES permits.[129]

Other Pollution Controls. Onshore facilities will also be subject example, under the Noise Control Act of 1971,[130] DEP is empowered to set standards of noise emission and to require the registration of persons engaged in noisemaking operations. Both air and noise pollution regulatory programs administered by DEP incorporate applicable federal limitations and requirements as well as state requirements generated under the authority of state police powers.

4. Impact Assessment and Resource Management Laws

Environmental Impact Assessment. Although New Jersey has no general environmental protection act which requires the preparation of an EIS before state agency permits can be granted, it has imposed similar requirements under other legislation and regulations. DEP requires the "registration" of persons engaged in operations which may pollute the environment and requires the filing of "reports" by them in accordance with departmental regulations.[131]

In addition, an EIS must accompany any application for a construction permit under the Coastal Area Facility Review Act (see earlier discussion).[132] This impact statement must include a listing of adverse environmental impacts which cannot be avoided if the facility is constructed and operated and a description of alternatives to all or any part of the proposed work.

Coastal Zone Management. Like other coastal states, New Jersey is developing a management program pursuant to the Coastal Zone Management Act of 1972. In the interim, the Coastal Area Facility Review Act gives the state a high degree of control and enforcement over land uses in the coastal zone.

E. NEW YORK

As with neighboring Connecticut and New Jersey, New York's primary marine mineral resources consist of sand and gravel suitable to meet construction needs in the metropolitan New York region. Three major deposits have been described and studied:

1. *New York Bight*—vast sand and gravel deposits in this area which ranges from the entrance of New York Harbor to the coast of New Jersey and Long Island
2. *Long Island Sound*—major sand deposits in the larger part of the sound controlled by New York, but prevented by statutes from exploitation[133]
3. *South Shore of Long Island*—major sand deposits, but probably not susceptible of exploitation because of concerns over coastal erosion and the protection of shellfish

Therefore, for a variety of reasons, ranging from environmental degradation (coastal erosion, concerns about releasing toxic materials captured in sediments, etc.) to the protection of established interests (tourism, beachfront property values, shellfishing, etc.), much of this large resource is not available for exploitation, despite nearby markets and ease of access to minerals lying in shallow waters.

1. Authorization of Offshore Exploration and Extraction

Laws and Institutional Structure. In order to remove sand, gravel, or other materials from the submerged lands of the state of New York, one must obtain a license from the state Office of General Services (OGS).[134] However, extraction of materials from waters bordering Long Island is prohibited by the state, except where the U.S. Army Corps of Engineers has determined that such operations are also necessary for improvement of navigation. Application for a submarine mining license, initiated by the dredger and not the job owner, is submitted to the OGS Bureau of Surplus Real Property and must contain a description of the exact area to be dredged, the name and port of registry of the vessel to be used, and a statement of the amount and destination of materials to be extracted.[135] In addition to a $50 filing fee, the applicant must furnish a surety bond of $50,000 and a liability bond of not less than $1 million. The application to OGS will not be acted upon until OGS receives a copy of the Corps of Engineers permit, and the Corps of Engineers, in turn, will not issue a permit until the applicant obtains a water quality certification from the state Department of Environmental Conservation. (The procedure for obtaining water quality certification is detailed on the following pages.) OGS may issue a mining license without formal public participation, as there is no provision in OGS regulations for a public hearing. The mining license is renewable annually but may not be transferred or assigned without OGS approval.

Policies of State Agencies. Officials of OGS feel that, within reasonable environmental and navigational limits, revenue from the sale of dredged sand and gravel should be maximized. OGS would also like to develop control over the site selection or origin as well as over the use of the dredged materials.

OGS will not issue a mining license until the applicant obtains clearances from the Corps of Engineers and DEC. Although it has no official role in issuing these other permits, OGS does try to help the applicant for dredge mining by urging the other agencies to speed up the paperwork on the application.

The DEC, which has regulatory powers over water quality, shellfish, and wetlands, has a more cautious approach to submarine mining. The Department feels that further information on the environmental effects of dredging sand and gravel must be developed before dredging activities in New York should be expanded. As a result, DEC has limited its approval of dredging to an area near New York Harbor.

Mining Experience to Date. Dredging of sand and gravel is currently taking place in only two areas, both near New York Harbor. Most of the dredging is being done on the east bank of the Ambrose Channel, the main shipping route to New York City. Since the current in this area is from east to west, dredging the east bank reduces the need to dredge the channel itself.

Aggregates removed from the New York Harbor area have been used for highway construction in New Jersey (as of 1974) and commanded a price of $3.93/cu.yd.[136] Since the dredger's 1974 costs were estimated to be no greater than $1.50/cu.yd.,[137] the OGS royalty of $.25/cu.yd. provided the state with approximately 10 percent of the dredger's profit.

2. Other Laws Affecting Offshore Operations

Monitoring of Operations; Sanctions. Once the dredger begins work, he must report to OGS each month on the amount of material removed and pay the appropriate royalty (presently 25¢/cu. yd.). OGS has the right to inspect the dredge site, vessels, and structures used in the operations, and the accounting records, at any time[121] and may terminate the license if its terms are violated. OGS and the Department of Environmental Conservation work together on monitoring the mining operations and enforcing the license conditions.

Water Quality Control. Before a dredger can receive a mining license from OGS or a permit from the Corps of Engineers, he must obtain water quality certification from DEC. To do so, the dredger must apply to the Division of Water Resources for the certification and publish in local newspapers a notice detailing the proposed work.[139] A public hearing may be held at the discretion of DEC. The Department's decision on the application is based largely on whether any disposal of dredged material would comply with federal ocean dumping criteria.

Authority over the Marine Environment. The dredger must also obtain a permit from DEC's Division of Fish and Wildlife and may be denied if the discharge of industrial wastes or other deleterious substances from the proposed operation would be injurious to fish or shellfish.[140] Dredging in shellfish grounds, in fact, is presumed to be a violation of state law. Any violation of DEC permit requirements may be subject to both civil and criminal penalties. Wilful noncompliance with water pollution control laws is a misdemeanor;[141] violation of DEC permit requirements or conditions is punishable by civil penalties in an action brought by the Department or the attorney general.[142]

3. Laws Affecting Onshore Facilities and Operations

Shore Land Use Controls: *Wetlands Regulation.* The Tidal Wetlands Act of 1973 restricts certain activities in tidal wetlands and adjacent areas.[143] Among the activities normally prohibited is the dredging or dumping or sand, gravel, or mud. The DEC may allow such operations to be conducted in wetlands by granting a "moratorium permit," but only if the applicant establishes that he will suffer unique and serious hardship if the permit is denied.[144] The applicant also has the burden of showing that his proposed activity is not contrary to the state's policy of protecting its tidal wetlands.

Other Shore Land Use Controls. Separate permits are required from DEC for various other shoreline activities, some of which may be relevant to marine mining, for example, a permit for excavating or placing fill in the navigable waters of the state,[145] or a permit for the construction of a dock, pier, or wharf.[146] Both types of permits are common to coastal states. An applicant for these permits in New York must furnish the Department with a detailed description of the proposed operation and publish notice of the activity for any such application.

Water Quality Control. Onshore elements of offshore mining systems, such as facilities for refining and separating dredged materials, must meet DEC water quality standards. The discharge of wastes from such onshore facilities is subject to regulation under the Federal Water Pollution Control Act and is prohibited without an NPDES permit, as is discussed in Chapter 8.[148]

4. Impact Assessment and Resource Management Laws

In June 1975, New York enacted an environmental act which requires an EIS for every state and local agency action which may have significant environmental effects. The act defines "action" to include the issuance of permits, leases, and licenses, and the promulgation of policies and regulations, with overall responsibility for implementation in DEC.[149] Therefore, any development of a state program, or any approval of mineral exploitation activities, will fall into this new legal framework.

Also, under DEC regulations, applicants for certain permits, including stream protection and industrial waste disposal system permits, must prepare an environmental report on the proposed project which includes a written description of the activity and a detailed analysis of its environmental effects.[150] The Commissioner of DEC may hold a public hearing, at the applicant's expense, on the environmental issues raised by the project.

The state is now developing its coastal zone management program in order to qualify for federal funding. The program will apply to both the Atlantic and the Great Lakes' coasts of the state, and it is likely that marine mining will not figure largely in the state's proposed program but will continue to be employed as an adjunct to the state goal of channel maintenance.

F. TEXAS

Marine minerals off the Texas coast include calcium carbonate in the form of accumulated shells of various coastal organisms and possibly some heavy mineral sands. Extensive shell mining has historically been conducted in estuarine waters, and mining for shells may move further out into the Gulf of Mexico.

Since the primary interest of marine miners is in shell deposits, the future of marine mining in this region will depend largely on state leasing of such deposits within the 3 marine leagues or 10.5 miles of state submerged lands and on federal leasing of other deposits on the OCS. The state's accommodation or acceptance of necessary shoreline facilities for handling and processing will be necessary. Given the state's orientation toward allowing economic uses of its coastal region despite environmental costs, manifest in its agencies and procedures concerned with coastal proposals, and given the absence of rigorous environmental review procedures, it is likely that necessary shoreline facilities will be sited largely as dictated by the market conditions governing the availability of coastal land.

1. Authorization of Offshore Exploration and Extraction

Laws and Institutional Structure. The offshore shell and other mineral resources of Texas are controlled by the Parks and Wildlife Commission under a permitting procedure. One seeking to mine such resources from the islands, reefs, bars, lakes, and bays of the state must apply to the Commission for a permit.[151] If the Commission finds that the proposed operations will neither damage any oyster beds and fish-inhabiting waters nor interfere with navigation, a permit may be issued.

The applicant must briefly describe the proposed work to be done, including the type of equipment to be used, the method of dredging operation planned, the proposed depth of the dredging, drawings of the location, and specifications of the project.[152] The applicant must simultaneously publish notice of the proposed work and the complete application in the daily newspaper of greatest circulation in the county to be affected by the work. Following application and publication, the Commission's Department of Parks and Wildlife is required to hold a public hearing on the proposal. At the hearing, any person may appear and present evidence orally, by affidavit, or by deposition. In deciding whether to issue the permit, the executive director of the Department must consider three primary criteria: the effect of the proposed operations on oyster beds and fish-inhabiting waters; the effect of the work on navigation; and the requirements of industry for the materials in question and their relative value to the state of Texas for commercial use. In addition, the director may also consider such factors as the applicant's past performance, degree of financial responsibility, the existence of the materials in the area, the effect of the work on recreational activity, and the effect of the work on commercial fishing.

Within a reasonable time after public hearing, the director must grant or deny the permit and set forth complete findings of fact supporting the decision. No permit may be granted for a period longer than one year, and the director may attach conditions to the permit as necessary, including the furnishing of a surety bond and payment of royalty to the department. In the event that the materials removed from bay bottoms are used as fill materials, a surety bond is required to cover the cost of the materials, calculated at 25¢ per cubic yard. Otherwise, the permittee must pay "the established price" of the materials as they are extracted. The permittee is also warned that the prices of marl, sand, gravel, and shell are subject to change by the Parks and Wildlife Commission with the approval of the governor.

As a result of the enactment of the Coastal Public Lands Management Act of 1973,[153] a miner of marine sand, shell, or other minerals must also obtain an easement from the Texas General Land Office. The consideration for the easement is set on a case-by-case basis, usually by means of negotiation.[154]

Policies of State Agencies. *[No evidence of the prevailing attitude of state officials toward marine mining has been developed, but a relatively developmental approach can be inferred from the history of coastal developments permitted by state officials.]*

Mining Experience to Date. Shell dredging in the bays and estuaries of Texas started in 1880. The use of shovel and wheelbarrow in the 1880s gave way to the mechanical dredge in 1905 and to the hydraulic dredge in 1912. In 1916, a method was found to utilize shell in cement manufacturing. Another boost to the shell industry occurred in 1929 with the discovery of a process to make lime from shell. In 1973, the shell dredging industry in Texas had delivered more than 100 million cubic yards ($7.7 \times 10^7 \, m^3$) of oyster shells to manufacturers, who then turned them into more than 100 billion pounds ($4.5 \times 10^{10} \, kg$) of products.

Concentrated dredging started in the early 1950s in San Antonio Bay. This is the only bay in Texas where the oyster shells contain the chemical constitutents necessary for the production of white cement. San Antonio Bay also has the advantage of being of shallow depth and immediately accessible to the Intracoastal Waterway. From 1969 to 1973, three companies have held nonexclusive permits to mine shell in San Antonio Bay and have operated from 3 to 5 dredges, all hydraulic. Average combined annual production is about 7 million cubic yards (6 million m^3).

There has been no experience with shell mining in the open ocean and OCS off Texas. There are two main deterrents: First, although shell resources in the Texas Gulf have been estimated to be in the hundreds of millions of tons, there have been no reliable estimates of the reserve; second, no mining technology has been proven for hard rock dredging in the hurricane-prone environment.

2. Other Laws Affecting Offshore Operations

Monitoring of Operations; Sanctions. The permit holder is required to submit monthly reports on all materials removed from public waters at the approved location,[155] including the amounts removed and their destination. The permittee is also required to keep permanent records, and failure to do so may result in cancellation of the permit.

The Parks and Wildlife Department may suspend or revoke a permit if the permit conditions are violated.[156] Specifically, if the use of "excessive equipment" is causing siltation or other damage to oyster beds or fish-inhabiting waters, the director may limit the quantity or type of equipment used in any particular area. The director also has authority to order an immediate halt to dredging within one-half mile of shore, dredging in waters less than 4 feet deep, or dredging that is causing siltation of exposed reef. Refusal to cease dredging upon request of the director can result in a 30 day suspension of the permit or, in aggravated cases, in revocation of the permit.

The Department has expressly stated that it may be an important public necessity to halt dredging violations without delay because of the threat of immediate and irreparable harm to the marine resources of the state.[157] Therefore, the Department requires all permit holders to have onboard each operating dredge a person with authority to stop all dredging upon request of the Department. Special remedies may be ordered: Any reef areas which become seriously silted will be repaired with a shell pad at least 1 foot thick; if siltation caused by a permittee results in measurable oyster mortality, compensation will be sought by the Parks and Wildlife Commission. If dredging operations in a particular area result in a history of siltation problems, the director has the discretion to delete the tract from existing and future permits for dredge mining.

Water Quality Control. The Water Quality Board is vested with authority to regulate all discharges into waters of the state.[158] All discharges are subject to control by rule, regulation, or permit, and the Board has specific authority to issue permits subject to conditions governing the character and quality, quantity, and location of the discharge.[159] The Board is the principal authority in the state with respect to water quality, and all other state agencies, including the Parks and Wildlife Department, must coordinate activities related to water pollution control with the Board.[160] Parks and Wildlife, however, enforces Water Quality Board rules, regulations, and permits where a violation affects aquatic life and wildlife.[161]

3. Laws Affecting Onshore Facilities and Operations

Shore Land Use Controls. Texas shoreland use controls related to onshore facilities and operations are primarily vested in local and county government. Islands, peninsulas, and public beaches bordering the Gulf of Mexico are, however, presumptively within the public domain under Texas law[162] and are subject to special protections against removal of sand, gravel, marl, or shells in such areas or within 1,500 feet therefrom.[163] Similarly, sand dune areas on barrier islands and peninsulas are subject to special protection.[164] In the case of both statutes, a special permit is required from the County Commissioners Court.[165]

Water Quality Control. The discharge permit authority of the Water Quality Board (WQB) governs onshore as well as offshore operations. Onshore processing facilities require a permit from the WQB for any discharges into the waters of the state and are also subject to the requirements of the NPDES permit program of the Federal Water Pollution Control Act, as is discussed in Chapter 7.

4. Impact Assessment and Resource Management Laws

Texas has no statewide requirement for the preparation of environmental impact statements by state agencies nor any permit-associated requirements for comprehensive environmental analysis of proposed action.

The state has recently established a Coastal and Marine Council, consisting of 16 appointed members, to assist in preparing a comprehensive management and planning program of coastal resources.[166] This planning task formulated by the state appears to have substantially the same objectives as the development of a state coastal management program as envisioned by the federal Coastal Zone Management Act.

CONCLUSIONS

This brief survey of policies, institutions, and regulations of six states with important marine minerals has served to illustrate some of the major features of the state context for offshore mining and to provide some basis for speculation on the future of offshore mining of state-owned submerged lands.[167]

One of the most obvious features of the state context is the diversity of interests, institutions, policies, and procedures among the 30 coastal states. Offshore mining ventures that intend to exploit deposits that lie on or in the submerged lands of several states will have several dramatically different political and regulatory environments to cope with. For example, a regional venture to exploit the sand of Long Island Sound in both the New York and Connecticut sections will face two very different sets of procedures, criteria, requirements, sanctions, policies, and attitudes. A venture on a national scale, with intentions to exploit deposits of similar minerals of nonadjoining states such as California and Florida, will probably face even greater differences. Therefore, nearshore mining ventures of more than state dimensions are likely to be discouraged. However, operations in a state or local context can be profitable. For example, a plot of sand 1 mile × 1 mile × 15 feet deep will yield 15 million cu. yd., which can be translated into a net profit of about $45 × 10^6$. This is a very "local" operation and demonstrates that marine mining does not have to be conducted on a multistate basis.

This extraordinary diversity among the states is not likely to be diminished by developments under the Coastal Zone Management Act, since the act and subsequent implementing regulations of the federal Office of Coastal Zone Management afford the states considerable discretion in determining boundaries, acceptable uses, and policies and criteria for development of their coastal regions, offshore and onshore. Some uniformity among the state regulatory agencies may be brought about by the continued promulgation of federal air, water, and noise pollutant limitations applicable to marine mining, but these regulatory limitations are only a few of the many elements of state level decision making on offshore developments and their onshore facility requirements.

Another significant feature of the state context for marine mining is the fragmentation of authority and review requirements within each state. Each state has many agencies with authority applicable to some aspect of marine mining. Each agency has its own functions, objectives, traditions, analytical methods, review procedures, applicant requirements, sanctions, and modes of public participation. Many may require similar reports. None may call for specific information of importance. All are subject to judicial review. Coordination of procedures and requirements is a chronic problem exacerbated by the presence of federal and local authorities as well. Delays and inefficiencies result, and this "multistop" approach probably does less to ensure coherent environmental and economic review of a proposed mining venture than a well-designed "one-stop" review process could accomplish.

Study of the state context also yields some interesting generalities. Agencies with authority over some aspect of marine mining, which may be found in a coastal state, include, for example:

1. *The navigational safety, public works, or channel dredging type of authority*, which is generally concerned with the coastal shipping and dredging activities and is generally sympathetic to marine mining, economic development, or at least to the sale of dredged

materials, provided the activities conform to applicable standards, and which must coexist with federal authorities and their frequently pre-emptive functions

2. *The general environmental, wetlands protection, or fish and wildlife type of authority*, which is generally reluctant to authorize major new coastal activities or projects and which employs generic and numerical pollution control standards, as well as qualitative criteria for environmental assessment in ad hoc review procedures, but is usually not required to conduct a "balancing analysis" such as cost-benefit to justify its decisions

3. *State facility siting boards or commissions* responsible for major coastal construction, which employ broad economic and environmental review criteria to evaluate each proposed facility on an essentially ad hoc basis, without an enforceable planning framework for the coastal region

4. *Coastal and resource planners* working on the development of coastal zone management and conservation plans, who may be multiple use, no-growth, or exploitive in their orientation, and who represent a growing influence over all other authorities;

5. *Mineral leasing authorities*, who generally allow exploitation, provided the inputs from other agencies yield a net favorable result in analyses used for decision making.

Given this array of authorities that may be found in a coastal state, the distinct preference among potential large-scale marine miners is to avoid attempts to work state-owned mineral deposits and to await the promulgation of a federal program for exploring and extracting the mineral resources of the outer continental shelf. The more centralized and perhaps more objective and balanced aspects of federal regulation and project evaluation, which will inhere in a federal program for the OCS, could promise fewer risks and more certainty to such potential marine miners. Even though transport and extraction costs may be higher for the OCS, the vagaries and complexities of state regulatory authorities may discourage those capable of mining the state submerged lands.

Notably missing from the array of state authorities discussed are true resource management agencies with long-term policies for conserving and wisely developing state marine mineral resources, with systems perspectives on the interrelationships among resources, environment, and the state and regional economy. Unfortunately, no trend toward the development of state level resource management was discerned.

Finally, some predictions can be put forth as a result of this review of the states. Only relatively small, localized marine mining ventures will possibly take place in state waters, to meet local needs. These ventures will be short lived, economically fragile, incapable of affording and employing sophisticated and environmentally beneficial technologies. Major ventures with substantial commitment to new techniques and efficient operation could take place on the OCS, following promulgation of final federal regulations, but will remain dependent on state and local decision making for critical coastal land-based facilities for handling, transport, and processing of marine minerals.

NOTES

1. 33 U.S.C. §§1251-1376 (1972).
2. 16 U.S.C. §§1451-64 (1972).
3. 33 U.S.C. §1344 (1972). See discussion of Corps permits.
4. 33 C.F.R. §209.120(d)(4).
5. 33 C.F.R. §209.120(c)(1) & (g)(5) (1974).
6. 42 U.S.C. 4321 et seq.
7. 16 U.S.C. 1453 (1972).
8. *Id.* §1455.
9. *Id.* §1456.
10. *Id.* §1455(b)(2).
11. *Id.* §1455(b)(5).
12. *Id.* §1455(b)(3).
13. *Id.* §1456(e)(1).
14. This requirement is expressly stated in regulations of the Department of Commerce issued pursuant to the CZMA. 15 C.F.R. §920.1 and 923.4 (1974).
15. 16 U.S.C. §1457 (1972).
16. See 11 Alaska Administrative Code (hereafter cited as AAC) §76.400-76.550 (1973).
17. *Id.* §76.525.
18. *Id.* §76.485.
19. Alaska Statutes (AS) 38.05.250(a).
20. AS 38.05.250(b) and 11 AAC 86.530.
21. AS 38.05.250(c) and 11 AAC 82.500.
22. AS 38.05.250(b); 11 AAC 86.545; 11 AAC 82.400-11 AAC 82.480.
23. AS 43.65.010.
24. Published by the Committee on Interior and Insular Affairs, U.S. Senate, 93d Cong., 2d sess., (July 1974).
25. AAC §76.500.
26. *Id.* §76.495.
27. See "General Information and Instructions for Applicants for a Waste Discharge Permit or for a Certification of Reasonable Assurance," issued by the

Alaska Department of Environmental Conservation. See also the DEC's application form for a certification of reasonable assurance.

28. 11 AAC §76.525 (1973). See also AS §16.05.870 (1974).

29. AS §16.05.890 (1974).

30. *Id.*

31. *Id.* §46.03.100.

32. " 'Industrial waste' means a . . . solid . . . or other waste substance or combination of them resulting from a process of industry . . . or from development of a natural resources. However, gravel, sand, mud, or earth taken from its original situs and put through . . . dredges or other devices for washing and recovery of precious metal contained in them and redeposited in the same watershed . . . is not industrial waste." *Id.* §46.03.900.

33. See the application form for a waste discharge permit, issued by the Department of Environmental Conservation. See also the information sheet, note 27, *supra.*

34. See information sheet, note 27, *supra.*

35. Personal communication, Mr. Dale Wallington, director of Division of Land Use and Urban Development, Department of Environmental Conservation, (1974).

36. Cal. Pub. Res. Code §30000 (1976).

37. Cal. Pub. Res. Code §6301 (West 1956).

38. The discussion of competitive bidding for mineral leases is taken from Cal. Pub. Res. Code §6890-6900 (West 1972), 2 Cal. Admin. Code (hereafter cited as CAC) §1900 et seq. (1969), 2 CAC §2200 et seq. (1969), and personal communications with Mr. A. Willard, senior mineral resources engineer, California State Lands Division (1974).

39. The discussion of prospecting permits and preferential leases is taken from Cal. Pub. Res. Code §6891-96 (West 1958); and 2 CAC §2200 et seq. (1969).

40. Personal communication, Mr. A. Willard, California State Lands Division (1974).

41. *Id.*

42. The discussion of the policies of the Department of Fish and Game is taken from personal communication with Mr. D. Lolluck, chief, Environmental Services Branch, California Department of Fish and Game (1974).

43. *Id.*

44. The information on mining in Monterey Bay is taken from personal communications with Mr. E. Welday, California Division of Mines and Geology (1974).

45. *Id.*

46. The Discussion of Monitoring of the operations of lessees and permittees is taken from 2 CAC §2205 (1969), *Id.* §1910, and California State Lands Commission Prospecting Permit.

47. 2 CAC §1911 (1969); and California State Lands Commission Prospecting Permit.

48. See generally, Cal. Water Code §13000 et seq. (1971).

49. The discussion of the certification procedure followed by the San Francisco Bay Regional Water Quality Control Board is taken from personal communications with Dr. T. Wu and Mr. D. Whitsel of that board (1974).

50. The discussion of the certification procedure followed by the Los Angeles Regional Water Quality Control Board is taken from personal communications with Mr. R. Hertel, executive officer of that board (1969).

51. The discussion of the Department of Fish and Game is taken from Cal. Fish & Game Code 200 et seq. (West 1972), and from personal communications with Mr. D. Lullock, chief, Environmental Services Branch, California Department of Fish and Game (1974).

52. Cal. Fish & Game Code §5653 (West Supp. 1975).

53. Cal. Gov. Code §66600 et seq. (West 1966).

54. Candlestick Properties, Inc. v. San Francisco Bay Conservation & Dev't Com'n., 11 Cal. App. 3d 557, 89 Cal. Rptr. 897 (1st Dist. 1970).

55. Cal. Pub. Res. Code §6890 (West 1956).

56. Cal. Harbors & Nav. Code §4001-10 (West 1955).

57. Cal. Water Code §13000 et seq. (West 1971).

58. *Id.* §13050.

59. 32 Op. Cal. Att'y Gen. 139 (1973).

60. Cal. Water Code §13260 (West 1971). The discussion of the procedures followed by the water quality boards is taken from Cal. Water Code §13260-67 (West 1971).

61. *Id.* §13320, 13321. The discussion of the procedures and policies of the State Water Resources Control Board is taken partly from personal communications with Dr. L. Kaplow of the state board (1974).

62. Cal. Pub. Res. Code §21000 et seq. (West Supp. 1974).

63. Friends of Mammoth v. Board of Supervisors of Mono County, 8 Cal. 3rd 247, 502 P.2d 1049, 104 Cal. Rptr. 761 (1972).

64. Cal. Pub. Res. Code §21065(c) (West Supp. 1974).

65. *Id.* §21160.

66. 2 CAC §2912 (1973). See generally, 2 CAC §2901 et seq. (1973).

67. Calif. Pub. Res. Code §§30600 and 30601. Cf. *Id.* §§30610 and 30610.5 for limited exceptions.

68. *Id.* §30103.

69. *Id.* §30106.

70. *Id.* §§30600 and 30601.

71. *Id.* §§30519(b) and 30601.

72. *Id.* §§30210-13 and 30220-24.

73. *Id.* §§30250-55 (development) and 30260-64 (industrial development).

74. *Id.* §30240. See also, *Id.* §§30107.5 and 30230.

75. *Id.* §30230.

76. *Id.* §30233(a)(4).

77. *Id.* §30101. However, that section limits the meaning of "coastal-dependent development and use" in terms that indicate absolute necessity for coastal siting in order to function. Thus it is not clear that onshore processing facilities will be viewed as coastal-dependent in California.

78. *Id.* §30260.

79. *Id.* §30610.5.
80. *Id.* §§30411, 30412, and 30416.
81. *Id.* §30402.
82. *Id.* §30401.
83. See, for example, studies of the New England River Basins Commission.
84. Conn. Gen. Stat. Ann. (hereafter cited as CGSA) §25-10 (1975).
85. *Id.* §25-11.
86. The description of the application process is drawn from personal communications with the Connecticut Department of Environmental Protection.
87. CGSA §25-12 (1975).
88. *Id.*
89. Personal communication, Department of Environmental Protection.
90. CGSA §25-17.
91. Personal communication, Division of Water and Related Resources.
92. Personal communication, Division of Water Compliance.
93. Personal communication, Aquaculture Division.
94. Personal communication, Division of Water and Related Resources.
95. CGSA §§ 26-221, 224. (1975).
96. *Id.* §§22a-28 et seq.
97. *Id.* §22a-29.
98. *Id.* §22a-32.
99. *Id.* §22a-34.
100. *Id.* §25-7b.
101. *Id.* §25-7d.
102. *Id.*
103. *Id.* §25-54i.
104. *Id.*
105. *Id.* §25-54j.
106. *Id.* §25-540, 25-54p.
107. *Id.* §25-54q.
108. *Id.* §22a-7.
109. *Id.* §22a-16.
110. Conn. Stat. Ann. §22a-1a to 1f (1975).
111. CGSA §22a-8 (1975).
112. New Jersey Statutes Annotated (hereafter cited as NJSA) §12:3-22 (1970).
113. Bureau of Marine Lands Management, Department of Environmental Protection, "Rules Applicable for Permit Applications," 1971.
114. Personal communications, Bureau of Marine Lands Management and Natural Resources Council (1974).
115. *Id.*
116. Personal communication, Natural Resource Council (1974).
117. Natural Resource Council, Coastal Moratorium Resolution, July 9, 1969.
118. Personal communications, Department of Environmental Protection, (1974).

119. *Id.*

120. NJSA §58:10–23.23 et seq. (Supp. 1977).

121. *Id.* §23:2-2 (1970).

122. *Id.* §23:9–36 (1970).

123. *Id.* §13:19-1 et seq. (Supp. 1977).

124. *Id.* §13:19-10.

125. *Id.* §13:9A-1 et seq. (Supp. 1974).

126. *Id.* §13:1B-8 (Supp. 1977).

127. *Id.* §12:5 et seq. (1970).

128. *Id.* §40:68-12 (1970).

129. *Id.* §26:2E-8 (Supp. 1977).

130. *Id.* §13:1G-5 (Supp. 1977).

131. *Id.* §13:1D-9(c) (Supp. 1977).

132. *Id.* §13:19-7 (Supp. 1977).

133. See note 83, *supra,* and note 167, infra, for considerable discussion of the legal, environmental, and other apsects of exploiting sand and gravel from Long Island Sound.

134. N.Y. Public Lands Law §3(5) (McKinney 1973).

135. See 6 N.Y. Code of Rules and Regulations §272.1-.7 (1973).

136. Personal communication, New Jersey Turnpike Authority, 1974.

137. Gillespie, "Beach Nourishment by Offshore Dredging" (Paper presented at the Fifth Underwater Mining Institute, University of Wisconsin, Milwaukee, May 10, 1974).

138. 6 N.Y. Code or Rules and Regulations §272.4 (1973).

139. *Id.* §608.16.

140. N.Y. Environmental Conservation Law §11-0503 (McKinney 1973).

141. *Id.* §17-1933.

142. *Id.* §17-0701.

143. *Id.* §25-0101 et seq.

144. 6 N.Y. Code of Rules and Regulations 660.5 (1974).

145. N.Y. Environmental Conservation Law 15-0505 (McKinney 1973).

146. *Id.* 15-0503.

147. 6 N.Y. Code of Rules and Regulations 608 (1973).

148. N.Y. Environmental Conservation Law 17-0505 (McKinney 1973).

149. S.3540 and A.4533, passed June 24, 1975, amending the N.Y. Environmental Conservation Law.

150. 6 N.Y. Code of Rules and Regulations 615 (1972).

151. Texas Rev. Civ. Stat. (hereafter cited as TRCS) 86002 (Supp. 1977).

152. The description of the application process it taken from three documents issued by the Texas Parks and Wildlife Department, "Rules and Regulations for Issuance of Marl, Sand and Gravel Permits" (1970); "Marl, Sand and Gravel Permit Application Information"; and "Questionnaire, Permit Application Information." See TRC 5, §§86.003–86.005 (Supp. 1977).

153. TRCS 5415e-1 et seq. (Supp. 1974).

154. Personal communication, Mr. Doran Williams, attorney for Texas General Land Office, 1974.

155. See "Rules and Regulations," note 134, *supra.*

156. See "Definitions and Administrative Actions Pertaining to Violations of Shell Dredging Permits," issued by Texas Parks and Wildlife Department (1974).

157. *Id.*

158. Texas Water Code § 21.251.

159. Texas Water Code §§ 21.080 and 21.081.

160. Texas Water Code § 21.257.

161. Texas Water Code § 21.259.

162. Texas Civil Stat. art. 5415d. See also Seaway v. Attorney General, 375 S.W. 2d 923 (Tex. Civ. App. 1964), ref. m.ne.

163. Texas Civil STat. art. 5415g. The act applies to only those areas situated outside the boundaires of an incorporated city, town, or village. However, art. 5415g, §11A, prohibits excavation or removal from any beach within an incorporated city, town, or village.

164. Texas Civil Stat. art. 5415h.

165. Texas Civil Stat. art. 5415g, § 2, and art. 5415h, § 4.

166. TRCS 4413 (38) (Supp. 1974).

167. Other recent studies which are informative on the state context for marine mining include:

J.L. Goodier, *U.S. Federal and Seacoastal State Offshore Mining Laws* (Washington: Nautilus Press, 1972).

N. Wakeford and D. MacDonald, *Legal, Policy and Institutional Constraints Associated with Dredged Material Marketing and Land Enhancement* (Vicksburg, Miss.: U.S. Corps of Engineers, Contract Report D-74-7, 1974).

Legal and Institutional Aspects of the Texas Coastal Zone (Division of Planning Coordination, Office of the Governor, State of Texas, 1973).

J. Soden, *Marine Mining in the New Hampshire Coastal Zone* (Exeter, N.H.: Southeastern New Hampshire Regional Planning Commission, 1976).

New England Offshore Mining Environmental Study (Massachusetts Department of Natural Resources, and U.S. Department of Commerce, NOAA, Washington, D.C. April 1973).

Long Island Sound: Mineral Resources and Mining (Boston, Mass.: Interim Report, New England River Basins Commission, July 1973).

F. Turkheimer, "Copper Mining from Under Lake Superior: the Legal Aspects," *Natural Resources Lawyer* 7, 1 (1974):137-55.

M. Grant, *Rhode Island's Ocean Sands* (University Rhode Island, Kingston, R.I., Marine Tech. Report No. 10, 1973).

M. Baram and W. Lee, *A Report on the Legal and Other Critical Issues Associated with the Offshore Extraction of Sand and Gravel in Long Island Sound* (Waltham, Mass.: U.S. Army Corps of Engineers, New England Div., Contract Report no. DACW33-74-M-0675, 15 March 1973).

"Louisiana Coastal Law," miscellaneous issues, Louisiana State University, Office of Sea Grant Development, Baton Rouge, La.

✳ *Chapter 10*

Frameworks for Harmonizing Government Decision Making

As marine mining prospects ripen, coordination of federal and state planning and decision making becomes critical.

Discussion in the preceding chapters has dealt on a dis-aggregated basis with the several federal and state agencies with regulatory and developmental authority.

However, federal and state planning and decision making must also be reviewed from an aggregated perspective to ensure that the separate exercise of such functions by these agencies adds up to a coherent decision-making framework for marine mining.

In this regard, two innovative federal laws now provide the major frameworks for the harmonization of actions by separate federal and state agencies: the National Environmental Policy Act and the Coastal Zone Management Act.

A. National Environmental Policy Act

The National Environmental Policy Act[1] was enacted to maintain and restore environmental quality by improving federal agency decision making on proposed agency actions. The act, commonly called NEPA, requires agency assessment of the environmental and other effects and the resource commitments likely to arise from proposed agency actions (at program and project levels) before such actions are indeed undertaken. Section 102 of the act[2] states:

The Congress authorizes and directs that, to the fullest extent possible: (1) the policies, regulations, and public laws of the United States shall be interpreted and administered in accordance with the policies set forth in this Act, and (2) all agencies of the Federal Government shall—

(A) utilize a systematic, interdisciplinary approach which will insure the integrated use of the natural and social sciences and the environmental design arts in planning and in decision-making which may have an impact on man's environment;

(B) identify and develop methods and procedures, in consultation with the Council on Environmental Quality established by title II of this Act, which will insure that presently unquantified environmental amenities and values may be given appropriate consideration in decision-making along with economic and technical considerations:

(C) include in every recommendation or report on proposals for legislation and other major Federal actions significantly affecting the quality of the human environment, a detailed statement by the responsible official on—

(i) the environmental impact of the proposed action,

(ii) any adverse environmental effects which cannot be avoided should the proposal be implemented,

(iii) alternatives to the proposed action,

(iv) the relationship between local short-term uses of man's environment and the maintenance and enhancement of long-term productivity, and

(v) any irreversible and irretrievable commitments of resources which would be involved in the proposed action should it be implemented.

This legislative mandate has served to broaden in one bold stroke the scope of factors to be considered in federal decision making.

Preparation of an environmental impact statement must precede any federal agency decision or recommendation on a proposal which will "significantly" affect the human environment.[3] Any proposed action qualifies as sufficiently federal which either is directly undertaken by a federal agency, is supported in whole or in part by federal funding, or involves a federal lease, permit, license, or other entitlement to use.[4] Thus, agency actions subject to NEPA include developmental and certain other activities of the agencies themselves, as well as agency decisions authorizing or funding certain activities by other governmental or private interests.[5]

Since the enactment of NEPA, the U.S. Council on Environmental Quality has promulgated guidelines which suggest suitable environmental assessment methods and responsibilities for all federal agencies, including dissemination of assessments to interested parties.[6] With few exceptions, these detailed assessment guidelines have been adopted by the agencies and further adapted to better apply to each agency's functions.[7] Numerous judicial decisions construing NEPA have provided further information to the agencies as to what constitutes acceptable assessment practice.[8]

NEPA has been exhaustively reviewed elsewhere,[9] and its usefulness, limitations, and controversies have become well understood over the past several years; thus this discussion will focus briefly on special aspects of the NEPA experience believed to be of most relevance to the social control of marine mining.

Although a number of environmental impact statements, which document assessments, have now been completed on offshore developments, particularly on oil and gas exploration and leasing programs,[10] few relate to marine mining. The major assessment on marine mining to date has been conducted by the Bureau of Land Management of the U.S. Department of the Interior and has resulted in the issuance of a "draft" environmental impact statement on BLM's proposed Operating and Leasing Regulations for Hard Mineral Mining on the Outer Continental Shelf.[11]

This EIS relates to a proposed program of marine mining under federal auspices and to BLM (with U.S. Geological Survey) rulemaking to govern exploration and extraction of marine sand, gravel, and phosphorite resources only. The statement is general, loosely descriptive, lacking in adequate baseline and other data as to environmental effects and resource utilization, but contains a useful summary of mining techniques and some preliminary analysis of possible types of ecological implications.

In accordance with NEPA dissemination and review procedures,[12] the EIS has been reviewed critically by various interested parties and by other agencies with authority and expertise relevant to marine mining.

Section 309 of the Clean Air Act, as amended,[13] requires the administrator of the Environmental Protection Agency to "review and comment in writing on the environmental impact of any matter relating to duties and responsibilities" of the EPA. This has been interpreted to mean that

> wherever an agency action related to air or water quality, noise abatement and control, pesticide regulation, solid waste disposal, generally applicable environmental radiation criteria and standards, or other provision of the authority of the Administrator is involved, Federal agencies are required to submit such proposed actions and their environmental impact statements, if such have been prepared, to the Administrator for review and comment in writing.[14]

EPA comments on this EIS, somewhat critical, are now part of the

BLM record and will presumably figure in subsequent BLM decision making and any judicial review initiated by affected interests.

A final EIS may be issued with the promulgation of final rules by BLM, if and when such BLM action is taken.[15] In any case, separate and more discrete EISs can be expected to be developed by BLM and USGS to precede any other of their "major actions" which may relate to marine mining. Examples of such "major actions" and the BLM (with USGS) EISs they may trigger include the following:

- Announcement of any leasing program for marine mining of a specific offshore region
- Award of any major lease within a specific region, whether an exploratory, development, or production lease, as defined by BLM[16]
- Decision to suspend or terminate any leasing program or lease
- Promulgation of any substantial additional regulations for sand, gravel, or phosphorite or for mining of other hard minerals
- Authorization of construction or installation of structures or pipelines, to the extent that such facilities did not figure in preceding EISs

In addition, "major actions" which may be undertaken by other federal agencies and include some marine mining may also be subject to NEPA and necessitate EISs, for example:

- Promulgation of regulations governing mining-related activities, such as effluent limitations for new sources (EPA), and navigational and dredge mining limitations (Corps of Engineers)
- Approval of programs or projects for the construction of major offshore facilities which are premised on use of marine sand and gravel, such as deepwater ports (Department of Transportation),[17] and artificial islands for nuclear power plants (Nuclear Regulatory Commission)[18]
- Approval of programs or projects for onshore construction or land extension activities which will utilize marine sand and gravel, such as beach erosion control (Corps of Engineers, Soil Conservation Service) airport extension land fills (Department of Transportation, Corps of Engineers), and highways (Department of Transportation).[19]
- Approval of dredging programs or projects for the primary or incidental purposes of commercial recovery of sand and gravel or other minerals (Corps of Engineers). One such project has already been assessed by the corps[20]

- Approval of federal subsidization of dredge construction for commercial recovery of marine minerals (Maritime Administration); approval of experimental or prototype mining or dredging programs or equipment (BLM, Corps of Engineers)

Therefore, the BLM's draft EIS is merely the first of a sequence of EISs which can be anticipated if marine mining is developed further. In each case, a lead agency must assume primary assessment and decision-making responsibility (likely lead agencies are noted above), and EPA and other federal and state agencies, as well as other interested parties, can be expected to provide critical feedback prior to lead agency decision making.[21]

The *Council on Environmental Quality Guidelines* suggest,

Agencies in such cases should consider the possibility of joint preparation of a statement by all agencies concerned, or designation of a single "lead agency" to assume supervisory responsibility for preparation of the statement. Where a lead agency prepares the statement, the other agencies involved should provide assistance with respect to their areas of jurisdiction and expertise. In either case, the statement should contain an environmental assessment of the full range of Federal actions involved, should reflect the views of all participating agencies, and should be prepared before major or irreversible actions have been taken by any of the participating agencies. Factors relevant in determining an appropriate lead agency include the time sequence in which the agencies become involved, the magnitude of their respective involvement, and their relative expertise with respect to the project's environmental effects.[22]

Joint statement preparation and designation of a "lead agency" each have certain advantages. Jointly prepared statements would probably reflect greater coordination and sharing of expertise but would not possess the advantage of the "lead agency" concept in terms of ultimate definition of responsibility for administration and enforcement.

In this fashion, NEPA can be expected to foster more systematic and environmentally sensitive decision making at program and project levels; patterns of review and cooperation among several federal agencies and among federal, state, and local tiers of government; and the development of analytical methods and information on the offshore context for marine mining.

Programmatic EISs can be expected to be general and somewhat vague, but should be sufficiently specific to guide program design and generic regulatory decisions. Projects should be consistent with their programmatic contexts, and project EISs may be able to incorporate considerable information from preceding program EISs, but should also be more focused and specific.

The history of NEPA is, to a considerable extent, one of litigation in federal courts, with parties seeking judicial review of agency actions for a number of reasons related to the task of impact assessment.[23] Many of the early bases for litigation have now been diminished, as agencies are now more familiar with and willing to comply with judicial criteria. Therefore, previously common problems of agency failure to conduct an appropriately timed or otherwise procedurally adequate assessment should not beset the future application of NEPA to actions related to marine mining.

Problems remain, however, and these are substantial. The substantive adequacy of EISs on actions related to offshore activities is a predictable problem. Little is known about the offshore environment, baseline data are largely nonexistent, analytical methods for predicting consequences of offshore activities are uncertain, and large safety or weighting factors will be advisable for dealing with the considerable uncertainty surrounding very critical issues, such as the prospects of coastal erosion and possible adverse effects on ecological processes, many of which are ultimately of commercial significance. Because of this chronic problem, the selection of leasing sites and mining techniques must be well considered and be founded on careful assessment in full recognition of such uncertainties.

A second and also chronic NEPA problem relates to the use of an EIS in agency decision making. Too often, it appears that decisions in fact precede the assessment process and that the issuance of an EIS constitutes compliance with what is perceived as a bureaucratic exercise but does not reflect a good faith effort to enlarge the factual record for decision making. Fortunately, public interest groups and opponents of intended agency actions have made full use of the judicial system, and the judiciary have been relatively vigilant in ensuring that EISs have indeed been used in agency deliberations.[24]

Other problems can be expected to arise from time to time. NEPA is a full disclosure law in the sense that agency findings are to be incorporated in the EIS and that the EIS is to be published. However, agencies conducting assessments of their intended actions on proposed leasing and other mining activities will necessarily be reliant on the proprietary data of private interests to some extent. Such data are commonly withheld from government disclosures to the public despite the spirit of NEPA and the requirements of the Freedom of Information Acts applicable to the administrative agencies.[25]

A final problem worth noting here is one of enforcement under NEPA. Following the publication of an EIS and an agency decision and the inception of mining-related activity, the lead agency may allow a substantial departure from the activity as originally proposed, assessed, and approved. Such departure may be necessary to ensure the economic viability of the private parties involved in light of unanticipated difficulties, yet may incur substantial environmental impacts. Although such changes are to be allowed only after they have been separately assessed and approved, time and other constraints may not permit the running of a full NEPA assessment process, or the agency may choose to avoid this implementation of NEPA in the midst of a previously assessed and approved project. By the time judicial review is conducted, the departure from the originally assessed activity may have run its full course, with significant environmental effects. Yet no judicial decisions have yet held that NEPA provides for the remedy of environmental restoration.[26]

Despite costs and delays incurred in NEPA compliance, and despite the uneven quality of the EISs and uncertainties about their actual use, the NEPA experience continues to provide increasing benefits to the public and is now being extended to state agencies by the enactments of over 20 state governments[27] (see the discussion of six states in Chapter 9). These benefits include a greater concern by government agencies for environmental attributes, for risks to human health, for interdisciplinary analyses and planning, for harmonization of hitherto fragmented decision making, for use of the expertise of other agencies, and for their own accountability before the courts. Somehow, we are all better off for NEPA, and the statute is a very important feature of the public management framework for marine mining.

B. THE COASTAL ZONE MANAGEMENT ACT

The other major legislative enactment which provides a framework for the harmonization of federal and state decision making is the Coastal Zone Management Act.[28] This statute was enacted by Congress in 1972 to foster the development, by each coastal state, of institutional reforms and management practices necessary for rational, multiple use management of its coastal zone. The Act affirms each state's authority to manage its coastal zone and provides various incentives for the establishment and operation of state coastal zone management programs.

As discussed in previous chapters, the coastal zone of the United States includes onshore and offshore regions of critical environmental and economic importance, marked by numerous interests in competition: recreation, conservation, esthetics; commerce based on shipping, recreation, industry, fishing, and energy; national security; communications; and the housing, transport, employment, and waste disposal needs of expanding coastal metropolitan centers. Authorities at work allocating coastal resources and regulating these interests are to be found at local, state, regional, federal, and international levels: local zoning boards and conservation commissions; state wetland and other agencies; regional port authorities; various federal agencies for pollution control, navigation, and operational safety; and several international commissions. The advent of marine mining will threaten these established interests and pose new and complex problems of regulation and resource allocation for these authorities.

Congress, in its enactment of the Coastal Zone Management Act (CZMA), therefore concluded that

> (g) In light of competing demands and the urgent need to protect and to give high priority to natural systems in our coastal zone, present coastal State and local institutional arrangements for planning and regulating land and water uses in such areas are inadequate.
>
> (h) The Key to more effective use of the land and water resources of the coastal zone is to encourage the coastal States to exercise their full authority over the lands and waters in the coastal zone by assisting the coastal States, in cooperation with Federal and local governments and other vitally affected interests, in developing land and water use programs for the coastal zone.[29]

and accordingly provided in the Act's declaration of policy that

> The Congress finds and declares that it is the national policy (a) to preserve, protect, develop, and where possible, to restore or enhance, the resources of the Nation's coastal zone, . . . (b) to encourage and assist the States to exercise effectively their responsibilities in the coastal zone through the development and implementation of management programs to achieve wise use of the land and water resources . . . giving full consideration to ecological, cultural, historical and esthetic values as well as to needs for economic development, (c) for all federal agencies engaged in programs affecting the coastal zone to cooperate and participate with state and local governments and regional agencies in effectuating the purposes of this title, and, (d) to encourage the participating of the public, of Federal, state, and local governments, and of regional agencies in the development of coastal zone management programs.[30]

The Act thereupon prescribes a staged program to achieve the congressional objectives.

In the first stage, the Secretary of Commerce is authorized to provide federal financial assistance to the coastal states for *development* of their coastal management programs. Following development, a state may submit its program for federal approval in the second stage and secure subsequent *operational* funding. To qualify for federal approval and second stage funding, a state's management program should include

1. An identification of the boundaries of the coastal zone
2. A definition of permissible land and water uses within the coastal region
3. An inventory and designation of areas of particular concern within the coastal zone
4. An identification and analysis of the legal authorizations for exercise of regulatory jurisdiction by the state agency involved
5. Broad guidelines for assignment of specific priorities to each conflicting use
6. A description of the organizational structure selected to implement the management program
7. Definition of the term *beach* and establishment of a planning process for protection of and access to public beaches and public areas of environmental, recreational, historical, esthetic, ecological, or cultural value
8. A planning process for siting and managing the impacts of energy facilities in the coastal zone;
9. A planning process for assessing the effects, lessening the impact, and restoring areas damaged by shoreline erosion[31]

The Secretary can provide up to four-fifths of the costs of a state's program development (first stage funding) for 3 years,[32] but no state is allowed to receive more than 10 percent of the correspondent annual appropriation.[33] Upon completion of the first stage, program approval by the Secretary of Commerce[34] enables the coastal state to receive further matching grants for program operation by state officials.

In order to receive these second stage monies for operation, the state must demonstrate that

1. The state program was developed in accordance with applicable regulations and in full consultation with relevant federal agencies, state agencies, local governments, regional organizations, port authorities, and other interested parties

2. The state has coordinated its program with existing local and regional plans applicable to the coastal zone and has made provision for continuing consultation with the agencies involved
3. The state has held public hearings during program development
4. The program has been reviewed and approved by the governor
5. The governor has designated a single responsible agency to receive and administer grants (but not necessarily to manage the coastal zone)
6. The state has organized to implement the program
7. The state has the necessary legal authority
8. The management program provides for "adequate consideration of the national interest involved in the *siting of facilities necessary to meet requirements which are other than local in nature*"
9. The program establishes for preservation and restoration of specific areas on the basis of their "conservation, recreational, ecological, or esthetic values"[35]

The federal government can thereupon provide up to four-fifths of projected state operational expenditures,[36] with no state allowed a grant exceeding 10 percent of the total available federal funds.[37]

The geographic-demographic region subject to the Act is vaguely defined and left for state determination. The Act provides that the boundaries of the "coastal zone" encompass the "coastal waters (including the lands therein and thereunder) and the adjacent shorelands."[38] The seaward limit is naturally the boundary of the state jurisdiction in the territorial sea, but the landward boundary is more difficult to define. The basic administrative necessities to be considered in delineating this boundary may be derived from two important and interactive objectives—protection of the aquatic environment and regulation of shoreline development.

Since a primary purpose of coastal zone management is to maintain the physical, chemical, and biological balances of the coastal waters, the estuarine systems, wetlands, and transitional areas of major tributaries feeding into coastal waters must be included within the zone. Anadromous fish spawn in these waters, and many other important marine species depend on the estuaries and wetlands for their sustenance. The coastal waters, estuaries, and major tributaries are therefore physically and biologically inseparable, and the legislation provides for the inclusion of such areas.

The *coastal zone* is defined in the legislation to extend inland "to the extent necessary to control shorelands, the uses of which have a direct and significant impact on the coastal waters."[39] State-by-state determinations of the inland boundary are now being made.

Obviously, the inland boundary will substantially determine the efficacy of the coastal management program. The state role in federal marine mining policy has been strengthened, for better or worse, by the Act and its boundary flexibility. Coastal sites chosen for the onshore activities and facilities that are needed to support offshore marine mining will normally fall within the coastal zone as it will come to be defined by most states. State siting and other regulation of such onshore activities injects the states, with their limited perspectives, into federal programs for offshore marine mining.[40]

The Coastal Zone Act has not affected the constitutional prerogatives of the federal government to regulate activities offshore[41] —whether in the territorial sea where concurrent state authority over uses of the territorial seabed has been established by the Submerged Lands Act[42], or beyond (on or over the outer continental shelf) where federal authority for resource use, facility siting, and regulation virtually pre-empts any state authority.[43] However, federal deference to approved state management programs is stressed by the Coastal Zone Act. Federal agencies are required to conduct their activities and plan developments in a manner that is "to the maximum extent practicable, consistent with approved state management programs."[44] Furthermore, each applicant for a required federal license or permit in the coastal zone is required to certify compliance with the applicable state management program, though the Act provides for exceptions.[45] These interjurisdictional aspects are discussed subsequently.

The Coastal Zone Management Act does not modify federal requirements and state programs established under the Clean Air Act and the Water Pollution Control Act. The requirements of these statutes are to be incorporated into the coastal zone management programs instituted by the states.[46] (The application of these statutes to marine mining is reviewed in prior chapters of this book.) The Secretary of Commerce has delegated his authority under the Coastal Zone Management Act to the National Oceanic and Atmospheric Administration (NOAA). NOAA has promulgated regulations prescribing conditions for availability of development grants and approval of state coastal zone management programs.[47]

Examination of the evolving responses of the states to the Coastal Zone Management Act is both premature and beyond the scope of this study. However, discussion of the basic administrative options available to the states for program formulation is appropriate. The state structure should make provision for coordination of agencies and interests with overlapping or complementary responsibilities and jurisdictions. This coordination function should take place at several levels; intrastate, interstate, and state-federal, in keeping with the objectives of this Act and its policy declaration.

Intrastate administrative coordination must involve the development, in most states, of a new mechanism that will insure that local and state officials work in a prescribed program for efficient, multiple objective planning and decision making on coastal zone issues. In some states, "home rule" politics and the political significance of local autonomy will preclude development of any state "super" agency for the coastal zone. In other states, regional substate commissions may be politically feasible and justifiable on the basis of environmental, demographic, and other features of their coastal zones. Probably in only a few states will authority be vested in a new state level agency or commission with extensive powers for coastal management.

The optimal structure is left for each state to determine by the terms of the Act, which provides that federal approval of a state management program must be based, in part, on state use of

> any one or a combination of the following techniques for control of land and water uses within the coastal zone:
> (A) State establishment of criteria and standards for local implementation subject to administrative review and enforcement of compliance;
> (B) Direct state land and water use planning and regulation; or
> (C) State administrative review for consistency with the management program of all development plans, projects, or land and water use regulations . . . proposed by any state or local authority or private developer, with power to approve or disapprove.[48]

Irrespective of the intrastate arrangements of an institutional nature that may be developed by any state for its program, the program must ultimately provide the authority

> (1) to administer land and water use regulations, control development in order to ensure compliance with the management program, and to resolve conflicts among competing uses; and
> (2) to acquire fee simple and less than fee simple interests in lands, waters, and other property through condemnation or other means when necessary to achieve conformity with the management program.[49]

Federal regulations developed pursuant to these provisions have not provided more specific guidance or criteria to the states and have thereby reinforced state autonomy for coastal matters.[50]

While *interstate arrangements* are encouraged, no guidance, incentives, or action-forcing provisions appear in the original Act. The 1976 amendments provide incentive, however, by increasing federal share funding for interstate program development and implementation to nine-tenths of the costs to be incurred, a 10 percent incentive for coordinated over individual state activity.[51] Given the dismal history of regional interstate cooperation in the United States, this marginal incentive may not be sufficient.

State-federal coordination is provided for in the act in uncharacteristic detail. State programs will not be approved "unless the views of federal agencies principally affected by such programs have been adequately considered."[52] Further, federal agencies "conducting or supporting activities directly affecting the coastal zone" or undertaking "any development project in the coastal zone of a state" shall act in a manner which is to the "maximum extent practicable, consistent with approved state management programs."[53]

But coordination is also forced by the Act in the case of "any applicant for a required Federal license or permit to conduct an activity affecting land or water uses in the coastal zone" of a state with an approved management program. In such a case, the Act prohibits issuance of the federal license or permit "until the state or its designated agency have concurred with the applicant's certification." Exceptions allow the Secretary of Commerce to waive this prior condition on federal licensing upon a determination that the proposed activity is "consistent with the objectives" of the Act or necessary for the national security.[54]

The 1976 CZMA amendments deal particularly with OCS exploration and development activities. Although the primary concern of Congress in enacting the 1976 amendments was offshore oil and gas development activity, the pertinent amendments are not limited to such development. Thus, after a state management program has been approved,

> any person who submits to the Secretary of the Interior any plan for the exploration or development of, or production from, any area which has been leased under the Outer Continental Shelf Lands Act . . . and regulations under such Act shall, with respect to any such exploration, development or production described in such plan and affecting any land use or

water use in the coastal zone of such state, attach to such plan a certification that each activity which is described in such plan complies with such state's approved management program and will be carried out in a manner consistent with such program.[55]

No federal official or agency may grant any license or permit for any activity described in such a plan unless the affected state concurs in the certification. State concurrence is presumed as a result of state failure to object to the certification. If the Secretary of Commerce, pursuant to procedures established by the Act, finds such activity to be consistent with the objectives of the CZMA or otherwise necessary in the interest of national security, state concurrence may be waived.

A significant incentive to the states for development of their coastal zone management programs is provided by these provisions of the Act. The incentive is a new basis for state involvement in the regulation of various activities such as those associated with marine mining, including both offshore activities and the siting and construction of processing facilities which would require federal licenses, with involvement premised on a state environmental and developmental plan for the coastal region in which the proposed activity would occur. This provides an opportunity for state involvement on a broad basis in decision-making processes for such activities, processes hitherto limited, in the usual case, to developers, local zoning officials, and federal pollution control and navigation officials.

Further, judicial review of a federal agency decision to license a proposed coastal activity should now include consideration of and reference to the state management program, and thereby confirm the use of state planning frameworks for decision making by federal officials on coastal matters. If this occurs in subsequent disputes brought to court, it will mark a major step forward in American land use decision making—recognition and adherence to a resource allocation-growth management plan—a step which has not been previously accomplished by NEPA and other environmental legislation at federal and state levels.[56]

CZMA therefore provides a new framework for coordinating the decision making of local, state, regional, federal, and international authorities applicable to marine mining, whether such marine mining occurs on state submerged lands or on the federal outer continental shelf. For the case of marine mining on state submerged lands, a state's programs or authority for minerals exploration, leasing, transport, and processing will be developed and conducted in a manner presumably consistent with the various elements of the state's coastal zone management program. (See Chapter 9 for discussion of such developments in six coastal states.)

For the case of marine mining on the federal OCS, those facilities and activities attending federally approved exploration and leasing which fall within or intrude upon a state's coastal zone (e.g., an *onshore* minerals processing plant or staging area for OCS mining activities, pollution of *state* waters or erosion of *state* beaches arising from OCS mining, etc.) will be subject to various provisions of the coastal zone management programs of one or more states and necessitate federal-state coordination within the CZMA framework.

As discussed earlier, applicants for federal licenses or permits to conduct any activities "affecting land and water uses in the coastal zone" are required to secure state coastal zone program approval that their proposed activity complies with and will be conducted consistent with the state's program before action by the cognizant federal agency. "No license or permit shall be granted by the Federal agency until the state . . . has concurred with the applicant's certification." Under the 1976 CZMA amendments, these provisions are extended to OCS leasehold exploration, development, and production. However, the Secretary of Commerce is provided with the discretion to authorize federal license or permit issuance without prior approval by the state program when he determines that the applicant's proposed activity "is consistent with the objectives of this title or is otherwise necessary in the interests of national security."[57] The implications and enforcement potential of this grant of authority to the Secretary are as yet unclear, and proposed NOAA regulations implementing the authority[58] have generated substantial controversy.

Another provision of the statute authorizes the Secretary of Commerce to require that the state program provides "for a method of assuring that local land and water use regulations within the coastal zone do not unreasonably restrict or exclude land and water uses of regional benefit."[59] Program approval must also include federal assessment of the extent of the state's consideration of the interests of the federal agencies (§ 306[c][1]); and the requirement that the proposed state program "provides for adequate consideration of the national interest . . . in planning for, and in the siting of, facilities necessary to meet requirements which are other than local in nature" (§ 306[c][8]). These new federal-state relationships raise constitutional and other issues which also await future resolution.[60]

As discussed in Chapter 9, coastal states are now in the process of developing coastal zone management plans for the federal Office of Coastal Zone Management, for approval, funding, and implementation of their § 307 authority over coastal activities such as offshore extraction of sand and gravel and the siting of onshore facilities.

Much of the future of U.S. marine mining, with its requirements for processing facilities, transportation, and handling in the coastal zones of the states, will therefore depend on the workings of 30 different coastal zone management programs exercised by the coastal states. Some states, such as Alaska, have already demonstrated their strong interest in fostering marine mining and attendant coastal developments. Other states, such as Oregon and Massachusetts, may exercise their coastal zone management programs to prohibit the siting of mineral processing facilities and of transport and handling facilities, thereby chilling commercial interests in carrying out mining of the adjoining submerged lands and continental shelf. Therefore, the developing federal lease program for OCS marine mining will to a considerable extent be controlled by local and state interests which will be increasingly influential in the management of their coastal zones. The otherwise somewhat innocuous CZMA therefore assumes a significant role in the future of marine mining, and provides a surprisingly prescient and appropriate administrative framework and conceptual basis for federal-state coordination.[61]

NOTES

1. 42 U.S.C. 4321 et seq., enacted January 1, 1970.

2. 42 U.S.C. 4332.

3. Council on Environmental Quality, "Guidelines: Preparation of Environmental Impact Statements," 40 CFR 1500, 38 FR 20550, January 28, 1974.

4. C.E.Q. Guidelines, 40 CFR 1500 2(a).

5. For recent developments regarding programmatic environmental impact assessments, see Kleppe v. Sierra Club 8 ERC 2169, U.S.S. Ct. (1976).

6. See note 3, *supra*, for CEQ guidelines. See 40 C.F.R. 1500.6(e), 1500.7 (d), and 1500.9(d) for CEQ stress on availability of impact assessments for public review.

7. See R. Druley, "Federal Agency NEPA Procedures," Minographed 23, *Environment Reporter* (Bureau National Affairs) 7, 10 (July 9, 1976), for analysis and citations.

8. See F. Anderson, "The National Environmental Policy Act," in *Federal Environmental Law*, E. Dolgin and T. Guilbert (St. Paul: West Pub., 1974); and *Annual Reports* of the U.S. Council on Environmental Quality.

9. See note 7, *supra.*

10. Several EISs have been developed for oil and gas activities offshore by

the Council on Environmental Quality, the Department of Interior, the U.S. Coast Guard, and other agencies.

11. Draft Environmental Statement, "Proposed Outer Continental Shelf Hard Mineral Mining Operating and Leasing Regulations," Bureau of Land Management, U.S. Department of the Interior, February 1974. Proposed regulations published in 39 DR 4105-4113, February 1, 1974. Note that Department of the Interior compliance with NEPA requirements for programmatic actions on other public resources has been the subject of considerable litigation. See, for example: NRDC v. Morton, 5 ELR 20327 (D.D.C. December 30, 1974) re: grazing programs; Sierra Club v. Morton, 5 ELR 20383 (D.D.C. June 6, 1975) re: wildlife refuges; Sierra Club v. Morton, 5 ELR 20155 (D.C. Cir. January 3, 1975); and Kleppe v. Sierra Club, 8 ERC 2169, ——U.S.——(June 28, 1976).

12. See for example, the "comments" submitted to BLM by Robert Blumberg, director, Division of Mineral Resources, Department of Natural Resources, Commonwealth of Massachusetts, February 13, 1974; and EPA "Comments" submitted by Sheldon Meyers, director, Office of Federal Activities, EPA, Washington D.C. (1974).

13. 42 U.S.C. 1857h-7 (December 31, 1970).

14. 40 C.E.R. 1500.9(b).

15. Inquiries to BLM indicate that development of the final EIS and final rulemaking has been deferred as a result of the priorities accorded oil and gas development.

16. See BLM's proposed regulations, note 11, *supra.*

17. Pursuant to Department of Transportation authority under the Deepwater Port Act of 1974, 33 U.S.C. 1501 et seq., enacted January 3, 1975.

18. The Nuclear Regulatory Commission and the Council on Environmental Quality are preparing EISs related to the construction of "floating" nuclear power plants on artificial islands.

19. Friends of the Earth v. Coleman, 5 ELR 20259 (9th Cir. March 10, 1975).

20. *Final Environmental Impact Statement: Ross Island* on proposed commercial dredging of sand and gravel, U.S. Army Corps of Engineers, Portland District, Portland, Oregon, October 1974.

21. See note 12, *supra.*

22. 40 C.E.R. 1500.7(b).

23. See note 7, *supra.*

24. See Calvert Cliffs Coordinating Committee v. Atomic Energy Commission, 449 F.2d 1109 (D.C. Cir., 1971).

25. 5 U.S.C. 551 et seq.

26. Ogunquit Village Corp. v. Soil Conservation Service, 7 ELR 20381, lst Cir. (1977).

27. See annual reports of the U.S. Council on Environmental Quality for documentation of state adoption and modifications of the federal NEPA requirements.

28. 16 U.S.C. 1451 et seq., enacted October 27, 1972, as amended.

29. 16 U.S.C. 1451.

30. 16 U.S.C. 1452.

31. 16 U.S.C. 1454(b).

32. 16 U.S.C. 1454(c).

33. 16 U.S.C. 1454(e).

34. 16 U.S.C. 1454(d).

35. 16 U.S.C. 1455(c).

36. 16 U.S.C. 1455(a).

37. 16 U.S.C. 1455(b).

38. 16 U.S.C. 1453(a).

39. *Id.* Also see § 923 of NOAA Coastal Zone Management Approval Regulations, 40 F.R. 1683 (January 9, 1975).

40. This important state role has been explicitly recognized in other laws also: the Deepwater Port Act of 1974, for example, which provides for federal licensing and regulating of deep-draft facilities on the outer continental shelf under federal jurisdiction—subject, however, to approval by those "adjacent coastal states" with coastal zone management programs either in operation or under development. 33 U.S.C. 1508(b)(1) & (c).

41. 16 U.S.C. 1456(e).

42. 43 U.S.C. 1311(d). Numerous cases have been brought in the Supreme Court to refine and construe the exact limits of state and federal power. In the most recent of these, U.S. v. Maine, 95 S. Ct. 1155 (1975), 13 Atlantic states sought to justify claims of jurisdiction beyond the 3 mile territorial sea by asserting sovereignty over the seabed as direct successors in title to the crown of England. The Court determined that previous decisions precluded such an interpretation, and found on the basis of a special master's report that the historical foundation for such a claim was inadequate in any case.

43. 43 U.S.C. 1331, et seq., enacted August 7, 1953.

44. 16 U.S.C. 1456(c)(1) & (2).

45. 16 U.S.C. 1456(c)(3).

46. 16 U.S.C. 1456(f).

47. 16 U.S.C. 1463; NOAA Regulations on Coastal Zone Management Program Development Grants, 15 C.F.R. 920, 38 FR 33044 (November 29, 1973), amended 40 FR 16832 (April 15, 1975); and NOAA Coastal Zone Management Approval Regulations, 15 C.F.R. 923, 40 FR 1683 (January 9, 1975).

48. 16. U.S.C. 1455(e)(1). Also see regulations cited in note 47, supra for virtual restatement of the amorphous language used in the act itself.

49. 16 U.S.C. 1455(d)(1)(2). Also see regulations cited in note 47, *supra.*

50. Note 47, *supra.*

51. Compare 16 U.S.C.1455(a) and 1456(a) with 16 U.S.C. 1456(b).

52. 16 U.S.C. 1456(b).

53. 16 U.S.C. 1456(c)(1)(2).

54. 16 U.S.C. 1456(c)(3)(A).

55. 16 U.S.C. 1456(c)(3)(B).

56. See discussion in M. Baram, *Environmental Law and the Siting of Facilities* p. I, sec. 4 (Cambridge, Mass.: Ballinger, 1976), on the failure of the states and courts to require planning frameworks for decision making on specific development proposals.

57. 16 U.S.C. 1456(c)(3).

58. 41 FR 42878, September 28, 1976.

59. 16. U.S.C. 1455(e)(2).

60. See Baram, note 56, *supra*, part II, on coastal zone management, which discusses these and other constitutional questions.

61. See "Coordination of Federal and Federally Assisted Programs and Projects", U.S. Department of the Interior, 41 F.R. 8808–15 (March 1, 1976), for federally promulgated "interim directives" prescribing federal-state coordination methods applicable to various coastal and offshore activities, but presently excluding marine mining.

✳ *Chapter 11*

Principles and Recommendations:
Towards Resource Management

INTRODUCTION

In the preceding chapters, a technology assessment of marine mining was conducted for the overall purpose of guiding federal and state decision making. The assessment, in the absence of national and state policies for natural resources or materials, was focused on the potential regulation of marine mining practices, to ensure that technologically, economically and environmentally feasible methods of marine mining would be employed and to ensure that the commitments and externalities associated with marine mining would be socially acceptable.

In this chapter, the need to develop principles for resource management of offshore hard minerals is discussed. Principles developed for oil and gas and other publicly owned resources are reviewed as to their suitability. The chapter concludes with a presentation of recommendations for governing the exploitation of the resources and for allocating information.

A. ALLOCATION OF RESOURCES

1. Traditional Considerations
Various principles for allocating oil, gas, timber, grazing lands, and other publicly owned resources have been developed prior to the advent of marine mining.

Consideration of such principles for state offshore hard minerals may be forthcoming in the processes now being undertaken by each coastal state to develop coastal zone management programs. However, investigation of the status of several such programs, discussed in Chapter 9, reveals that each state is preoccupied with planning to accommodate multiple uses of its coastal zone and with structural modification and coordination of existing institutions and regulatory authorities. Such developments may eventually involve consideration of principles for resource allocation, but there is no evidence that such a task is being directly and vigorously addressed.

At the federal level, despite a number of studies conducted by Congress, the Department of the Interior, and their consultants and contractors, there has been little consideration of principles to govern the use of offshore hard mineral resources. For example, the Department of Interior's "Proposed Outer Continental Shelf Hard Mineral Mining Operating and Leasing Regulations"[1] and accompanying environmental impact assessment[2] simply provide that the "Department's leasing goals" are "to achieve orderly and timely resource development, protection of the environment, and the receipt of fair market value for leased mineral resources,"[3] pursuant to Departmental authority provided by § 5 of the Outer Continental Shelf Lands Act of August 7, 1953.[4] However, this statute, and the Submerged Lands Act,[5] were enacted because of interests in offshore oil and gas resources, and their legislative history fails to reveal significant Congressional consideration of principles for hard minerals allocation and exploitation.[6] The National Academy of Sciences report, "Mining in the Outer Continental Shelf and in the Deep Ocean,"[7] similarly fails to grapple with the task of considering or developing principles for hard minerals allocation, and after stating some initial assumptions about national needs and minerals potential, focuses on how to conduct certain exploration and exploitation practices.

Nevertheless, others have unofficially considered or attempted to articulate principles of resource allocation for marine minerals in general, for oil and gas, and for deep ocean minerals, and these provide some bases for considering and developing principles applicable to the subject of this study, hard mineral resources off-shore.

Krueger, in 1970, examined administration of the Outer Continental Shelf Lands Act[8]

with a view toward determining whether their administration provided for the maximum benefit to the general public,[9] [and defined] this general policy objective [as] a composite of the following more specific, but quite broad, policy objectives that emerged from a consideration of the various treaties, statutes and administrative pronouncements regarding our nation's offshore:

1. Efficient resource management—the objective of best effecting the prudent use of resources through their intelligent management by the federal government.[10]
2. The encouragement of private participation—the objective of permitting qualified, responsible representatives of the private sector to participate in the development of outer continental shelf resources.[11]
3. The maximization of revenue to the federal government—the objective of effecting the greatest direct financial return to the resource owner.[12]
4. The encouragement of multiple use of resources—the objective of coordinating management of the various resources and uses of the continental shelf to minimize conflicts.[13]
5. The advancement of knowledge and the development of technology—the objective of learning more about the offshore and its resources and achieving the technological capability to safely permit the scientific exploration and resource development.[14]
6. The protection of environmental quality—the management objective of preserving, and in some cases restoring, the natural condition of the environment.[15]

This statement of general principles applicable to offshore minerals resource allocation is derived from an analysis of federal resource-related laws, treaties, and regulations. (See footnotes 9–15 which contain Krueger's footnotes and citations for his principles.)

Another set of principles has been presented by the Director for Ocean Resources of the Department of the Interior for the case of deep seabed hard minerals (manganese, copper, etc.):

It is clear that mineral resources of the ocean bottom are of considerable importance to the United States, not only for the potential they offer of a secure source of metals necessary for our economic prosperity, but also for the accompanying benefits to our balance of payments position. Accordingly, it is the Administration's policy to follow a course of action which will assure that these minerals are available for the future to American consumers and to United States industry. To satisfy this policy, the arrangements for seabed mining must guarantee that (1) American companies are entitled to mine these minerals under conditions which assure a stable, secure and fair investment climate; (2) the environment is protected from degradation; and (3) the public is assured a fair return for the disposition of such mineral resources. . . . other factors do create a sense of urgency. These involve our lead in prospecting, technology and market-ing, as well as the need to maintain industrial initiative and momentum. . . . It is in the nature of our society and our economic system that the market place and potential for profit-making stimulate technological initiative. We in the government do not decide that a particular mineral resource is worth developing for our future needs and then develop the resource ourselves. Neither do we give direct subsidies to our mining in-dustry. . . . The public is clearly the beneficiary of this process. To keep this process going, however, government must assure that it does not take actions which hamper this kind of industrial initiative. . . .

Our role in resource management is to assure sufficient rewards to pri-vate industry from resources exploitation so as to encourage the develop-ment of the resources. We should not, however, permit the exploitation of the resource to result in windfall rewards. The bulk of the rewards should be preserved to the public. . . .

From a resource management perspective legislation which might be designed . . . should assure that:

1. Mineral resource development occurs at an economically efficient rate.
2. It occurs under rational rules and regulations.
3. Mineral resource development occurs in an environment sufficiently competitive to ensure that the bulk of economic rewards are passed through to the consumer and the general public.
4. Conditions under which development occurs are consistent with the U.S. need for a secure resource base.
5. Mineral resource development is consistent with our concerns for the ocean environment.

. . . such legislation, if enacted now, would have to provide for very sub-stantial data turnover requirements, since the sole source of informa-tion about the mineral resource, topography, mining recovery system and metallurgy would be the industry.[16]

This statement provides insights into the economic concepts and resource allocation principles of a particular presidential administra-tion. Assumptions about the economy, the role of competition and industry in assuring public benefits, the relationships between gov-ernment and industry in new economic and technological sectors, pervade this statement and would have to be critically examined by Congress and other decision makers considering deep ocean mining. Such principles would also have to be carefully reexamined for the case of hard minerals offshore—because the needs for such re-sources, the industries, and technologies involved, and the risks and economic conditions of marine mining, differ substantially from those for deep-ocean mining.

2. New Considerations and the Importance of Prototype Leasing

As these two sets of "principles" demonstrate, we do not systematically allocate, but allow and encourage (or at least do not discourage), industrial exploitation of publicly owned mineral resources under conditions which presumably ensure that *environmental costs* and *economic benefits* to the public will be acceptable. Yet *environmental costs* are incurred, and we have historically failed to impose adequate safeguards on resource exploitation activities and restoration responsibilities on the authorized exploiters, apparently because of the remoteness of effects from such activities (on public lands or offshore areas) from the public and the consequent low level of public concern and pressure on decision makers. Since many of the environmental "costs" are unquantifiable, in that they relate to wildlife and esthetics, or not fully appreciated because they will become manifest only after a long period of time, environmental costs have not been adequately considered in government decision making on publicly owned resources.[17]

Similarly, assumptions about the *economic benefits* to the public likely to arise from private exploitation of publicly owned resources have frequently not held under actual conditions. The economic benefits are generally considered to be

1. Revenues from leasing programs (bids, royalties)
2. Employment
3. Lower prices of goods for consumers
4. Balance of payments improvements
5. Overall economic health because of stable resource availability conditions

However, the economic results of private exploitation of our publicly owned resources have never been tested against other models or forms of public exploitation and joint public-private exploitation which are employed in other countries, which may provide a greater measure of economic benefit to the public in certain cases (without "destroying free enterprise" or otherwise irreversibly changing our economic system). Therefore, our traditional approaches to resource allocation should not be applied unexamined to marine mining for offshore hard minerals.

For example, appropriate offshore mining of sand and gravel will require equipment not used or possessed at present by the U.S. dredging industry, if lower prices for such materials and minimization of environmental harms are major objectives (see Chapter 4). The purchase or lease and use of such equipment therefore will be necessary and may be more readily accomplished through a joint program involving firms in the U.S. dredging industry, construction and materials industries, and public agencies at the state or federal level (e.g., Corps of Engineers, Department of the Interior, etc.).

A willingness to examine traditional principles and to develop new mechanisms for allocating publicly owned mineral resources offshore should characterize future marine mining developments at state and federal levels, and the coastal zone management program offers a framework for such developments. These approaches can also be examined as "alternatives" in the environmental impact statements to be developed pursuant to the Natural Environmental Policy Act,[18] thereby enabling comparisons of both economic benefits and environmental costs associated with alternative principles and procedures.[19]

Several new principles for allocating publicly owned resources, which have evolved in recent years, must now be considered. These new principles include

1. Enhanced protection and restoration of environmental quality[20] —the inclusion of benefits and costs of any action to extract, transport, process, use, or dispose of any material";[21] the proper valuation of such environmental costs (admittedly a difficult task); and the inclusion of restoration costs and benefits as well in the analysis
2. Pursuit of "a national policy of conservation of materials, energy, and environmental resources,"[22] with concomitant responsibilities to find substitute products, diminish consumption, and enhance recycling
3. Willingness to impose moratoria on what we are capable of technologically achieving—e.g., marine mining—until "orderly development" is assured through government coordination[23]

4. Willingness to sanction prototype or demonstration leasing programs for purposes of carefully learning more about the offshore environment and the implications of possible exploitation programs.

Discussion in preceding chapters has dealt with various legal and policy developments which manifest these new values. But the concept of a cautious approach to resource allocation, based on demonstration projects and feedback from such prototypical activities under close government supervision, is relatively new in the field of mineral exploitation. The need to conduct such projects offshore before the advent of government leasing programs is enhanced by the absence of baseline data and the many difficulties (time, funds, skills, etc.) that would be faced in developing such data.

The Department of the Interior has recognized the value of a "prototype leasing" approach in its programmatic environmental impact statement:

> Prototype leasing offers the benefits of actual field testing and monitoring of commercial mining systems while simultaneously providing useful, valid data. From these data, a set of leasing and operating regulations for hard mineral mining could be established. These would result in a sound program of mineral resource development having a minimum deleterious environmental effect with maximum economic return. The regulations would then permit full-scale leasing.[24]

Project NOMES, to demonstrate and evaluate sand and gravel mining in Massachusetts Bay, is then discussed as the first of several prototype projects. The project would involve the design and testing of monitoring techniques, evaluation of impacts on key biological and water quality parameters, and study of long-term postmining processes, such as biological restoration. This project, critical to the determination of resource allocation and exploitation policies, was never undertaken. Reasons for its termination appear to include some, but limited, expressions of local public concern over "strip-mining" the bay, state government uncertainties, and the failure of the federal and state agencies involved to find a commercial or public use for the dredged materials. No plans have been announced to revive the project or to initiate other projects elsewhere, such as on the OCS, where public acceptance would be more likely because risks to coastal interests would be less likely.

The elements of a prototype leasing program have been considered by the National Academy of Sciences in their study of shelf and deep ocean mining and by several industrial interests. The Inter-Holland Corporation, a major Dutch designer and builder of hopper dredges and other marine mining equipment has, for example, proposed the following elements:

1. Prior to commencement of mining operations, the appropriate agency of the U.S. Government should conduct a baseline study of the mining sites.
2. The lessee should be responsible for conduct of a continuous monitoring program during the course of his mining operations to provide a record of changes from conditions existing prior to development operations established by the baseline study. The details of this data collection program should be set forth in terms of the lease. The lessee should be entitled to credit the cost of the above environmental monitoring program against royalty and/or bonus payments to the U.S. Government.
3. Immediate payment of the full bonus bid to acquire the prototype lease would create an undesirable economic burden on development. To reduce this burden, the bonus could be payable over a period of time, say five equal installments.
4. The primary lease term should be for a sufficient period of time to allow for amortization of the major investment required for mining equipment and shore terminal facilities.
5. Prototype lease operations should proceed only under approved development plans and continued acceptable performance by the lessee. Development plans must provide for compliance with all applicable state and federal regulations.
6. Early production incentive should be provided which would permit, under certain circumstances, the credit of a portion of development cost during the early years of the lease against bonus and royalty payments to the government.[25]

Prototype leasing or other means of demonstration and learning[26] should precede the advent of marine mining under federal and state auspices.

Finally, it should be stressed that this discussion of the need to examine and articulate principles for resource allocation of such minerals relates not only to the "how to" question—how to lease and otherwise exploit publicly owned offshore minerals in the public interest—but also the even more important "why" question—why (and therefore when) should we go offshore to exploit such minerals. Mere technical competence, mineral discoveries, industrial economic feasibility, and the lobbying of interest groups are not reasons enough. Obviously, relatively compelling circumstances should be found before programs for mining the sea bed are to be authorized.

The "why" question therefore requires identification of justifying circumstances. Those circumstances which are measurable could include the following, singly or in combination:

1. Industrial need for resources in light of depletion of existing supplies onshore or of disruption of foreign sources, with subsequent effects on productivity and jobs
2. Federal need for such resources essential for national security
3. Lower prices for essential consumer goods and services, after full consideration of externalities and clean-up or restoration costs
4. Undesirability of further exploiting certain onshore mineral deposits, because of significant environmental effects or disruptions of the human environment and land use patterns.

In answering the "why" question, the need for technological leadership and industrial growth will inevitably be raised. However, technological leadership in marine science and engineering can be developed through other activities which do not require exploiting publicly owned resources which may be more essential for the use of future generations; and industrial growth without an underlying rationale of satisfaction of government and consumer needs for essential goods and the creation of new jobs would appear to be a questionable basis for launching marine mining. Kreuger has concluded that

> The real issue is not whether the hard mining industry needs special incentives in order to develop offshore minerals, but whether it serves any policy objectives to provide them. It is questionable whether it does at this point in time. From the standpoint of efficient resource management hard minerals are being obtained from other sources. From the standpoint of multiple use of resources and the protection of environmental quality, the offshore is better left unmined, particularly with due regard for the fact that some forms of hard mining, such as dredging, can be expected to cause much greater pollution and much more interference with other uses than petroleum development. From the standpoint of maximization of revenue to the federal government, there would seem to be little to be gained by supporting offshore development by the hard mining industry, at least on the basis proposed by it. The goal of encouragement of private participation in offshore development and of the advancement of knowledge of the development of technology would be served by giving encouragement to the hard mining industry. These goals are being satisfied in large part by the involvement of the petroleum

industry in the offshore, however, and it may be that the petroleum industry through its advanced knowledge and technology will be able to undertake development of other minerals without the special development of other minerals without the special incentives sought by the hard mining industry.[27]

Therefore, the first task for government in developing principles for resource allocation applicable to hard minerals offshore is to develop and apply criteria to determine public needs and thereby answer the "why" question. Given favorable findings, the second stage of determining principles relating to "how to" considerations should follow and should be marked by the extensive use of demonstration projects. Only through such a staged approach to the development of principles for resource allocation can federal and state governments responsibly discharge their stewardship function over publicly owned resources.

B. EXPLOITATION OF RESOURCES

1. Use of Preceding Analysis

This is the third and final stage of analysis which should precede government authorization of specific marine mining activities. It has been preceded by a sequence of analyses which can be summarized as follows:

First Stage of Analysis. Conduct a technology assessment to generate information and to develop a framework for organizing such information on marine mining and perceiving social control options. This task constitutes the major part of this study, and includes consideration of the following:

Forces promoting marine mining (Chapter 1)
Methods of technology assessment (Chapter 2)
Minerals availability and working experience (Chapter 3)
Technologies available for marine mining systems (Chapter 4)
Environmental and resource implications (Chapter 5)
Legal and regulatory considerations for social control (Chapters 6–10)

The information generated on these subjects can be organized in a general framework for analysis from which social control options can be derived (see Figure 2–2).

Second Stage of Analysis. Consider principles for allocation of publicly owned mineral resources offshore to enable decision makers to answer two fundamental questions (see Part A of this chapter):

1. Why exploit? Under what conditions of need should we exploit, in light of the information contained in the technology assessment?
2. How to exploit? What socioeconomic considerations should govern allocation and exploration in light of the information contained in the technology assessment?

If a decision is reached on allocating certain minerals for conservation and others for exploitation at specific levels, sites, and rates, then the specific features of resource exploitation programs can be considered.

2. Elements of Exploitation Program

This third and final stage of analysis involves the development of appropriate principles of *managing* exploitation, and their application in an administrative program. The exploitation mechanism may be a leasing program such as that suggested by the Department of the Interior in its proposed regulations[28] or another formal, administrative mechanism. In either case, it must be capable of incorporating several provisions needed to implement the results derived from the preceding stages of analysis as depicted in Figure 11-1.

Elements of the leasing program proposed by the Department of the Interior have been discussed earlier in this study and will not be repeated here. Nor will alternative mechanisms to leasing be discussed, since it is assumed that those principles of an exploitation mechanism indicated in Figure 11-1 will remain relatively constant, irrespective of the mechanism to be chosen.[29] Figure 11-2 summarizes the Interior Department's proposed leasing system.

Important issues relating to the economics of mining are not dealt with in this study. These include the adequacy of public revenues; the means by which such revenues can be optimized and acquired (bidding for lease tracts, royalties on minerals recovered, etc.); the importance of competition in assuring low prices for minerals and high bids for exploitation rights; bond and insurance requirements for extraction companies; criteria for evaluating the financial soundness of competing marine miners; linkages between exploration and extraction rights; and preferences to be accorded explorers who now want to exploit. These issues, and others relating to resource economics and the economics of mining and the mining industry, have not been dealt with in this study and should be dealt with at the time specific minerals are sought to be exploited

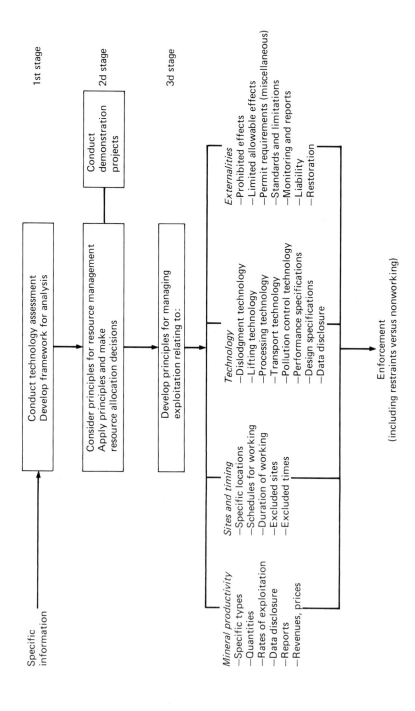

1st stage

2d stage

3d stage

Conduct
demonstration
projects

Conduct technology assessment
Develop framework for analysis

Consider principles for resource management
Apply principles and make
resource allocation decisions

Develop principles for managing
exploitation relating to:

Specific
information

Technology
—Dislodgment technology
—Lifting technology
—Processing technology
—Transport technology
—Pollution control technology
—Performance specifications
—Design specifications
—Data disclosure

Externalities
—Prohibited effects
—Limited allowable effects
—Permit requirements (miscellaneous)
—Standards and limitations
—Monitoring and reports
—Liability
—Restoration

Sites and timing
—Specific locations
—Schedules for working
—Duration of working
—Excluded sites
—Excluded times

Mineral productivity
—Specific types
—Quantities
—Rates of exploitation
—Data disclosure
—Reports
—Revenues, prices

Enforcement
(including restraints versus nonworking)

Figure 11-1.   Development of Principles for Managing Resource Exploitation.

Lease types	(Three stages) A. Exploratory B. Development C. Production
Lease term	A. Exploratory—two years, renewable once for two more years B. Development—two years, renewable once for two more years C. Production—ten years, subject to readjustment at the end of each succeeding ten-year period
Block size and number	A. Exploratory—36 blocks, not to exceed 207,360 acres B. Development—9 blocks, not to exceed 51,840 acres C. Production—3 blocks, not to exceed 17,280 acres
Rental fees per acre per annum	A. Exploratory—$0.10 B. Development—$0.25 C. Production—$1.00

		Year 1	Year 2	Subsequent
Minimum expenditures	A. Exploratory	$40,000	$50,000	$60,000
	B. Development	$125,000	$150,000	$175,000
	C. Production		—None—	

Royalties per annum	Set by lease. Minimum of 2 percent of gross value at point of shipment to market.

Figure 11-2. Proposed Leasing System for OCS Hard Minerals.

Source: Dept. Interior Environmental Impact Statement, "Proposed OCS Hard Mineral Mining Operating and Leasing Regulations," 1974, p. 254, figure 16.

since the minerals sought and the sites, firms, and technologies will determine which of the different sectors of the mining industry will be involved in exploitation, which markets and pricing factors are relevant to such analyses, and which economic relationships among the many to consider deserve priority.[30]

The principles to be implemented in the mechanisms chosen for exploitation, identified in Figure 11-1, are briefly discussed here, largely on the basis of information provided in preceding chapters.

Provision Specifying Minerals Authorized for Exploitation. This provision should specify the types of minerals to be taken, quantities authorized, and allowable rate of extraction for the authorized site or area. Scheduled reports should be provided the authorizing government agency to assure that work is indeed taking place.

Nonworking by authorized miners should not be permitted because of implications on the price structure for such minerals and should result in termination of authorization and reauthorization for other miners. These features of the exploitation mechanism accord with the proprietary responsibilities of governmental agencies administering the commercial recovery of publicly owned resources. Taking of unauthorized minerals or excessive amounts of authorized minerals can be expected to be a common problem, and the authorizing agency should vigilantly restrict operations to the established parameters of exploitation. Unlicensed or unauthorized operations should not be permitted, and this will entail the development of a surveillance and policing function, possibly to be conducted by the U.S. Coast Guard on the outer continental shelf.[31] Penalties, fines, performance bonds and restoration requirements of sufficient deterrence should be established for such violations.

Provision Specifying Sites and Timing for Exploitation. This provision should specify the sites and scheduled periods for minerals recovery in accordance with government jurisdiction over the offshore lands. Further, it should designate excluded or prohibited zones to prevent risks to the coastal ecosystem such as beach erosion, to prevent risks to presently competing interests such as shellfishing and pipelines, and to preclude mining activities that would obstruct or render impossible certain desired future uses of the region, such as the rehabilitation of an ecosystem, in accordance with government cognizance of the multiple uses and tolerable externalities for the region in question.[32] Siting should also be established to effectuate certain positive purposes as well, such as the siting of dredge mining in shipping channels to improve navigability[33] or to remove polluted sediments of the seabed.

Working schedules should be similarly specified to accommodate competing interests, such as shipping, and to maintain externalities within established limits—e.g., to assure that sediment plumes are not maintained for periods sufficient to reduce ecosystem processes or to assure that working activities do not interfere with certain critical stages in ecosystem processes such as spawning or migration of certain species.

Provision Requiring Desired Technologies and Performance. This is a critical aspect of the administrative mechanism, as it can ensure that authorized miners employ those technologies in each phase of marine mining that

- Are technologically and economically feasible for the scale of mining activities authorized
- Have the capability for minimizing the most critical externalities or social costs for the site region
- Enable fair returns on investment to the miners
- Promote the state of the art of low social cost marine mining in the United States

As discussed in Chapters 4 and 5, different new techniques are available and should be evaluated on a mineral and site-specific basis by the cognizant government agency for selection and appropriate "technology forcing" on the nascent marine mining industry. The exploitation of hitherto unexploited marine resources owned by the public provides a rare opportunity for government regulation, the opportunity, uninfluenced by existing economic constraints, to value and include social costs in the analyses underlying the several regulatory decisions that will have to be made. Optimization of either industrial profits or public revenues, or of a balancing approach considering only these factors, is obviously an inappropriate method for determining the types of technologies to be used in exploiting public resources. Social costs and benefits must be determined through processes open to public input and included in subsequent processes of regulatory decision making. (The environmental impact statement provides a context for eliciting public inputs, and therefore those EIS's to be done should evaluate alternative technologies as well as alternative sites and exploitation projects.)[34]

Once the desired technologies are established on a site-and-mineral-specific basis, government authorities may choose to employ either or both of the following methods for forcing such technologies:

1. The application of *performance specifications* (e.g., limitations on water quality or depth of seabed dredged) which would apply irrespective of the technology to be used by a miner
2. The application of *design specifications* (e.g., prescription of hopper dredge design, effluent control techniques, etc.) which would essentially prescribe the technologies to be used by a miner

Performance specifications used by government in regulation have traditionally been more acceptable to industry, because they usually are based on current practice and therefore present little that is new and enable the practice of "business as usual." They are also easy to violate and difficult to enforce, because government enforcement requires proof of actual harms and sufficiently evidenced causal relationships between harms and source and the relative absence of synergistic factors.[35] Violations in the marine environment would be difficult to prove because of lack of baseline data, storms and other natural events, and other factors. However, to the extent that these difficulties can be overcome in a cost-effective manner by government monitoring and industrial reporting, performance specifications based on what has been proven (largely overseas) should be stringently set and used so as to force advanced technologies while allowing the marine miner discretion in choosing the specific technological methods and equipment to be used.[35a] This would accomplish miner compliance with the specifications while allowing miner choice of advanced technologies most suitable to his level of activity and financial capability.

Design specifications have traditionally been imposed by government on industrial activities to force quick and sure compliance with governmentally determined levels of public safety or other important government objectives. Therefore, design specifications have been promulgated by the Nuclear Regulatory Commission which are applicable to the proprietors of nuclear power plants.[36] In this manner, government expertise in technologies and hazards can be efficiently translated into specifications and forced on industry.

However, problems with this approach should be noted for the case of marine mining: There is no government expertise based on operating experience, and the manner in which such design specifications are promulgated and applied to industry may inadvertantly freeze technological development and the initiatives of our marine industries. Both problems can be avoided, however. Government expertise can be quickly acquired by research (there is time for research, as marine mining is not urgently required), by observation of foreign activities, and by the sponsorship of prototype or demonstration projects to test out the different advanced technologies.

Government specifications in the proper regulatory format need not have their chilling effects either. Formal rule making by government agencies is indeed a cumbersome process which could lead to the casting of specifications into "concrete" standards, definitely a chilling prospect for a young industry. The promulgation of design specifications as generic guidelines applicable to classes of mining activity or sites but providing the prospective miner with opportunity to convince the agency that alternative designs would achieve desired performance and be more cost effective as well would appear to be a suitable method. Again, the Nuclear Regulatory Commission's (NRC) approach can be considered: The NRC's *Regulatory Guides* recommend technological specifications which presumably reflect the most advanced feasible methods of keeping certain risks (radiation) "as low as reasonably achievable," which are based on established procedures for soliciting expert opinions, and which nevertheless afford potential NRC licensees and the NRC itself the flexibility to recognize and implement newer, less costly, more effective technologies on a case-by-case basis. Although the NRC experience is not one of convincing performance, it nevertheless offers a structural approach worth considering for forcing good designs on the regulated industry.

Therefore, given a thorough understanding of the advanced technological state of the art of marine mining as practiced elsewhere, and given the time to conduct research and demonstration projects, government authorities have the responsibility to use both performance and design specification approaches as circumstances warrant.

Provision Requiring Performance Within Acceptable Levels of Social Costs or Externalities. As amply discussed in Chapter 5, various onshore and offshore effects of marine mining have been identified and measured, despite the absence of complete baseline data for the marine environment. And as discussed in Chapters 6 through 10, numerous federal and state agencies have regulatory jurisdiction over mining activities and have established various standards and other limitations and permit procedures to ensure that the social costs of marine mining are kept within limits as required by Congress. Such social cost aspects of marine mining are intimately associated with the preceding discussion of "forcing technology" on the industry, and therefore provisions should be consistent with the capabilities of the prescribed technologies, but not compromised by inadequate technologies.

In addition to substantive considerations of social cost, the mechanism for exploitation should designate appropriate interagency procedures and permit sequences to reduce costly confusion among potential miners and agencies. Ideally, in terms of administrative efficiency, a "one stop" process should be developed at state and federal levels so that, for example, potential marine miners would face one broad regulatory proceeding which would incorporate the concerns and responsibilities of all federal and state agencies, with one subsequent opportunity for judicial review of the regulatory decision. However, this is a matter of considerable bureaucratic and legal complexity and can wait until the level of actual mining activity justifies such reform proposals.[37]

3. Allocation of Information

Finally an issue which pertains to most of the foregoing must be discussed: the allocation of information generated by those conducting authorized demonstration, exploratory, and extraction activities. Controversy over the government acquisition of raw information from industry working public resources under government permit has now been generally resolved in favor of such government acquisition. Therefore, government licenses and permits for offshore exploration and production activity generally include provision for the development, disclosure, and submission of certain types of data by industry working under such authorizations to government.

Industrial compliance is always uncertain because of the government's lack of knowledge as to what data are available, and the ease with which important data can be withheld by industry. Therefore, government acquisition of raw information from marine miners should be a practical problem of retrieval, but not a legal problem of authority. In contrast to oil and gas, hard minerals offshore have been principally explored by the federal government and not by private interests, and this can serve to create a more favorable context for government-industry partnership on information generation and allocation for the hard minerals case.

However, government acquisition from industry of processes for interpreting data and the industrial interpretations of such information, and government allocation or disclosure of such information to the general public, remain major controversies. For the oil and gas case, the Department of the Interior is permitted but not compelled to withhold from public disclosure "geological and geophysical information and data, including maps, concerning wells" under one of the several exemptions of the Freedom of Information Act of 1968.[38]

Proposed regulations of the U.S. Geological Survey, however, would provide for U.S.G.S. acquisition of processed data or interpretations from industry and eventual disclosure to the public.[39] This has brought about strong opposition, as expected, from the oil and gas industry. The American Petroleum Institute (API), for example, has contended that government disclosure of proprietary data and its interpretations by industry (also proprietary) would have these adverse effects:

1. Lead to a sharp decrease in independently conducted geological and geophysical work.
2. Decrease competitive bidding at lease sales.
3. Reduce substantially the level of bids on each tract sold.
4. Result in fewer bids.
5. Discourage the drilling of exploratory wells, for fear of providing competitors with information bearing on adjacent, unleased tracts.
6. Lower the rate of oil and gas discoveries, and thereby increase the cost of these resources to the consumer.[40]

Others appearing on behalf of industry have threatened legal action to test the validity of the proposed information disclosure regulations.[41]

The application of this "chamber of horrors" approach to marine mining for hard minerals by other industrial interests is likely as marine mining exploration and extraction regulations are developed. Nevertheless, a strong government position on industrial data disclosure to government and government disclosure to the public is necessary for the case of marine mining if our approach to marine mining is to be responsive to public values and state and local attitudes and if our regulatory processes are to function in the open manner sought by reformers. A National Academy of Sciences' committee studying continental shelf mining adopted at least part of this:

> After issuing a production license, government should have access to all technical data and interpretations held by the licensee. The federal government should have as one of its objectives the accumulation of as complete a data base on subsea minerals as possible. In this connection, government should be encouraged to accelerate its own data collection.[42]

For the case of marine mining, data and information recommendations can be depicted in the matrix format shown in Table 11-1.

Authority to conduct demonstration, exploration, extraction, and monitoring activities should provide for industrial disclosure of all information, raw and processed, to the federal and state agencies involved. This enables the development of a coherent data base for further governmentally sanctioned exploitation programs and would be based on the consideration that publicly owned resources are being subjected to commercial recovery and that no commercially owned property is involved. Industrial claims that processed information contains or consists of trade secrets or proprietary information are valid, but should be waived in the public interest because

Table 11-1.   Marine Mining and Information Allocation

Marine mining activity		Data and disclosure	
	1. Industrial proprietary information used to determine analytical and mining procedures	2. Raw data acquired from authorized activity	3. Resultant processed data or interpretations from industrial analysis and working
Demonstration projects	All to government[a]	All to government[a]	All to government[a]
Exploration			
Preproduction	Industry retention	All to government[a]	All to government[b]
Postproduction	Industry retention	All to government[a]	All to government[b]
Extraction (production)	Industry retention	All to government[a]	All to government[b]
Environmental and safety monitoring	All to government[a]	All to government[b]	All to government[a]

[a]Denotes subsequent government disclosure to the public.
[b]Denotes careful time phasing of such data disclosure to public.

the information is essential to securing the necessary data base for further exploitation and more efficient regulations, and such waivers should therefore be a condition for government authorization. Similar approaches to the allocation of information have been developed in other fields of governmental regulation, such as those other fields where government authority over industrial activity is complete as in the fields of nuclear power and aerospace.

However, the information independently generated by industry with its own funds for conducting analyses and designing mining procedures falls within traditional concepts of trade secrecy—particularly if such information was not generated under government license or other authorization. Disclosure of such information can be required as a condition for authorization by government, but is likely to have significantly chilling effects on the interests of the already developed and competitive marine industries in marine mining. A judicious approach is called for, and could consist of the approach indicated in Table 11-1 that disclosure of such information to government would occur only (1) insofar as it relates to environmental and safety monitoring (to thereby provide assurance to government that industrial self-monitoring will be adequate), and (2) insofar as it was generated or employed in the context of demonstration projects, which are of course designed to enhance full government learning on marine mining.

The issue of subsequent disclosure of such information to the public remains and must be considered in the context of regulatory decision making and administrative procedures designed to enhance informed participation by all levels of government and by the public. The Department of the Interior has, in its proposed offshore mining regulations, sought a simple solution of nondisclosure, presumably in reliance on the exceptions to the Freedom of Information Act which enable agency nondisclosure of trade secrets[43] and certain geological information:

> *260.82 Public Inspection of Records.* Geological and geophysical interpretations, maps, and data and commercial and financial information required to be submitted under this part shall not be available for public inspection without the consent of the lessee so long as the lessee furnishing such data, or his successors or assignees, continues to hold a lease of the lands involved.[44]

This approach appears unjustifiably broad in light of the foregoing analysis of information allocation, and as indicated in Table 11-1 by an [a], the public interest in disclosure by government of all data acquired from industry from demonstration projects, all raw data, and all data pertaining to environmental and safety monitoring would appear to be (1) critical to informed public participation in resource allocation and exploitation regulation stages of government decision making, (2) without chilling effect on marine industries, and (3) justified by public ownership of the resource at stake.

However, government disclosure of processed data from exploration and extraction activities, while in the interest of open regulatory processes, would have uncertain, but probably significant, effects on industrial willingness to exploit. Such data should therefore be considered for disclosure under a time-phased program to insure that inequitable uses of such data by mining competitors will not occur.

These are admittedly judgments, somewhat informed and somewhat intuitive, as to how the difficult data allocation issue should be resolved.[45] By disaggregating "data" into their specific types and by carefully studying the competing public and private interests at stake, the federal and state agencies should be able to reach reasonably appropriate decisions on data allocation and avoid simplistic responses to the consistent industrial demand for nondisclosure. A full disclosure objective should be adopted and implemented to the extent reasonable, in light of such considerations—particularly since the resources involved are in the public domain, most exploration has been undertaken by government agencies, and industrial interest and technological advancement and revenues will flow only as a result of such government efforts on, and public acceptance of, marine mining.

NOTES

1. 39 F.R. 4105-13 (February 1, 1974).

2. Bureau of Land Management, U.S. Department of the Interior, Washington, D.C., February 1974.

3. Draft Environmental Impact Statement, note 1, *supra*, and p. 000.

4. 43 U.S.C. 1331 (a) (1953).

5. 43 U.S.C. 1301 et seq. (1953).

6. See R. Krueger, "An Evaluation of the Provisions and Policies of the Outer Continental Shelf Land Act," *Natural Resources Journal* 10, 4 (1970): 763-810; and "The Background of the Doctrine of the Continental Shelf and the Outer Continental Shelf," *Natural Resources Journal* 10 (1970): 442-514.

7. Marine Board, Assembly of Engineering, National Academy of Sciences, Washington, D.C. (1975).

8. See note 6, *supra*.

9. From R. Krueger, note 6, *supra;* and 43 U.S.C. § 1391 (1964). This was stated as being the policy objective of Congress [sometimes hereinafter referred to as PLLRC]. 78 Stat. 985, 43 U.S.C. § 1400 (1964). The objectives were identified and evaluated in Nossaman, Waters, Scott, Krueger & Riordan, *Study of the Outer Continental Shelf Lands of the United States* [hereinafter referred to as Nossaman OCS Study] (Springfield, Va.: Clearinghouse, 1968), § 11.1.

10. From Krueger, note 6, *supra*. The Truman Proclamation of 1945, the Marine Resources and Engineering Development Act, and the legislative history of the Outer Continental Shelf Lands Act all evidence the objective of best effecting the prudent use of resources through their intelligent management by the federal government. Proclamation No. 2667, 3 C.F.R. 67 (1943-48 Comp.); 33 U.S.C. §§ 1101-24 (1966). *See also* Nossaman OCS Study, note 1 §§ 1.5, 1.12.

11. From Krueger, note 6, *supra*. The Outer Continental Shelf Lands Act and the regulations promulgated pursuant thereto clearly contemplate that the development of minerals in the outer continental shelf be undertaken by qualified, responsible representatives of the private sector. 43 U.S.C. 1391 et seq. The Marine Research and Engineering Development Act also recognizes the desirability of "[t]he encouragement of private investment enterprise in exploration, technological development, marine commerce, and economic utilization of the resources of the marine environment." 33 U.S.C. § 1101(b)(3) (1966).

12. From Krueger, note 6, *supra*. While there are indications in the legislative history of the Outer Continental Shelf Lands Act that the generation of revenue was a secondary consideration, its subsequent administration, particularly in

recent years, clearly indicates that a basic policy objective has been to maximize revenue to the federal government from the sale of mineral leases. This was particularly manifest in the 1968 Santa Barbara lease sale. See Nossaman OCS Study, note 1 §4.16.

13. From Krueger, note 6, *supra*. This objective has been repeatedly acknowledged as necessary by many branches of the federal government. The act for the classification of public lands which was passed contemporaneously with the law creating the Public Land Law Review Commission defined "multiple use" as follows:

[T]he management of the various surface and subsurface resources so that they are utilized in the combination that will best meet the present and future needs of the American people; the most judicious use of the land for some or all of these resources or related services over areas large enough to provide sufficient latitude for periodic adjustments in use to conform to changing needs and conditions; the use of some land for less than all of the resources; and harmonious and coordinated management of the various resources, each with the other, without impairment of the productivity of the land, with consideration being given to the relative values of the various resources and not necessarily the combination of uses that will give the greatest dollar return or the greatest unit output.
43 U.S.C. §1415(b) (1964).

14. From Krueger, note 6, *supra*. This policy is implicit in the Truman Proclamation and the administration of the Outer Continental Shelf Lands Act. It is made explicit by the Marine Resources and Engineering Development Act and is also evidenced in the Convention on the Continental Shelf. The Marine Resources and Engineering Development Act provides:

(b) The Marine Science activities of the United States should be conducted so as to contribute to the following objectives:
(1) . . .
(2) The expansion of human knowledge of the marine environment.
(3) The encouragement of private investment enterprise in exploration, technological development. . . .
33 U.S.C. §1101 (1966).

15. From Krueger, note 6, *supra*. This policy objective is evidenced in a number of recent federal acts, particularly the recently enacted National Environmental Policy Act of 1969, which provides that "the policies, regulations, and public laws of the United States shall be interpreted and administered in accordance with" the act's environmental protective policies, and that federal agencies shall use environmental design arts in their planning and by July 1, 1971, propose changes to their statutory authority and regulations to conform to the act's purposes. 83 Stat. 852 (1969). This policy is also evident in the Conventions on the Continental Shelf and High Seas. See Krueger, *International*

and *National Regulation of Pollution from Offshore Oil Production* (Proceed. Colum. Conf. Int'l & Interstate. Reg. Water Pollution, 1970).

16. Supplemental Statement of Leigh S. Ratiner, Director for Ocean Resources, Department of the Interior, on behalf of the Interagency Task Force of the Law of the Sea, in *Deep Seabed Hard Minerals*, Hearings before the Subcommittee on Oceanography of the Committee on Merchant Marine and Fisheries, U.S. H. Rep., 93d Cong., 1st sess. (1973).

17. U.S. Council on Environmental Quality, *Sixth Annual Report* (Washington, D.C., 1975), p. 237.

18. 42 U.S.C. 4321–47 (January 1, 1970).

19. *Natural Resources Defense Council v. Morton*, 458 F. 2d 827 (D.C. Cir. 1972) is an important decision construing NEPA and defining agency responsibilities for the consideration of alternatives (in this case, offshore oil leasing alternatives). Department of the Interior compliance is evidenced by its "requests for Comments on Possible Oil and Gas Leasing," for use in EIS preparation. See, for example, 38 F. Reg. 18390 (1973).

20. All studies of resource management now cite this principle, since the enactment of NEPA in 1970.

21. See "Conclusions and Recommendations," *Man, Materials and Environment* (Washington, D.C.: National Academy of Sciences, 1973), p. 5.

22. See *Mineral Resources and the Environment* Washington, D.C.: (National Academy of Sciences, 1975), p. 18 and elsewhere.

23. As proposed, for example, by Congressmen Hughes and Dodd in H.R. 5588, 94th Cong., 1st sess. (March 26, 1975): "a bill to declare a moratorium on the sale of leases in frontier areas of the OCS for the purpose of exploiting mineral reserves."

24. *Draft Environmental Impact Statement on Proposed Outer Continental Shelf Hard Mineral Mining Operating and Leasing Regulations* (Washington, D.C.: U.S. Department of the Interior, 1974), pp. 258–61.

25. Personal communication with Robert Ziegler, vice president, Inter-Holland Corporation.

26. A carefully considered design for research and the collection of baseline data suitable for application to any offshore activity, including marine mining, is provided by H.R. 1363, U.S. H. Rep., 94th Cong., 1st sess. (1975).

27. See Krueger, note 6, *supra*, at 780.

28. See note 24, *supra*.

29. See Krueger, note 6, *supra*. Also see J. Jacobson and T. Hanlon, "Regulation of Hard-Mineral Mining on the Continental Shelf," *Oregon L. Rev.* 50 (1971): 425–61, for discussion of various elements of leasing programs.

30. See W. Lee et al., *Opportunity Brief on Offshore Mining for Sand and Gravel* (Cambridge, Mass.: MIT Sea Grant Program, 1976), for an example of an analysis of economic and pricing considerations in a mineral, site, and industry-specific context.

31. See P. Swatek, "A Conservationist's Perspective on the Prospect of Nearshore Sand and Gravel Mining," (Paper presented at National Academy

of Sciences workshop on "Environmental Aspects of Submarine Mining," Washington, D.C., January 9, 1975), for discussion of the difficulties of enforcement. U.S.G.S. enforcement failings in the oil and gas context are discussed in *Outer Continental Shelf Oil and Gas Development and Coastal Zone,* Committee on National Ocean Policy, U.S. Senate, Washington, D.C. (1975).

32. The Sierra Club has undertaken a designation of zones or sites for the exclusion of mineral leasing and other exploitation activities proposed for onshore public lands. See "Testimony of Donald Carmichael for the Sierra Club before the Senate Committee on Interior and Insular Affairs on S. 1040, S. 3009, S. 3010, S. 3085 and S. 3086, Washington, D.C., March 29, 1974, in *Mineral Development on Federal Lands,* Hearings before the Subcommittee on Minerals. Materials and Fuels of the Committee on Interior and Insular Affairs, U.S. Senate, 93d Congress, 2d session (1974).

33. See discussion of New York State in Chapter IX.

34. See discussion of NEPA in Chapter X.

35. The reader is referred to analyses of performance specification approaches of the early air and water pollution control acts (pre-1970 and pre-1972 respectively).

35a. In their assessment of OCS oil and gas, D. Kash et al concluded that . "U.S.G.S. should establish equipment requirements in terms of the objectives to be achieved. While these requirements should include detailed performance standards for all pieces of equipment effecting safety and environment, design specifications should not be allowed to act as a deterrent to technological development. . . ." *Energy Under the Oceans,* U. Okla. Press, 1973, p. 257.

36. See 10 C.F.R. various provisions.

37. "One-Stop" regulatory procedures for power plant and transmission line siting have evolved in various states. However, only New York state has substantially achieved the "one-stop" goal for state and local regulatory functions. See M. Baram, *Environmental Law and the Siting of Facilities: Issues in Land Use and Coastal Zone Management,* Ballinger Press, Cambridge, Mass. (1976), Part I, Section 4.

38. 5 U.S.C. 551 et seq. Relevant exemptions are provided for trade secrets (552(b) (4)) and geological information concerning wells (552(b) (9)).

39. See Draft Environmental Impact Statement on Proposed Amendment to OCS Lands Act, U.S. Geological Survey, Washington, D.C. (1976).

40. Hearings on the provisions of the proposed amendment to OCS Lands Act pertaining to "Geological and Geophysical Data Submission and Disclosure" conducted by USGS (note 38 supra) elicited numerous statements of opposition from the oil and gas industry, such as "Testimony of Dr. W. Laird, American Petroleum Institute", Washington, D.C. July 15, 1974, from which the quotation is taken.

41. See Statement of L. Funkhouser, Standard Oil of California, presented at the hearings held by U.S.G.S. (note 39 supra)

42. *Mining in the Outer Continental Shelf and in the Deep* Ocean, National Academy of Sciences, Washington, D.C. (1975), p. 65.

43. See note 38, supra.

44. "Proposed Hard Mineral Leasing Regulations", U.S. Dept. Interior, Bureau of Land Management, 39 F. Reg. 4105–4113, February 1, 1974.

45. The difficulties of disaggregating the data problem and recommending solutions which balance industrial federal and public interests are considerable. For a good example of grappling with the problem in the oil and gas context, See D. Kash, et al, *Energy Under the Oceans*, U. Okla. Press, 1973, pp. 152–159.

Index

About the Authors

Michael S. Baram is a lawyer and partner in the law firm of Bracken, Selig and Baram, Boston, Massachusetts. He is also a professor at Franklin Pierce Law Center, and previously served as a member of the faculty at the Massachusetts Institute of Technology. He has specialized in federal regulatory matters, particularly in the areas of environmental and natural resources law, and serves as a member of various committees of the National Academy of Sciences and the American Bar Association. He is currently chairing an American Bar Association Environmental Law Committee, and also serving on several advisory committees to federal agencies. His publications include various articles in *Science*, and other journals, and a book, *Environmental Law and the Siting of Facilities*.

William Lee received his Doctor of Science in Resources Systems Management from the Massachusetts Institute of Technology. His dissertation was entitled *When Values Conflict: An Application of Multiattribute Decision Analysis to Marine Sand and Gravel Mining*. He is now with the Environmental Systems Division, Woodward-Clyde Consultants, San Francisco. He is interested in the applicability of quantitative methods such as decision analysis in complex resources and environmental problems.

David A. Rice is a professor and associate dean at Boston University School of Law and a graduate of the University of Wisconsin and Columbia University School of Law. He has been a consultant to and authored major studies for the Massachusetts Legislature and Office of Coastal Zone Management and the State of North Carolina on legal aspects of coastal land use, beach access and coastal management program implementation. His other publications include the law casebook, *Consumer Transactions*.